GIGANTIC BOOK OF
CROSSWORDS

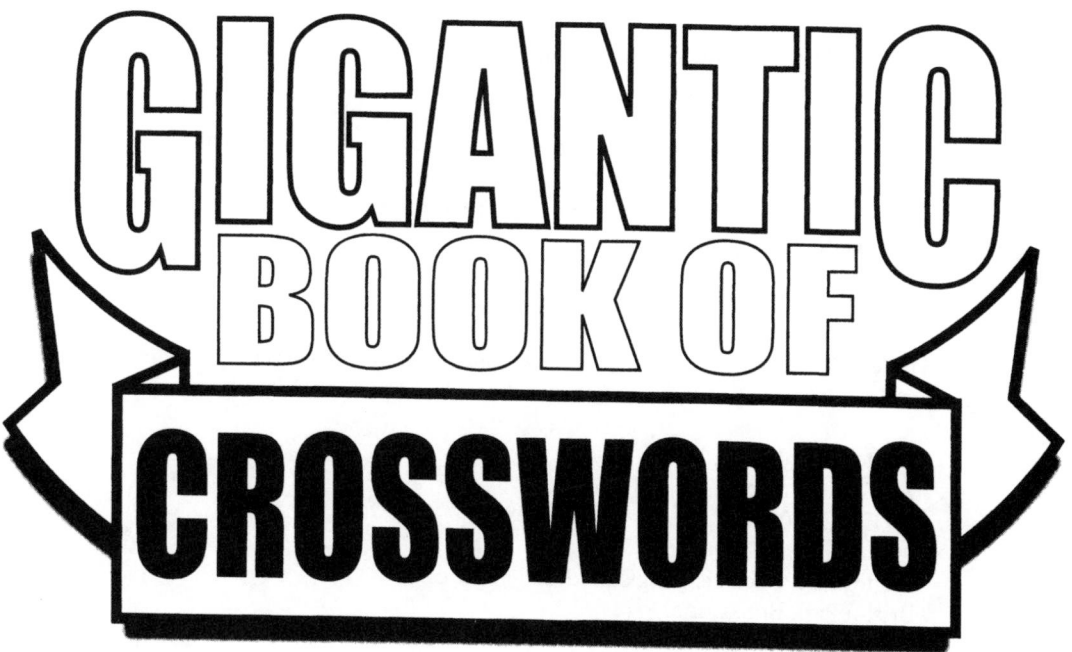

Richard Manchester

BRISTOL
PARK
BOOKS

First Bristol Park Books edition published in 1999.

Originally published as *The 2nd New Mammoth Book of Crossword Puzzles*
and re-issued as *Giant Grab A Pencil ® Book of Crossword Puzzles*

Bristol Park Books, Inc.
252 W. 38th Street
NYC, NY 10018

Bristol Park Books is a registered trademark of
Bristol Park Books, Inc.

Published by arrangement with Crosstown Publications.

ISBN: 978-0-88486-475-2

Printed in the United States of America

CONTENTS

PUZZLES

10. Reward her — as she rewarded you. *Rev. 18:6*
11. He . . . shall not uncover his head, nor — his clothes. *Lev. 21:10*
16. Thou shalt not tempt the Lord — God. *Matt. 4:7*
18. Jehoiada was the — of the Aaronites. *I Chr. 12:27*
20. Then do we with patience w— for it. *Rom. 8:25*
22. It . . . appeareth for a little time, and — vanisheth. *James 4:14*
23. Thou shalt bring her — to thine house. *Deut. 21:12*
24. Thy — and thy she goats have not cast their young. *Gen. 31:38*
25. The Land of —
26. The — Testament
28. He that — his life for my sake shall find it. *Matt. 10:39*
30. He hath received him — and sound. *Luke 15:27*
31. Before the cock —, thou shalt deny me thrice. *Luke 22:61*
32. The Garden of —

34. They shall come . . . from the no—. *Luke 13:29*
35. He shall rule them with a — of iron. *Rev. 2:27*
37. — entered into the ark. *Matt. 24:38*
40. — shalt thou make in the ark. *Gen. 6:14*
41. She . . . said unto — mother, What shall I ask? *Mark 6:24*
42. The Book of —el
43. Son of Seth
44. — called his wife's name. Eve. *Gen. 3:20*
46. They saw . . . the lame to —, and the blind to see. *Matt. 15:31*
48. — are ye fearful? *Matt. 8:26*
49. Sennacherib king of Assyria . . . thought to — them for himself. *II Chr. 32:1*
50. Fear —, Zacharias: for thy prayer is heard. *Luke 1:13*
51. He that hath an —, let him hear. *Rev. 3:6*
52. The children of Israel walked upon — land. *Ex. 14:29*
55. The LORD sent thunder and h—l. *Ex. 9:23*

Solution is on page 363

ACROSS

1. Light fixture
5. Garfield, for one
8. Air duct
12. Egg-shaped
13. Man's nick-name
14. Composer Stravinsky
15. Contradict
16. Turncoat
18. Notable period
19. Colony insect
20. Skeletal parts
21. Headland
23. In favor of
24. Protuberance
26. Clucker
27. Observed
30. Away from the wind
31. Contend
32. Heal
33. Man's nick-name
34. Angry
35. Thick soup
36. Male heir
37. Army vehicle
38. Spaghetti or macaroni
41. Prohibit
42. Steal from
45. Not guarded
47. Corncob, for one
48. Stash
49. Dined
50. On the Baltic
51. Drinks slowly
52. Naughty
53. Fender gouge

DOWN

1. Ore vein
2. Declare
3. Handcuffs
4. Work at (a trade)
5. Chili con —
6. Aid's partner
7. Decade number
8. Energy
9. Actor, Richard —
10. Knot; knob
11. Very: French
17. Poet's "black"
19. Gibbon
22. Grow older
23. Charge
24. Sack; pouch
25. Eskimo knife
26. Concealed
27. Unexpected event
28. Exist
29. Tiny
31. Actor Johnson
32. Stage "hint"
34. Groan
35. Ballpoint
36. Hearty dishes
37. Worn-out
38. Face: slang
39. Against
40. Cease
41. Greek letter
43. Unwrapped
44. Tempo
46. Apply lightly
47. Tablet

Medium

Solution is on page 364

10

ACROSS

1. Young dog
4. Halts
9. "Busy" insect
12. Anger
13. Fragrant purple bloom
14. Beam of light
15. Liverpool's country
17. Love very much
19. Even a bit
20. Shoplifts, for example
21. Stretch of land
24. Detested
25. Take a chance on
26. Put away in order, as papers
27. Supposing
29. Pen fluid
30. Certain card game
31. Garden tool
32. All right!
33. Worries
34. Soup dish
35. Bolts
36. Flower part
37. "Jaws" creatures
39. Chum
40. Natural hair dye
41. Highest
45. Bowlike curve
46. Wire thickness
48. Pub brew
49. Female deer
50. Fireplace "smolderer"
51. Kind of bread

DOWN

1. Crusty treat
2. Coffee-maker
3. Square — in a round hole
4. Slope
5. Very small
6. Ancient
7. Dad
8. Disperse
9. Wide
10. Actor, James — Jones
11. Sites of sight
16. Be without
18. Legal document
20. Store specials
21. Group of three
22. Skating arena
23. Inquire of
24. Backpacker's walks

26. Companions for spoons and knives
27. Hawkeye State
28. Collapsed
30. Parcel
31. Sizzling
33. Maize
34. Door "ringer"
35. Knight's spear
36. Not as bright
37. Food fish
38. Large sandwich
39. Book part
41. Bath place
42. Long item on a rabbit
43. Crafty, as a fox
44. Golf mound
47. P.M.'s complement

Easy

Solution is on page 364

SHANEANIGANS   HARD

by TED SHANE

You'll find zany definitions in this crossword by Ted Shane, so please look out for traps. For example, the definition for 42-Down is "Choice word" and the answer is ELSE. The clues are sly, so be careful.

Solution is on page 364.

ACROSS

1. Bossy girls can stall around here, but in time some jerk will take them in hand
5. They're a head of the corned beef
13. This follows a famous Tor in Canada
14. I'm inclined to think it's on the decline, too
15. ronam giP
16. Horse flopera
17. Set up a bar to
18. If a hot rod is headed SE, which way does its rumble seat face?
19. The source of Adam's Ale
20. If Papa is heading SSW with a willow switch, which way is Junior going?
22. He feels sick when people are too healthy: abbr.
23. Small quarters in exchange for large dollars: sing.
25. Lissen youse guys, dis one ain't no good, I want de — one
27. This is no dancer but it does a perfect split
28. They're in a position to offer a girl a proposal for a lifetime contract
31. We'd have peace if we could get them to go along with each other
32. Doubles or nothings
33. What the Russians have taken out of life
34. Things Dad finishes paying for on the 24th of December and starts paying for again on the 26th
36. Interoffice Flash-o-gram
37. Gargles on key
38. This star keeps getting Greta all the time
39. Short Italian posy

41. Professional Gardeners Amalgamated: there's many a sly dig here
42. What folks on diets do for food between meals
43. Glorified gossip distributor: abbr.
44. This floats around in an iceberg
46. These really do a-mount to something in Russia
48. Phifftetoo: Roman
49. A type of laid-away pay for a rainy day: plural
51. I could gopher this state: abbr.
52. It struck this maestro in the ear, made him wince, and knocked the curl out of his moustache: 2 wds.
53. The warden doesn't like his too hard-boiled: slang

DOWN

1. Place filled with the Juniors of happy parents getting a good rest: 2 wds.
2. The Jimmy Durante of the animal world
3. Routes that mst be trvld
4. It's a strong parent who can say this
5. This is apparently cut from the lamb that bore the Golden Fleece these days
6. A little assistance, please!
7. Good mixers
8. Convertible tops
9. Kind of is that is
10. A little entirely backwards
11. Red ball—sounds cheesy!
12. Pass it on!
16. What the new nylons did when she started to walk
19. He has a shy id
21. Politician's favorite fish

24. Bowser's treasures
25. Wholes in ones
26. What egotists constantly do to their I's
28. Jumpy Australian, fills his front sac, and hops around like a bear with a built-in pogo stick
29. Swinging and swaying to Caribbean blasts and woodwinds
30. Grandma called it inserting the proboscis in other folks' affairs, Congress calls it investigating
32. Prominent Antarctic citizen, keeps cool in white tie and tails

35. Gulp bubblewater correctly
36. This is hard hit during the wrestling season
38. Zoom juice
39. Invinegarates
40. Mountainous Greek combining form and cookie
42. Choice word
45. It's gnown for asking, "What's —?"
47. Industrialist that's taken to the hills
48. Twisted tale
50. Large economy-sized Jr.
51. Possessive I

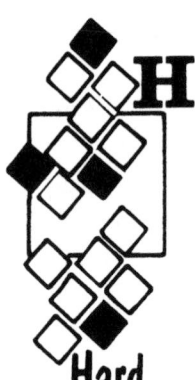

Hard

ACROSS

1. Palatial home
7. Breaks a traffic law
13. Exonerate
14. Wait a minute!: 2 wds.
15. Daring trick
16. Overturn
17. Gets a move on
18. Rich vein
19. Aunt: Spanish
20. A Gabor
21. — Jones's locker
22. Hit on the noggin: slang
23. Doormat word
25. "— and Bess"
26. Belated
28. "Robinson Crusoe" author
31. Male geese
35. Frothy beverages
36. Pub order
37. Famed person: abbr.
38. Luau fare
39. Yellowstone, for one
40. Skirt style, for short
41. — machine, amusement arcade device
43. Scope
44. Landed property
45. Small package
46. Took time off
47. Aquatic animals

DOWN

1. Kidney-shaped nut
2. On the move
3. Tattle: slang
4. Casks
5. Bed: French
6. "— tu, Brute!"
7. Disreputable
8. Vatican resident
9. Elevated railways
10. Newspaper chief
11. Catnapping
12. Furtive
16. Famous model: 2 wds.
18. Weak; ineffectual
21. Bird of peace
22. College student
24. Sounds made by 21-Down
25. Football kick
27. Moist
28. Spruce; stylish
29. Girl's name
30. Throws mock punches
32. Display; reveal
33. Excellent horseshoe throw
34. Barker's lines of chatter
36. Grew wan
39. Party spread
40. Trade center
42. Flying mammal
43. Betrayer: slang
45. Italian river

Solution is on page 364

ACROSS

1. Lamb's bleat
4. Not the top or bottom
8. Completely engrossed (in)
12. Circle segment
13. Clothed
14. A continent
15. Educator
18. Cut, as wool from a sheep
19. Ms. Bancroft
20. Ocean
22. Lock of hair
26. Pastors; clergymen
31. Hawaiian garland
32. Lincoln and Vigoda
33. Mine extract
34. Window ledge
35. Oolong, for one
36. Chitchat, as at a party: 2 wds.
38. Newsboy's cry
40. Affirmative vote
41. Woe!
44. Cello's "kin"
48. Quick to feel pity
52. Eye part
53. Waxer and waner
54. Small child
55. Bar brew
56. Dispatched
57. Certain Roman goddess

DOWN

1. Treble's partner

2. Foot part
3. Dull, steady pain
4. Makes points
5. Jackson 5's "— Be There"
6. Information
7. Paradise
8. Competitor in a speed contest
9. Cigarette residue
10. Pumpkin or pecan dessert
11. Road surface
16. Fertile desert spot
17. Picnic pests
21. Molecular unit
23. Charles Lamb's pen name
24. Exchange for money; vend

25. Smooth as —
26. Companion
27. Wild goat
28. Tidy
29. Time period
30. Depend (on)
34. Step
36. Bargain event
37. Pianist, Oscar —
39. Speeder's bane
42. Sleeve "fillers"
43. Foot covering
45. Mr. Preminger
46. Jump
47. Totals (up)
48. Vat
49. Resident of 7-Down
50. Word indicating a maiden name
51. Extremely long time

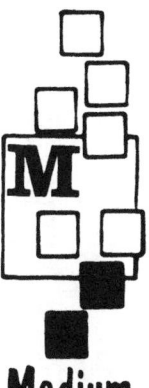

Medium

Solution is on page 364

ACROSS

1. Supreme Being
4. Misplaces
9. Salary
12. Ventilate
13. Spare; leftover
14. Dark bread
15. Smacks
17. New York baseball team
19. Church service
21. Understands
22. Fanatics
25. Relaxes
28. Either's partner
29. Breaks suddenly
31. Saucy
32. Neither's partner
34. Falls in flakes
36. Perish
37. Paradise
39. Consumed liquids
41. Exist
42. Stitched
44. Picked up the tab
46. Chopped
48. Spouse
49. Certain Post-office employees
52. Faints; falls (over)
55. In addition
56. Drench
58. Actress Farrow
59. Bandleader Brown
60. Lance
61. Solidify

DOWN

1. Car fuel
2. Lubricate
3. Theater offering
4. Piano instructions
5. Beast of burden
6. Pigpen
7. Epochs
8. More rational
9. Ironed
10. Affirmative word
11. Affirmative word
16. Chums
18. Retain
20. Remain in an upright position
22. Regions; areas
23. Wear away
24. Baseball or football
26. Clan
27. Spirited horse
30. Mass of bees
33. Compensation for good acts
35. Sports shoe
38. Adjacent (to)
40. Actress Jackson
43. Acts
45. Abounds (with)
47. Let fall
49. Actor Mineo
50. Dollar bill
51. Take to court
53. Fib
54. Used a chair
57. Brazil's continent: abbr.

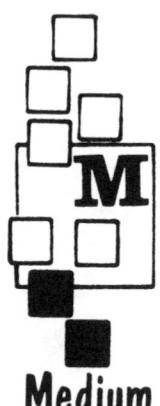

Medium

Solution is on page 364

ACROSS

1. Conserve
4. "Born Free" lioness
8. Pretense
12. Raconteur's collection
13. Merino mom's offspring
14. Nimbus
15. 1919 Sherwood Anderson work: 2 wds.
18. Seattle —, 1977 Kentucky Derby winner
19. Spry; nimble
20. Author Fleming
22. Make fun of
26. Sons: German
29. Turkish title
30. NT book: abbr.
31. Henry James novel: 3 wds.
34. Mantra sounds
35. Cover
36. Merits
37. Attack
39. Sea eagle
40. Howled (at)
42. Carry
46. 1930 Marc Connelly play (with "The") 2 wds.
50. "— Misbehavin'," musical revue
51. Affirm
52. Put away
53. Seed vessels
54. Lox store, for short
55. Parisienne's title: abbr.

DOWN

1. Peter Benchley novel
2. Indigo plant
3. Lion's pride
4. Overhead trains
5. Jacob's father-in-law
6. Complacent
7. Shorten
8. Farrier
9. Derisive cry
10. Arab name
11. Lea sound
16. "Dallas" name
17. Bit-by-bit fact finder
21. Of the wind
23. Stravinsky
24. Daybreak
25. Building wings
26. Portico
27. Electrical resistance units
28. Dame Myra —, pianist
29. Annex (with "on")
32. Frog perch: 2 wds.
33. South African tribesman
38. Aids, in a way
39. A Ford
41. Roof part
43. Utah city, near Provo
44. Word with "work" or "mate"
45. Ferrara noble family
46. Hiatus
47. Brazilian city, for short
48. Goal
49. Prefix with "monthly"

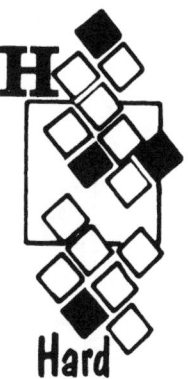

Hard

Solution is on page 365

Easy

ACROSS

1. Skip
4. Pea's "home"
7. Play division
10. Place for an ear-ring
11. Two-wheeled vehicles
13. Fired, as an arrow
15. Used oars
16. Adjusted again, as a clock
17. Wrinkles
19. Cut, as grass
20. More secure
22. Take part in a revolt
24. Scold constantly
26. Corn core
27. Singer, — Fitzgerald
28. Robert or Oliver
29. Drink, cat-style
31. Hawaiian greeting
34. Takes a chair
36. Thin, hard cookie
37. Name
39. Plant parts
41. "Over — Rainbow," Judy Garland hit
42. Ancient
43. Ease, as pain
44. Story
46. Item recorded in a journal
48. Grope (for)
49. Want
51. Exist
52. Dug, as an underground passageway
56. Sticky earth
57. Formal agreement
59. Musical group
60. Rescue
61. — Vegas, Nevada
62. Tell a fib
63. Small drink
64. Mr. Franklin
65. Carney and namesakes
67. Had an IOU
69. Passengers
72. Mr. Knotts
73. Merited
75. Tin container
76. Chief meal of the day, usually
78. Necessity
79. Shuts noisily, as a door
81. Heavenly body
82. Item for the blackboard
85. Skillet
86. Rule
88. Capital of Massachusetts
92. Judge's mallet
93. Lion's feature
94. Send out
96. Brazenness
97. Smallest bill
98. Festival
99. Scheme
101. Enjoy 76-Across
102. Vocalist's syllable
104. Paradises
106. Communion table
107. Tormé or Ott
108. Weary
110. Knowing
112. Flies, eagle-style
114. Deep pink
115. Fine fabrics
116. Vats
117. Strong longing
118. Mothers
119. Holy woman: **abbr.**

DOWN

1. In what way?
2. Fat
3. Foot levers
4. Wharf
5. Approves
6. Bambi, for one
7. Taking a nap
8. Tot
9. 2,000 pounds
10. Not high
11. Inhale and exhale
12. Harshly
14. Five pairs
15. Automaton
18. Uses a common seasoning
19. Burrowing animal
21. Flutter
23. Necklace piece
25. Strong wind
26. Beret, for one
30. Writing tool
32. Detested
33. Woe is me!
35. Branch of the U.S. Congress
36. Tender
37. Adolescent
38. Capri and Man
40. Narrow opening
43. Give temporarily
45. Make a mistake
47. Attempt
48. Enjoyment
49. Cleans, as furniture
50. Fished for congers
52. Recorded (music)
53. Toil
54. Tied, as a score
55. Lair
56. Female horse
58. Help
59. Auction offer
61. Boy
63. Solitary
66. Sight or taste
67. Above
68. Marry
69. Raced
70. Edge; border
71. Uppity person
72. Thick

74. Fishing-rod need
75. Walking aid
77. Twelve o'clock
79. Yellow-skinned fruits
80. Tastes
82. Conceit
83. Rave
84. Prevent
85. Ashen

87. Wither, as plants
89. Forest "residents"
90. Egg-shaped
91. Tennis need
93. Make angry
95. Browns, as bread
98. Web-footed birds
100. Fish of the salmon family
103. Broadcast

105. Enjoy a hot-weather sport
106. Noah's boat, and others
107. Woman's title: abbr.
109. Rogers or Clark
111. Montgomery's State: abbr.
113. Mr. Vigoda

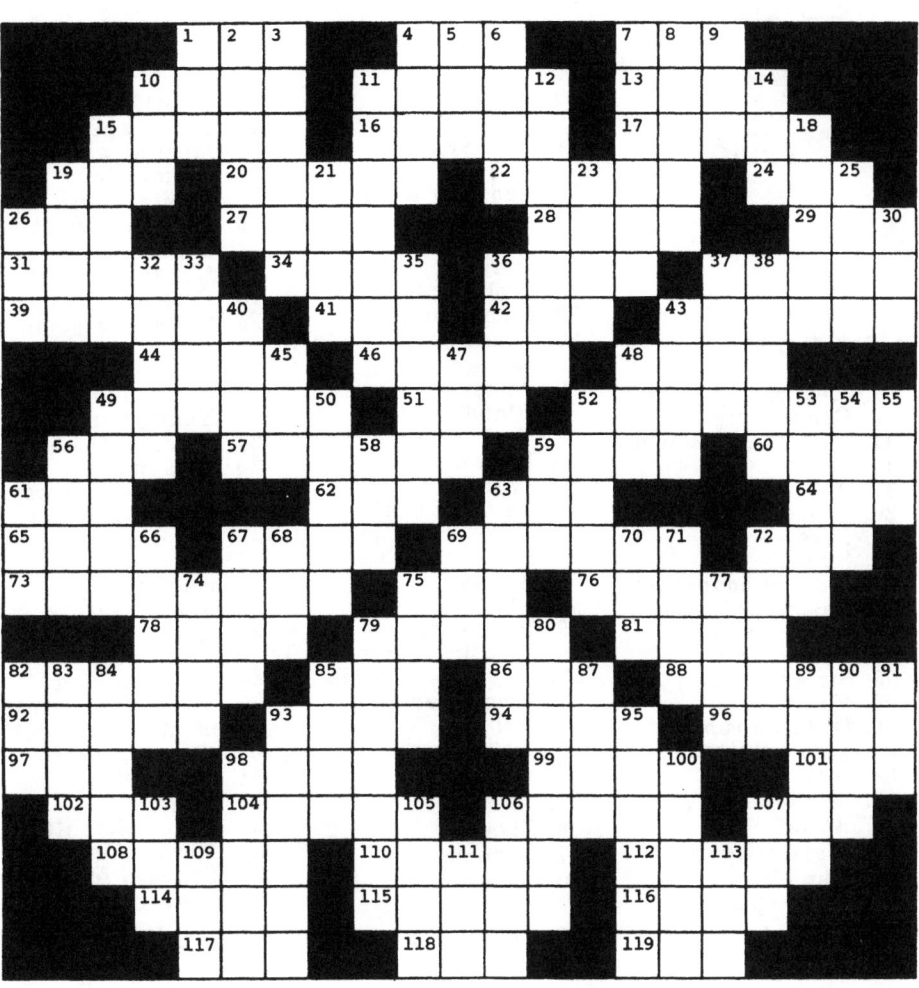

Solution is on page 365

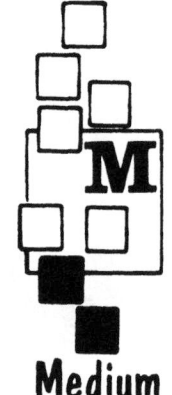

Medium

ACROSS

1. Meager
6. Chart; diagram
11. Portion of medicine
15. Deeds
19. Thick soup
20. Juliet's love
21. Level
22. Skin opening
23. Musical adaptation
25. Pasteboard item
26. Swing around
27. Row of seats
28. Strikes sharply
29. Wan
30. Distance runner
31. Distress signal
32. Girl
33. Ringlet
35. Racket
37. Walked vigorously
39. Small horse
40. Chess piece
41. Against
44. Employ
45. Pleat
46. Bailed
47. Also

48. Sheriff's group
51. Make —, hurry
52. Frosted
53. Acmes
54. Border (on)
55. Indefinite amount
56. Official positions
58. Succinct
59. Charged atom
60. Certain
61. Bonfire residue
62. Commotion
63. Chorus
65. Mountaineering spike
66. Skillful maneuvers
69. Elevate
70. Right now
71. Hockey disk
72. Shoe tip
73. Shoulder scarf
75. Keepsake
76. Baptismal bowl
77. Only
78. Wolf's call
79. Sports contest
80. Greek letter
82. Mimicked
83. Anger
84. Blunder: slang
85. Spring flower
86. Loud noise
87. Through
88. Tattered cloths
89. Make short, quick cuts
90. Admission card
93. Flash flood
95. Book part
96. Door in a fence
97. — Vegas, Nevada
99. Roman language
101. Drizzle
103. Not straight
104. Seasoning
105. Spoken
106. Choose
107. Auto device
110. Aware of the real nature: slang
111. Concerning: 2 wds.
112. Rub out
113. Sports palace
114. Composer of verse
115. Gaze

116. Clan emblem
117. Irritable

DOWN

1. Gaiters
2. Rare articles
3. Take into custody
4. At hand
5. Twice five
6. Thick lubricant
7. Frolics
8. Iowa city
9. Writing implement
10. Fiery
11. Transfer picture
12. Egg-shaped
13. Musical works
14. Terminate
15. Orbital point
16. Hobbyist's find: 2 wds.
17. Not false
18. Prophet
24. School mark
29. Use a lever
30. Intellect
32. Come in last
33. Young horse
34. Comprehension
36. Was in debt
38. Corrode, in a way
39. Sit for an artist
40. Bundles
42. Startled exclamation
43. Facial feature
45. Renown
46. Flax fabric
48. Two of a kind
49. Woodwind instrument
50. Kansas: 2 wds.
51. Trumpet
53. Trial
55. Three-piece item
57. Nautical cry
58. Stitched fold
60. Strongbox
61. Assistant
62. Actuality
64. Little brook
65. Card game
66. Food fish
67. Apple center

20

68. Planter's purchase
70. Large books
71. Cooking vessels
73. Tanker
74. Ripped
75. Mandarin orange variety
76. Turn over
77. Valuable fur
79. Butting animal
81. Great Lake

82. Small rodents
84. Cereal choice
86. The same
89. — Diego, CA
90. One behind another
91. Fills with joy
92. Natural ability
94. Guide
95. Petty gambler: slang
96. Honking birds

98. Wander
99. Fold of cord
100. Italian river
102. Measure of land
103. Use a mixer
104. Withered, to poets
106. Apple seed
107. TV unit
108. Paid athlete, for short
109. Gym pad

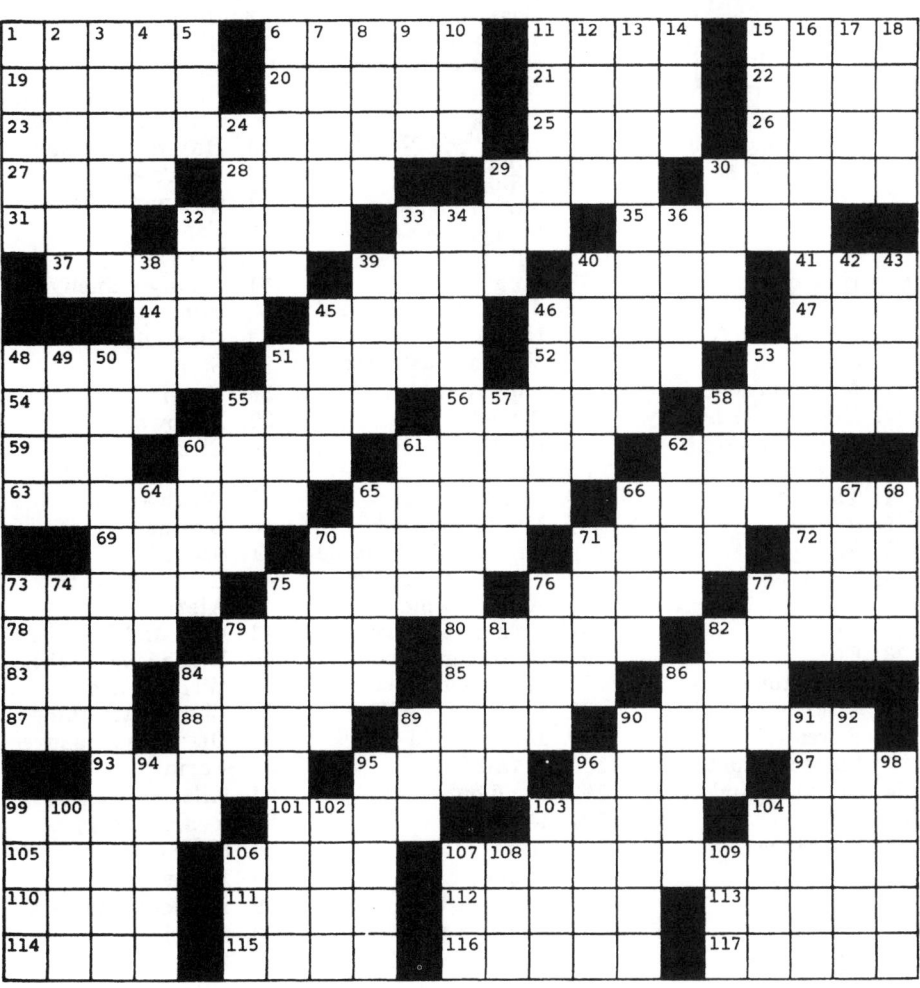

Solution is on page 365

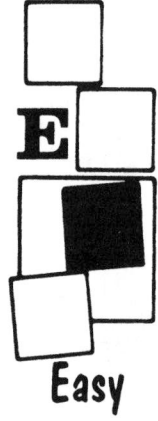

Easy

ACROSS

1. Cinnamon, for one
6. Jog
10. More mature
15. English resort city
19. Christmas song
20. Take on
21. Taunt
22. Region
23. Singly
24. Thought
25. Stringed instruments
26. Fuzz
27. Hamilton's bill
28. Creeping plant
30. Bureau
32. Picks up the tab
34. Stand behind
35. Task
36. Entrance
37. Fashion
40. Honks
41. Lass
42. Traveler's guide
45. Trotter
46. Worries
47. Jury

48. Be in the red
49. Andy's pal
50. School group
51. Labyrinths
52. Venetian-blind piece
53. Cushion
54. Use jointly
55. Highland musician
56. Tremble
57. Sports shoes
59. Heaped
60. Stares angrily
61. Like a sage
62. Coal worker
63. Journey
64. Makes as a profit
67. Strong winds
68. Makes believe
72. Valentine symbol
73. Ringlets
74. Adhesives
75. Not at home
76. Fairy-tale beast
77. Glides in the air
78. Magnificent
79. da Vinci's "— Lisa"
80. Chum
81. Vine or bush fruit
82. Empty space
83. Also-ran
84. Crafty
85. Loan
86. Shore
87. Most unsullied
88. Vallee, of film fame
89. Magicians' sticks
90. Asian staple
91. Lion's den hero
94. Challenged
95. Armored vehicle
96. Sack
99. Egg-shaped
100. Wrathful
102. Send out
104. Likeness
106. Aper
107. Memos
108. Shoe part
109. Artist's stand
110. Holiday nights
111. Machine parts
112. Foot digits
113. Marsh grasses

DOWN

1. Shoo!
2. Wan
3. Certain golf club
4. Anti
5. Raise
6. Meditate
7. Take a taxi
8. Raw metal
9. Instructors
10. "Do unto — ..."
11. Rental agreement
12. Dash
13. Sixth sense, for short
14. Brings back to the original condition
15. Haying machine
16. Diva's song
17. Camper's shelter
18. Fedoras
29. Frost
31. Bunny maneuvers
33. Bun
34. Game fish
35. Stop
36. Eatery
37. Fellows
38. Citizen of "The Eternal City"
39. Wear away
40. Bruins
41. Stared
42. Grinding tooth
43. Alert
44. Rose and Fountain
46. Emergency light
47. Writing need
50. Checkmate game
51. Distance measures
52. Form
54. Kilt
55. Yearns (for)
56. Slashes
58. Knowing
59. Medicinal tablets
60. Avarice
62. Wed
63. Elephant's snout
64. Uses an ax
65. Lawful

66. Ahead of schedule
67. Sentry
68. Botany specimen
69. Rope loop
70. Sand hills
71. Begin
73. Trite
74. Fescue
77. Young plant
78. Most happy

79. Additional
81. Sad and gloomy
82. Fido's treasure
83. More fortunate
86. Gentle touch
87. Brooch
88. Angers
89. Irrigate
90. Ranks
91. Rounded roof

92. Tel —, Israel
93. Title
94. Facts
95. Ceramic piece
96. Foundation
97. Ripened
98. Certain toothpastes
101. Fish eggs
103. Cow's cry
105. Actress West

Solution is on page 365

SPECIAL CHALLENGER CROSSWORD

"A MOVING EXPERIENCE"   **by EUGENE T. MALESKA**

Here is a real toughie for you. We have omitted giving you such helps as "2 wds.," "hyph. wd.," and "slang"; but in the spirit of fair play, all abbreviations and foreign words are so indicated.

ACROSS

1. Silent-siren Negri
5. — Dame de Paris
10. California army base
13. Archer's leather guard
19. Mimicked
20. Stem covering
21. Medieval poem
22. SCTV's home
23. Converse idly
26. Angel or jinni
27. Half a score
28. Buenos —
29. Mother-in-law of Ruth
31. Very: French
32. Samuel's teacher
33. Love: Scottish
34. German gentleman
35. Frightening
38. "Blacke's Magic" star
40. Tiny being
42. Appeased
45. Ages upon ages
46. "Bone up"
47. Gasconade
48. "— Jude," Beatles' album
49. Furnace feeders
51. Shelly —, jazz drummer
52. Only
53. Take measured steps
56. Where have you —?
57. Gratified completely
58. Action at Belmont
59. One: Spanish
60. Luau dish
61. Namely
63. Props for Solti and Muti

66. Sweet German bread
68. One-time basketball arena in Washington, D.C.
69. Actress Harper
70. Greek sun god
71. Up and about
72. Inquire after
73. Noun-forming diminutive
74. Antiquated
75. Baby animals
77. Scar on a car
79. Discard
80. "— Alice," Albee play
82. Resounds
83. Abstract notion
85. Metallic rock
86. Discontinue
87. "Space Oddity" rock star
88. "Our Gang" author
91. Most unpleasant
93. Palm leaf
94. More costly
96. Viscount Templewood
97. Congressman's "prize"
98. Dance step
99. Bombast
100. Appear
102. Age, as cheese
104. George or Marion Kerby, e.g.
106. Clay, today
107. Be agreeable to
110. Be patient
113. Bird or McHale
114. Summer drink
115. City that influenced farm boys?
116. Sharpen
117. Classify
118. "— Rosenkavalier"

119. Excalibur, for one
120. "Humdinger"

DOWN

1. Medium for Degas
2. Hamlet's girl
3. Like Elsa
4. Fuss; trouble
5. Vague idea
6. Dark yellow pigment
7. Bumbo or bogo
8. Lee's men, for short
9. Sound perception
10. Ball-bouncing game
11. Barber's tool
12. Per —
13. Belonging to a comic-strip character
14. Séance sound
15. "Peer Gynt" temptress
16. Suffer unrequited love (for)
17. Ms. Adams
18. "Peanuts" expletive
24. Quest of some scouts
25. Iago to Othello, e.g.
30. Archipelago component
34. Mortar trays
36. Job for Spade
37. Emulate Olivier
39. What the doctor ordered
40. To —, exactly
41. Capsize
42. Johnny-cake
43. Suffix with musket or profit
44. Color cloth
46. Flock of fowl
47. — the hatches
50. English horns' kin

24

51. "Pine Tree State"
52. Dole out
53. Promotional campaign
54. Prior: prefix
55. Be kept waiting
57. Dotted fabric
58. Pitcher's "boo-boo"
60. Walk wearily
62. Gallimaufries
63. Treat a turkey
64. Egypt's lifeline
65. Spore
67. Mariposa
69. "I Love Lucy" actress
75. Adman's "come-on"

76. Conical kiln
78. Site of Phillips University
79. Ancient portico
80. Cargo unit
81. Investor's option: abbr.
82. British noble
83. Scoter
84. Magician's word
86. Concern for Casey: abbr.
87. Trademark
89. Dreyfus trial subject
90. Greek
92. Shade of red

93. Probing remark
94. Ran
95. Bold poker player
97. Fine porcelain
98. Difficult puzzle
100. Humane organization: abbr.
101. Morays: old English
103. "If — a Hammer"
104. Torment
105. Poor-boy, in NYC
108. Raleigh's title
109. Outside: comb. form
111. Saturn's spouse
112. Sigma preceder

Solution is on page 365

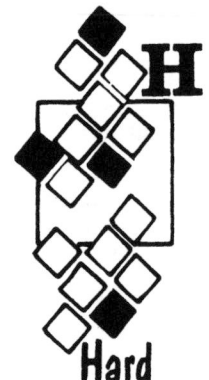

Hard

ACROSS

1. Pawns: slang
6. Famous name in tennis
10. Shadowbox
14. Meek one
15. Outline
16. A Great Lake
17. Product for the skin
18. Duad
19. Extremely
20. What astronauts train for: 2 wds.
23. Man's nickname
25. Gershwin, and others
26. Service station
29. Spouse
31. Wager
32. Trifle
33. Gets rid of
34. "The Invisible Man" author
36. "The Way We —," film
37. Word with "wave"
39. Board-game piece
40. Fertile spots
41. Obstacle
43. Decree
45. Makes confused
49. Russian plain
53. Blame: slang
54. Period
55. Spanish article
56. Certain horse
57. English college
59. From
60. Stadium cheer
62. Miss Ullmann
63. Lessee
65. Yearly
67. Rows
69. Moisture
70. Same
73. Greek letter
75. Suburb of Boston
79. Papal document
80. Nozzle
82. Nevada city
83. Moment
84. Express in greeting
85. Clothes: slang
87. Helix
89. Cover with a metal plate
90. Quiet!
91. Splendidly
94. Ruth's husband
96. Turkish title
97. Weeders
100. Concerned with
101. US playwright
102. Endorses
103. Pub order
104. Luge
105. Telegrams

DOWN

1. Monogram of FDR's successor
2. Triumphant exclamation
3. Criticized
4. Restrain
5. Ballet injury
6. Seemed
7. Narrow strips
8. Very small margin
9. Infuriates
10. Separate
11. Bishops
12. Publicize
13. King, in Madrid
21. Rowing team
22. Tank
23. Tiff
24. Move slowly along the ground
27. Triangular insert
28. Looks at
30. Despots
31. Ran together
35. Fibs
36. Dilute
38. Guitar's "cousin"
40. Fall month: abbr.
42. Scold
44. Land mass
45. Worry
46. Recent
47. Atop
48. Sneaky one: slang
50. Survey
51. Item for some beach-goers
52. Begrudge
55. Sea eagle
58. Pertaining to birth
61. Colors
64. Nothing
65. Concerning: 2 wds.
66. Cognizant
68. Burst
70. Recedes
71. Witty reply
72. Utmost
74. Wrote
76. 366-day period: 2 wds.
77. Objects
78. Very
80. Comedy's Phil
81. Word used with "shalt"
84. Hinder
86. Display a second time
88. Barber's item
89. Separate into shares
92. Man's name
93. Norse god
94. Apron part
95. United
98. Cereal grass
99. Draftee's group: abbr.

Solution is on page 365

DIAGRAMLESS

MEDIUM

This Diagramless is 15 boxes wide by 15 boxes deep.

ACROSS

1. Children's book, "Charlotte's —"
4. Journey segment
7. Dry, as the desert
9. "Miffed"
10. West Point students
13. Electrical mishap
14. Overly
15. Bangs (a door)
16. Shells out
19. Shipments from Detroit
20. Take —, happen
21. Old airplane: slang
23. Word with Patrick or Valentine
24. Sends via the post office
25. Once around the track
28. Swiss range
29. A la —, menu choice
30. Window glass
31. *Oui* or *Si*
32. Might; power
33. Exterior
34. Particle, as of soap
35. Scatter
36. Oceans
37. Newsman, Dan —
39. Commence
40. Bakery purchase
41. Bowling score
42. Messenger's chore
46. Chums
47. Paddock papa
48. Exist
49. Statute

DOWN

1. WAVE's "sister"
2. Stat for Dwight Gooden: abbr.
3. Offer
4. Weaving devices
5. Is mistaken
6. Obtain
8. Discover the true character of
9. Portion
11. Quality of sound
12. Turf
13. Bed boards
15. Weighing device
16. Loses one's footing
17. — out, succeeds
18. Less plentiful
20. Lacking color
22. Baptism is one
23. One's chance to speak
24. New Testament book
25. Afterward
26. Once more
27. For each
29. Shoreline
30. Free from pollution
32. Signal light
33. "...to see our-selves as — see us" (Burns)
34. Dreads
35. Move slightly
36. No longer fresh
38. Mimic
39. Practice boxing
41. Health resort
43. Be on the sick list
44. FDR program: abbr.
45. Grass moisture

Solution is on page 366

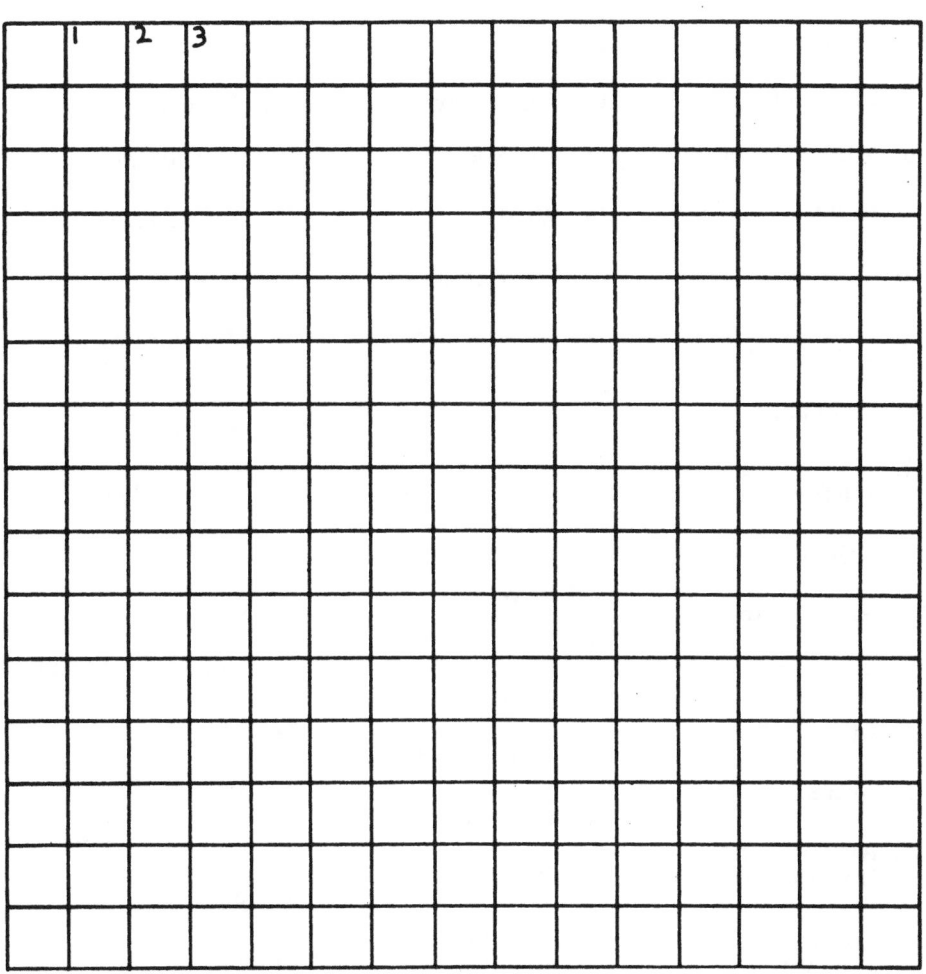

DIAGRAMLESS

MEDIUM

**This Diagramless is 15 boxes wide by 15 boxes deep.
Starting box is on page 377.**

ACROSS

1. Taxi passenger
5. Large pitcher
6. Miss Fitzgerald
7. Pump or loafer
11. Posed for a portrait
12. Yield
13. Misplaced
17. "It Had To Be —," old favorite
19. Call out to a ship
20. Nautical term
21. Spurns
23. Rips
25. Actual
26. Arthur Conan Doyle's duo: 3 wds.
33. Cliburn and Johnson
34. Della, of song
35. Rue
38. Shopper's event
39. Scent
40. Dine
43. Walked over
44. Taj Mahal site
45. Wrath
47. Scottish dance
48. Mr. DeBusschere
50. Paradise
51. Transmit

DOWN

1. Lawyer's charge
2. Shoemaker's tools
3. Receive and pass on
4. Muse of poetry
7. Student
8. Listen to and consider
9. Norse god
10. Congers
13. Wooden strip
14. Bread spread
15. Make airtight
16. Semester
18. Secondhand
22. Raven's cry
24. A few
25. Medical professionals: abbr.
27. — Diego, CA
28. Before: prefix
29. Try
30. Char
31. Norway's capital
32. Require
35. Bellow
36. Move sideways
37. Skin opening
41. Assistants
42. Commerce
46. Exact
49. Upshot

Solution is on page 366

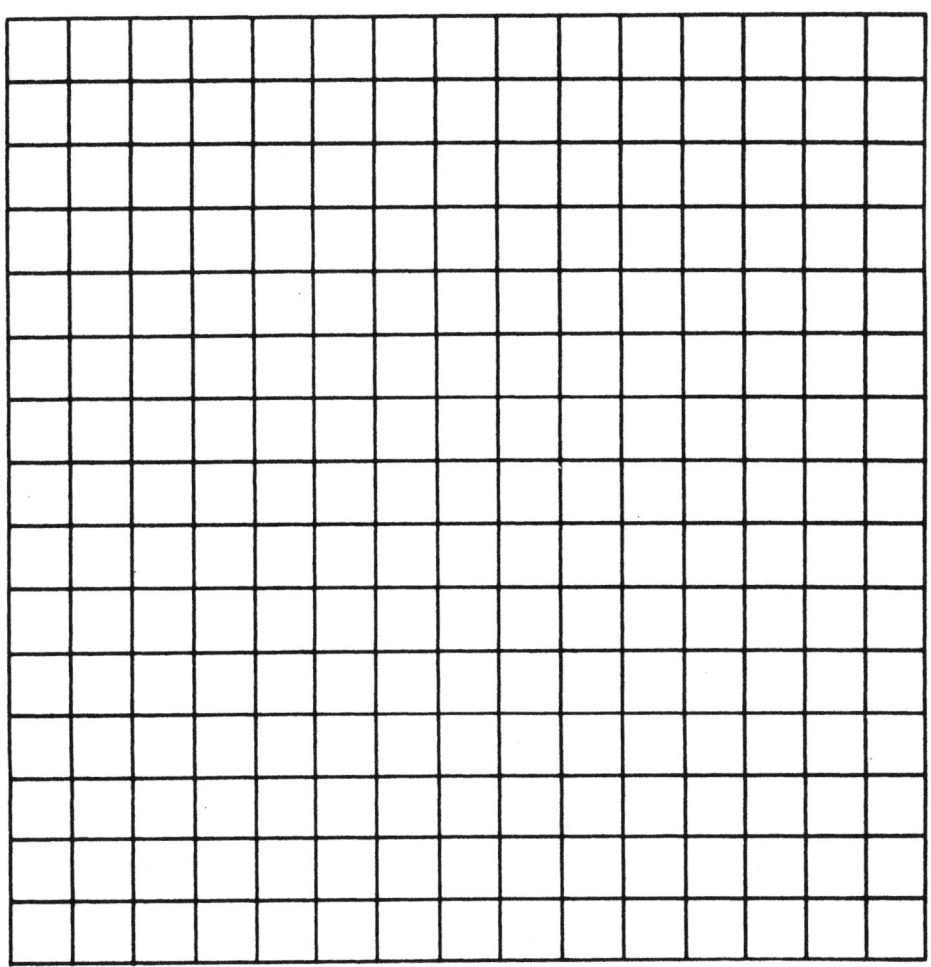

DIAGRAMLESS

HARD

**This Diagramless is 15 boxes wide by 15 boxes deep.
Starting box is on page 377.**

ACROSS

1. Deep cut

5. Killer whale

6. Theater sections

11. College VIP

12. Rapidly

13. Talus

16. Native-born Israeli

17. Jabber: slang

18. Sherlock Holmes, for one

20. Failure, as of memory

22. Howl; wail

24. Italian movie star

25. TV star, Tom —

27. Certain tests

28. Washington river and city

34. White vestment

35. Indian instrument

36. Kingdom

39. Low-lying stretch of land

40. Prevaricator

42. Cultivates

43. Not deceived by: slang

44. Approve

DOWN

1. Supreme Being

2. Region

3. Read hastily

4. Trickery: hyph. wd.

6. Highland maiden

7. Milky stone

8. Actor Kaplan

9. Light tan

10. Base, as of government

14. Endure

15. Fencing foil

19. Uproar

20. Entices

21. Anchovy sauce

23. Lounge lazily

25. Fly high

26. A Gardner

29. Aide: abbr.

30. New Zealander

31. Certain print type: abbr.

32. Shopping center

33. Greek war god

37. Connection

38. — Hari

41. Cowboy Rogers

Solution is on page 366

ACROSS

1. Fifth month
4. Singing group
9. What person?
12. Frost
13. Play —, pretend game
14. In what way?
15. Cake and coffee, for example
17. Shoulder covering
19. Rooster's mate
20. Stable booths
21. Change
24. In — of, regardless of
25. Guide
26. Use a razor
27. Mother
29. Hang down
30. Small rock
31. Marsh
32. All right
33. Pile, as of books
34. Drill (a hole)
35. Mako, for one
36. Planted (seeds)
37. Tables' partners
39. Cat's foot
40. Visit, as by a ghost
41. Ammunition
45. Circle part
46. Girl's name
48. Falsehood
49. Golf mound
50. Concluded
51. Lawyer's charge

DOWN

1. In the center: abbr.
2. Expert
3. Affirmative vote
4. Rallying cry
5. Brass instrument
6. Not at home
7. Exists
8. Uneasy; nervous
9. Sea mammal
10. Cry like a wolf
11. Night birds
16. Storage shelter
18. Detest
20. Child's punishment
21. Too
22. Plumbing problem
23. Label
24. Affect with surprise
26. Heavenly bodies
27. Greater amount
28. Grown old
30. See 24-Down
31. Gift adornment
33. Leg part
34. Soup dish
35. Liquid dressing
36. Lettuce dish
37. Informal talk
38. Tortoise's foe
39. Unmixed
41. Nip in the —, check early
42. Sprite
43. Bind (up)
44. Look at
47. One

Easy

Solution is on page 366

ACROSS

1. Owns
4. Ceases
9. Extreme degree
12. Tavern brew
13. Experiment
14. Exist
15. Actor Caine
17. Painting stand
19. Actor Hudson
20. Pounded heavily, as raindrops
21. Brook
23. Carefree
24. Permits
25. Alleys
26. California city: abbr.
28. Martino and Hirt
29. Blanket
30. Family member
31. Belonging to me
32. Best seller, sometimes
33. Short conversation
34. Singer Reddy
35. Elm's bounty
36. "Swipes"
38. Those people
39. Container
40. Keener
43. Up in the —, undecided
44. Prank
46. Half a pair
47. Young child
48. Express appreciation
49. Unusual

DOWN

1. Amateur radio operator
2. Actress MacGraw
3. Mysteries
4. Word with "smoke" or "hay"
5. "Star —," T.V. show
6. Lubricant
7. Harrisburg's State: abbr.
8. Railroad car
9. Mean
10. Beech or birch
11. Gripped
16. Garden tools
18. Swiss mountains
20. Quiz show group
21. — up, become silent
22. Depend (upon)
23. Safe place
25. Adores
26. Weight
27. Poker stake
29. Gather, like dust
30. Hair preparation
32. Well-groomed
33. Dear: French
34. Central core
35. "Jaws" "star"
36. Get out!
37. Threesome
38. Soon afterward
40. Health resort
41. Wrap up
42. Vermilion
45. Exclamation

Medium

Solution is on page 366

Medium

ACROSS

1. — Vegas
4. Driving impulse
8. Just
12. Actor,— Wallach
13. Emphasize
15. Take a chance
17. Seashores
18. Young dog
19. Speck
20. Allow to
21. Crafty
23. Delight
24. That woman
25. Some; no matter which
26. Greek letter
27. Rough, grating sounds
29. Play, "You Can't Take — With You"
30. Small stones
32. Memo abbreviation
33. Sour citrus fruit
35. Boy
36. Cut with an ax
37. Actor,— Torn
38. Annoy
39. Kitchen items
40. Behave
41. Passing fashion
42. Nothing
43. Sell in small quantities
45. Names (of books)
48. Exactly alike
50. Hardwood tree
51. Small hollow impression
52. Completed
53. Ironic, as a smile

DOWN

1. Table support
2. — carte: 2 wds.
3. Merely; only
4. Swallow eagerly
5. A single unit
6. Paid notice
7. Something used to lure game
8. Sunshine State: abbr.
9. Passageways between seats
10. Translate
11. Take a break
14. Decay
16. Purchase
19. Made twice as much
21. Lament; loud cry
22. Mediate
23. Quick thrust
24. Owns
26. "— Little Indians"
27. Bright color
28. Uses a needle
30. Soda
31. Slack; not rigid
34. Child's glove
36. Not solid
38. Legally sound
39. Cherry stone
40. Dry
41. In good physical condition
42. Cleopatra's river
44. Picnic pest
45. Yellowish-brown color
46. Organ of hearing
47. "The Firmament"
49. Person in charge of an army unit: abbr.

Solution is on page 366

ACROSS

1. Evergreen tree
4. Jungle weapon
9. Car-park area
12. Before: poetic
13. Word of greeting
14. Big fuss
15. Marriage; matrimony
17. Hot —, alcoholic drink
19. Noah's boat
20. Transport by truck
21. Intelligent
24. Fall back, as troops
27. Listen!
28. Cavities
29. Baton Rouge's State: abbr.
30. Wheel edge
31. Reacts to shocking news
32. Sardine can
33. 14th letter
34. Home plate, and others
35. Paper bag
36. Sahara, etc.
38. Radio parts
39. Country road
40. Deface
41. Florida city
43. — Bills, NFL team
47. Behave
48. Ledge
50. Fastener
51. Aye!
52. Beehive product
53. Kickoff gadget

DOWN

1. Not many
2. Make angry
3. Bright color
4. Not very tall
5. Actor, Gregory —
6. Huge deer
7. Actor Pacino
8. Revolves
9. Soup dipper
10. Strange
11. Plaything
16. "Happy" bird
18. Belonging to you and me
20. Assists
21. Tear (paper) into strips
22. Augusta's State
23. Body limb
24. "Love" flowers
25. "Wonderland" girl
26. Gasoline holders
28. It "makes waste"
31. Adorn, as with parsley
32. Dining bill
34. Ray of light
35. Swell of the sea
37. Bed planks
38. Chewy candy
40. Pack animal
41. Spring month
42. Winter driving hazard
43. Hogan of golf fame
44. Likely (to)
45. Tell a fib
46. Dollar bill
49. Sound from Santa

EASY

Solution is on page 367

ACROSS

1. Allow
4. Rallying cry
9. Actor Majors
12. Miss Gardner
13. Shelf
14. Shoemaker's implement
15. Nancy and Jimmy
17. Jacket part
19. Show the way
20. Franklin and Gazzara
21. Elbow, for one
23. Astronomer's study
26. Employs
27. Pursue
28. Mr. Martino
29. Fleur-de——
30. Decelerate
31. Bashful
32. Technical specialist: abbr.
33. Got up
34. Utensil
35. Vow
37. Darling
38. Marries
39. Frayed
40. Hurl
42. Sincere
45. Charged atom
46. Deserves
48. Paving need
49. Insect
50. Declare
51. Pigpen

DOWN

1. Statute
2. A Gabor
3. Adds up
4. Golf-shoe feature
5. Tend, as cattle
6. McMahon, and others
7. For example: abbr.
8. Set free
9. Pass, as time
10. Mama merino
11. Building wing
16. Berry and Follett
18. Singer Murray
20. "Dynasty" role
21. Mint —, drink
22. Dogwood
23. Stage
24. Lake —, Nevada
25. Underhandedly
27. Irritable
30. Spans
31. Shakespearean creations
33. So be it!
34. Ripped
36. Having debts
37. Steed
39. Desire
40. Little lie
41. Asner role
42. Historic age
43. Used a chair
44. Attempt
47. On

MEDIUM

Solution is on page 367

38

ACROSS

1. Throw out; evict
6. Muscle spasm
11. Not "with-it": slang
12. Prize
14. "Last Stand" general
15. United
16. Either . . . —
17. Rodent
18. Change; correct
20. Night before a holiday
21. Toward
22. Fence steps
23. Wood-splitting tools
24. Gives consent
26. Group of students
27. Roof edge
28. Beer suds
29. Sky-blue color
31. Itemizes again
34. Where the sun sets
35. Eucharistic metal plate
36. "— tu, Brute!"
37. "To be" form
38. Men, for short
39. One: Scottish
40. Thus
41. Bullfight cheer
42. Slip by, as time
44. Aide
46. Scraped harshly
47. Gratifies
48. Smacks

DOWN

1. Regard as identical
2. Righteous
3. Dine
4. Having artistic inventiveness
5. Wood-eating insect
6. Hag
7. Tear
8. Reverential fear
9. Parent, for short
10. Verifies
11. Fragment
13. Clothe
19. Certain trains
20. Tests
22. Intelligent
23. Actor Delon
25. Employ again
26. Cabbage salad
28. Chains; shackles
29. Flooded with water
30. Aughts; nothings
31. Hurried
32. Verb forms
33. Horse
35. Looks searchingly
38. Merriment
39. Engagement: abbr.
41. Choose
43. Botanist Gray
45. After "sol"

HARD

Solution is on page 367

ACROSS

1. Yarn; story
5. Surprise attack
9. Soda
12. Actor Alda
13. Land measure
14. Lobe location
15. Lease
16. Adolescent
17. Mistaken
19. Car-mishap result
21. Snakelike fish
23. Tell
27. Sprinkle (seeds)
31. Strange
32. Felix, for one
33. Water barrier
35. Canine
36. Scent
39. Truthfulness
42. Stay
44. For each
45. Press (clothes)
47. Get up
51. Precious stone
54. Castle's protective ditch
56. Shy; demure
57. Chablis, for one
58. Poker stake
59. Ram's mate
60. Give temporarily
61. Doe or buck

DOWN

1. Bull's-eye site
2. Pub brew
3. Arrive by plane
4. Go into (a building)
5. Baby's toy
6. Playing card
7. Anger
8. Cozy room
9. Church seat
10. Paddle
11. Expert
18. Tennis-court divider
20. Recent
22. Guided
24. Assists
25. Horse's gait
26. Irritable; tense
27. Wound mark
28. Concern
29. Tiny particle
30. Stadium cheer
34. Wipe (the floor)
37. Posted (a letter)
38. Atmosphere
40. More tidy
41. "To — is human . . ."
43. Wanderer
46. Not any
48. Frost (a cake)
49. Plant seeds
50. Organ of sight
51. Night bird
52. Crusted bakery treat
53. Advice columnist Landers
55. Devoured

EASY

Solution is on page 367

ACROSS

1. Young seal
4. A Barrymore
8. Summon
12. Commit a "boner"
13. Impolite
14. Bread spread
15. Black cuckoo
16. — and all, everybody
17. Word with "camp" or "strap"
18. Small window
20. Farm sight
22. Rogue
24. Car shelters
27. Memo
28. Volcano peaks
29. Musical tone
30. Poet's word
31. Fleece-lined jacket
32. "— Abner," comic strip
33. For instance
34. Masses of ice
35. Man's nickname
36. Make less important
38. Makes, as wicker chairs
39. Paddles
40. 16 ounces
41. Thailand, formerly
43. Hull
44. Wane
47. Highest point
48. Large amount
49. Flour grain
50. Jumble
51. Scorch
52. Tennis need

DOWN

1. Legume
2. Samovar
3. Secret
4. Parasite
5. Undersized plant
6. Dutch commune
7. You and me
8. Poisonous snakes
9. In a line
10. Mr. Durocher
11. Land parcel
19. Adam's wife
20. Relies (on)
21. Region
22. Massage
23. Like Eric the Red
24. Ravine
25. Cream of the crop
26. Preserves in brine
28. Wagons
31. Bartlett or Bosc
32. Lighthouse room
34. Finds fault with
35. Chess piece
37. Forms froth
38. Apple product
40. Actress Negri
41. Mr. Snead
42. Frost
43. Baked dish
45. By the —, incidentally
46. Wager
48. Writer's afterthought: abbr.

MEDIUM

Solution is on page 367

BIBLE CROSSWORD　　　MEDIUM

by RUSS CARLEY

Bible references in this puzzle are from the King James Version. You'll find it stimulating to solve, and may discover you know more about the Bible than you think you do.

ACROSS

1. He . . . gave also to — that were with him. *Luke 6:4*
5. Can the Ethiopian change his skin, or the leopard his —s? *Jer. 13:23*
9. — there be light. *Gen. 1:3*
12. The priest . . . bored a — in the lid. *II Ki. 12:9*
13. Blessed are the — in heart. *Matt. 5:8*
14. Seth . . . begat —s. *Gen. 5:6*
15. Have mercy — me. *Ps. 6:2*
16. He is r— from the dead. *Matt. 14:2*
17. I — no pleasant bread. *Dan. 10:3*
18. He — forth two of his disciples. *Mark 11:1*
20. Thy will be —. *Matt. 6:10*
22. His eyes were as a flame of f—. *Rev. 19:12*
23. They . . . cast him into the — of lions. *Dan. 6:16*
24. There was no —om or them in the inn. *Luke 2:7*
26. Man shall not live by bread —. *Matt. 4:4*
29. — mother in law saw what she had gleaned. *Ruth 2:18*
30. He that committeth — is of the devil. *I John 3:8*
31. How — wilt thou sleep, O sluggard? *Prov. 6:9*
32. A sower went out to — his seed. *Luke 8:5*
33. This is now — of my bones, and flesh of my flesh. *Gen. 2:23*
34. — I speak unto thee? *Acts 21:37*
35. A time of —, and a time of peace. *Eccl. 3:8*
36. Oh that I had — like a dove! *Ps. 55:6*
37. If thy right hand offend thee, cut — off. *Matt. 5:30*
38. A serpent — him. *Amos 5:19*

39. There came wise — from the east to Jerusalem. *Matt. 2:1*
40. A city that is set on an — cannot be hid. *Matt. 5:14*
42. Let there be no strife . . . between my — and thy herdmen. *Gen. 13:8*
46. I will not with ink and — write unto thee. *III John 13*
47. Ye shall eat . . . the roebuck and the fallow —. *Deut. 14:4, 5*
49. I will never l— thee, nor forsake thee. *Heb. 13:5*
50. —end unto me, and hear me. *Ps. 55:2*
51. They shall reign for — and ever. *Rev. 22:5*
52. Behold the fig —, and all the trees. *Luke 21:29*
53. — touched me? *Mark 5:31*
54. Because thou didst — on the Lord, he delivered them into thine hand. *II Chr. 16:8*
55. The kingdom of heaven is at —. *Matt. 3:2*

DOWN

1. Why hast thou — dealt with us? *Luke 2:48*
2. Now abideth faith, —, charity. *I Cor. 13:13*
3. —, the family of the Elonites
4. James . . . and John . . . were in the ship — their nets. *Mark 1:19*
5. Thou beholdest mischief and —. *Ps. 10:14*
6. He shall — the people together. *Deut. 33:17*
7. He said unto them, Exact no m— than that which is appointed you. *Luke 3:13*
8. Our vines have — grapes. *Song 2:15*
9. The fatness of his flesh shall wax —. *Isa. 17:4*

42

10. Neither suffer ye them that are — to go in. *Matt. 23:13*
11. Put it . . . upon the great — of their right foot. *Ex. 29:20*
19. How long will it be — they believe me. *Num. 14:11*
21. I have compassion — the multitude. *Mark 8:2*
23. His favour is as — upon the grass. *Prov. 19:12*
25. I will nourish you, and your little —. *Gen. 50:21*
26. We give thee thanks, O Lord God —ghty. *Rev. 11:17*
27. The full soul — an honeycomb. *Prov. 27:7*
28. They shall have . . . that which cometh of the sale of his patrim—. *Deut. 18:8*
29. Hope we have as an anc— of the soul. *Heb. 6:19*
30. Thou art the — of God. *Mark 3:11*
32. He — down. *Matt. 26:20*

33. He . . . — up their wounds. *Ps. 147:3*
35. He . . . causeth them to wander in the —ness. *Ps. 107:40*
36. The To— of Babel.
38. —ess them which persecute you. *Rom. 12:14*
39. Eat, drink, and be —. *Luke 12:19*
41. Lead us not — temptation. *Matt. 6:13*
42. He . . . hath lifted up his — against me. *St. John 13:18*
43. Call me not Naomi, call me —. *Ruth 1:20*
44. We shall be saved, — as they. *Acts 15:11*
45. He . . . healed them that had — of healing. *Luke 9:11*
46. The Lord . . . delivered me out of the — of the lion. *I Sam. 17:37*
48. Adam and —

Solution is on page 367

43

ACROSS

1. Parish priest
6. Military hat
11. Leg bone
12. Travesty's kin
14. Sarcastic
15. Sacred song
17. Be adequate
18. Common contraction
19. Album item, for short
20. Strange, in a way
21. Refusal
22. High and low
23. One hundred centavos
24. Small piece of jewelry
26. Pummels
27. Workbench item
28. Roman statesman
29. Formulate
31. Missions
34. Govern
35. Expose to great heat
36. Out of bed
37. At all
38. Soft cheeses
39. Exist
40. Currently popular
41. Laments
42. Italian island
43. French city: 2 wds.
45. Tumult
47. French city
48. Temptress

DOWN

1. Winner
2. Wading bird
3. Chew the —, ruminate
4. Capone
5. Italian painter
6. Gaiters
7. Nimbus
8. Limb
9. Boxing win: slang
10. Most strange
11. Dim
13. Children's toys: hyph. wd.
16. Kind
19. Tea
20. Criminal
22. Folklore creature
23. Flower part
25. Po Valley's land
26. European capital
28. King of Lydia
29. Opposite of robust
30. Small stream
31. Ireland, to poets
32. City on the Indian Ocean
33. Pike
35. Metal alloy
38. Beethoven's birthplace
39. African plant
41. — Tse-tung
42. Go astray
44. "— Lost Youth," Longfellow poem
46. Greek letter

HARD

Solution is on page 368

44

ACROSS

1. Mist
4. Tiny insects
9. Apply lightly
12. Female sheep
13. Cook in an oven
14. Frost (a cake)
15. Weave together
17. Garden implements
19. Beerlike brew
20. Shy; demure
21. Oyster gem
24. Jabs
25. Merit
26. Country roads
27. In the event that
29. Inquire
30. Rows, as of people
31. Dove's sound
32. Concerning
33. Beehive product
34. Weep loudly
35. Skating enclosures
36. Caesar or Waldorf
37. Playground attractions
39. Writing instrument
40. Glue
41. Birthday-cake decorations
45. Adam's wife
46. Saber
48. Valuable wood
49. Small, cozy room
50. Canvas shelters
51. Distorted

DOWN

1. Lawyer's charge
2. Possess
3. Receive
4. Ruffle
5. Misplace
6. Dine
7. While
8. "Diff'rent —," TV hit
9. Levees
10. Highest cards
11. Better than better
16. Caution
18. Fruit drinks
20. Cash
21. Bell-shaped fruit
22. Relieve
23. Noah's vessel
24. Window sections
26. Chain parts
27. Hawkeye State
28. Pleat
30. Most lengthy
31. Golden State: abbr.
33. Suggestion
34. Musical group
35. Ascended
36. Dispatches
37. Hastened
38. Flutter
39. Separate
41. Pro and —
42. Deep in pitch
43. Organ of hearing
44. Cloud site
47. You and I

EASY

Solution is on page 368

45

HARD

ACROSS

1. Clever
6. Popular garb
11. Cigar
12. Eradicate
14. Helmsmen
15. Restaurant
16. Gold: Spanish
17. Moral value
19. Self-esteem
20. Annoys
22. Sun: Latin
23. Heathen deity
24. Hawaiian feasts
26. — off, began, in a way
28. Divulge a secret: 3 wds.
33. Ancient instrument
34. Insipid
35. Deadly pale
38. Sweet potato
40. Knowledge
41. Greek letter
42. Flightless birds
44. Anger
45. Dress for 24-Across
47. Short snooze
49. Thoroughfare
50. Hard to solve
51. Window ledges
52. Perceive

DOWN

1. Saddle attachment
2. Island of Hawaii
3. In the past
4. Ceremony
5. Assays
6. Special celebration
7. Heroic poem
8. — *longa, vita brevis*
9. Widely known
10. Sweet sorghum
11. Pillaged goods
13. Implement
18. Impetuous person
21. Besmirch
23. Exemplary
25. Crafty
27. Abate
29. Auditions
30. Consecrates, in a way
31. Recite
32. One of the Seven Dwarfs
35. Shaw's "— and the Man"
36. Closes
37. Nymph of Moslem Paradise
39. Ridicules
42. *Affaire d'honneur*
43. Sensible
46. Man's nickname
48. Weight unit

Solution is on page 368

ACROSS

1. Night hooter
4. Forbidding; stern
8. Daring deed
12. Actor Marvin
13. Fishing cord
14. Speed contest
15. Private eye: abbr.
16. Ms. Sothern
17. Was concerned (about)
18. Elephant's "horn"
20. Car mishap result
21. Declare as holy
23. Park seats
26. Uncommon
27. Packing carton
28. Negative response
29. TV commercials
30. Coin-flip call
31. "My — Sal"
32. Chicago's State: abbr.
33. Items for a poker player
34. Stand up to; confront
35. Be worthy of
37. Kinds
38. Peel
39. Hospital section
40. Wild flower
42. Come in first
43. Sprite
46. Leer at
47. Small pie
48. Neither's partner
49. Solidifies
50. Thought
51. Pigpen

DOWN

1. Ancient
2. Tiny
3. Postman's deliveries
4. Drinking container
5. Skating area
6. Country hotel
7. "— and My Shadow"
8. Paris's country
9. Our planet
10. Expert pilot
11. Actor Knight
17. Pennies
19. Employ
20. Copes (with)
21. Pigtail
22. Cuplike spoon
23. Groom's mate
24. Make into a law
25. Foot bottoms
27. Slice (a turkey)
30. Linger
31. Flower sites
33. Stops
34. In favor of
36. "— the beans," reveal a secret
37. — Claus
39. Telegram
40. Canine
41. Grow old
42. Roll (of money)
44. Building site
45. Sauté
47. After "la"

EASY

Solution is on page 368

SHANEANIGANS   HARD

by TED SHANE

You'll find zany definitions in this crossword by Ted Shane, so please look out for traps. For example, the definition for 11-Down is "The Old Grind" and the answer is MILL. The clues are sly, so be careful.

Solution is on page 368.

ACROSS

1. Drink these very gin-gerly
9. Have their ups and downs; are often taken up only to be let down by women
13. Worst way to dish out steak and flattery
14. A lad that was a lamb
15. Gave up freedom and rights to enter into a union
16. How not to take a used-car salesman
18. Well-upholstered
20. They almost made the rounds, but were flattened in the end
21. Two tuney words after tra
23. Likenormously
25. What to do to troubles, collectors, and collisions
27. Mother's little shadow
28. Bullet served with rubber chicken at banquets
31. Realo Grande money
33. House of wacks
35. Mosquitoes' Mickey Finn: abbr.
36. Some of the interest is lacking
38. Sunday succulent, absorbed after Sunday supplement
39. When attached to the left, a conservative husband usually refuses them
41. Millions of things you can find for money
42. What a beautiful model can always be found in the best of
45. What to stay on with danger around
47. Messy party, according to the outsiders who plan to come in and clean up
49. Empire Stately tree
52. What the non-pushy get put
53. Gloomy Gus, Willie the Weeper, or Lachrymose Lou
55. Bridal shower
56. When he does this, it may be too taxing

DOWN

1. What Scotchmen do to the lawn with their teeth
2. Important St.
3. Describing cedar closets, rose gardens, and a perfume factory (attarboy, Shanel)
4. Front part of a train
5. Economically motionless
6. A famous racket
7. Where heap big brave makum his home: 2 wds.
8. Eye vision this
9. Kind of person with a lot of weight to throw around
10. This is the end of a Cinder
11. The Old Grind
12. Manufactures words
17. Non-muscular kibitzer—yells his head off urging 22 men to knock each other down
19. Kind of living a stripper makes
21. Less than half gladdened
22. eton fo namoW
24. This comes before payday
26. Has three legs and gets into hot spots
28. Corny things to relieve aching dogs
29. Taken in a hammock with a book

48

30. Small amounts
32. Cube root of one
34. Word for MacGloom and MacSullen
37. These get kicked over when wild oats are sowed
39. Call out the name of an evergreen: 2 wds.
40. Responses to some advances
42. Horseomatic drive

43. Member of the Arizona Braves
44. knird yt-tuN
46. The middleman for a seller
48. Good place to find a hot potato: abbr.
50. Gypsy whose story was told in brief
51. After altarations, women become attached to these: abbr.
54. Kind of famous Hollywood car

EASY

ACROSS

1. In favor of
4. 2,000 pounds
7. Chop (down), as a tree
10. Mimic
11. Performs alone
13. Before: poetic
14. Five pairs
15. "Carmen," for one
16. Tell a fib
17. Go into
19. Domesticated
21. Marry
23. Needlefish
24. Foundation
27. Outer garment for a showery day
32. In the past
33. Pieces of paper money
34. Fuss
35. Merited
37. Worry
38. Compete (for)
39. That woman
41. Filleted
44. Oscar or Emmy
48. Smallest bill
49. Senior
53. Deface
54. Highest card
55. Identifiable noise
56. Frozen water
57. Bright color
58. Cot
59. Morning mist

DOWN

1. Destiny
2. Not closed
3. What tenants pay
4. Spinning toy
5. Spanish cheer
6. Neither's "partner"
7. Ship's wheel
8. A Great Lake
9. Unwanted plant
11. Painful
12. Belonging to the Devil
18. Lamb's mom
20. Circle segment
22. Operate, as a car
23. Covers with a gold layer
24. Evil
25. Grow older
26. Distress signal
28. Pub brew
29. Rowing need
30. Fruit drink
31. Small child
33. Grooms' mates
36. First woman
37. Not many
40. Difficult
41. Wild hog
42. "— upon a time . . ."
43. Require
45. Among
46. Speed contest
47. Sketched
50. Tennis stroke
51. Payable
52. Conclude

Solution is on page 368

ACROSS

1. Glass container
4. Mixes
9. Fence opening
12. Mine output
13. Molar
14. Grow old
15. Tuck in: 2 wds.
17. Labor group
19. Ripped
20. Baseball great Musial
21. Aircraft
23. Increases: 2 wds.
26. Lariat
27. Assassinates
28. Not on your life!
29. Dollar bill
30. Extra
31. Poetic contraction
32. Exist
33. Harvests
34. Companion
35. Busy chores
37. Bakery items
38. Assistant
39. Walking stick
40. Indications
42. Accumulates: 2 wds.
45. Lyric poem
46. Reflection
48. Our country: abbr.
49. Turf
50. Short letters
51. Church seat

DOWN

1. Work

Solution is on page 369

2. "— You Lonesome Tonight?"
3. Bureaucratic routine delay: 2 wds.
4. Shop
5. Village
6. Charged particle
7. Direction: abbr.
8. Sleep: slang
9. Puts on, as weight
10. Time past
11. Author's need
16. Finished
18. Brief snoozes
20. TV headliners
21. Investigate thoroughly
22. Antisocial person

23. Open-handed blows
24. Join together
25. Sits for an artist
27. Digging tool
30. —, remits through the mail: 2 wds.
31. Shortens, as a hem: 2 wds.
33. "Singin' In the —"
34. Lion's "collar"
36. Stormed
37. Grottoes
39. Canary's home
40. Distress call
41. Marriage vow: 2 wds.
42. Took a chair
43. Put in service
44. Puppy's foot
47. "Show Me" State: abbr.

MEDIUM

ACROSS

1. Naughty
4. Office records
9. Pie — mode: 2 wds.
12. Self
13. In reserve
14. Chop off, as branches
15. Made a choice
17. Outline (a drawing)
19. Woody plant
20. Choir voice
21. Got to one's feet
23. Provides food
25. Damaged by use
26. Wild hog
27. That fellow
29. Tax organization: abbr.
30. Turns acidic
31. Angry
32. Myself
33. Sound an alarm
34. 5,280 feet
35. Rhymers
37. — -Dixon line
38. Pine Tree State
40. Bother
41. Group of eight
42. Enduring
45. Minute fraction: abbr.
46. New period in history
48. Actress Remick
49. Sound for "quiet"
50. Mean; unpleasant
51. Ram's mate

DOWN

1. River bottom
2. Ice or stone
3. Physicians
4. Lost color
5. Words of understanding: 2 wds.
6. Pot cover
7. Actor Wynn
8. Bird-hunting dogs
9. Ladd and Alda
10. Crazy: slang
11. Mimic
16. Golf club
18. Bright color
21. Do the crawl
22. Raced
23. Bridge groups
24. Merit
26. Watercraft
27. Angel's aura
28. Adam's garden
30. Add sugar
31. Rocket
34. Sail support
35. Throw (a ball) to the batter
36. Half a pair
37. Soft and thick
38. Velvety green plant
39. Makes a hole-in-one
40. True statement
42. — Angeles, California
43. Recent
44. Golly!: slang
47. Keystone State: abbr.

EASY

Solution is on page 369

ACROSS

1. Be flexible
6. Horse, e.g.
11. Archer's wrist guard
12. Gathers
14. Large ditch
15. Worldwide
16. Footnote abbreviation
17. Pallid
19. French article
20. Superlative ending
21. Robert Burns, for one
22. Otherwise
23. "Humdinger"
24. Expect
25. Flèche
27. Whistle sound
28. Corn
29. Change direction
30. Irene Dunne role
31. Musical group
32. Author's output: abbr.
35. Soviet security police: abbr.
36. Noted coloratura soprano
37. — Hari
38. Pencil part
40. Pain reliever, at times: 2 wds.
42. Glossy
43. Certain game players
44. Similar
45. Glorify

DOWN

1. Kaffiyeh wearers
2. Small crane
3. Sour
4. Enclosure
5. Molasses
6. Strength
7. Exclusively
8. Sci-fi item, for short
9. Cloudlike masses
10. Surveying instrument
11. Soft cheese
13. Weather word
18. Old French coin
21. Convinced
22. Pitcher
23. Ms. Minnelli
24. Spellbound
25. Fruit and wine punch: Spanish
26. — machine, arcade attraction
27. Ductile
28. Manufactures
29. Popular vehicle
31. Endured
32. Feminine name
33. Initiate
34. Is limp
36. Surreptitious look
37. Western sight
39. Emulate Debbie Armstrong
41. "Mr. Peepers" actor

HARD

Solution is on page 369

53

EASY

ACROSS

1. Cover (a present)
5. Paving material
8. Bitter quarrel
12. Shopper's carrier
16. Tresses
17. Singer Turner
18. Fairytale beast
19. Ones who walk back and forth
21. Assistant, as to a nurse
22. New rooms on an old house
24. Wide street
25. Football goal: abbr.
26. Wan
28. Actor Mineo
29. Rational
31. Pair of fives
32. — Hatteras, N.C.
33. Plead
34. Garden intruder
36. Mrs. Truman
37. Game tally
39. Car fuel
40. Rips
41. A la —, menu term
42. Train (a lion)

43. Camp bed
44. Creature
45. In favor of
46. Wrath
47. Writing tablet
48. Desire strongly
49. Horse's gear
53. Come back (to)
55. Stage in growth
56. Soft drink
57. Mr. Marvin
58. "I told you —"
59. Identical copy
60. Dromedary
61. Ocean
62. Tardy
65. Get on (a train)
66. Bargain events
67. Crooked
68. *Uno* or *une*
69. Dried plum
70. Certain drinks
71. Mate for Ma
72. Consumed food
73. Ventilates
74. Earth, for one
75. Snarl, as hair
79. Tooth doctor
81. Raves
82. Grow ill
83. Actor Howard
84. Pen "juice"
85. Prickly beauties
86. Country hotel
87. Magician's stick
88. Frozen rain
91. Bathtime bars
92. Perform in a play
93. Evergreens
94. Inky instruments
95. Paddles
96. Spanish cheer
97. Discover
98. Actress Gardner
99. Young goats
101. Fruit drink
102. Dispatched
103. Richmond's State: abbr.
105. Disposition; mood
107. Orange's "cousin"
111. Happily — after
113. Snoozes
114. A Great Lake
115. Blow (a horn)
116. Relax; take a nap
117. Strip of wood

118. Congressmen: abbr.
119. Underwater vessel, for short
120. Lays (a table)

DOWN

1. "— Price Glory?"
2. Surprise attack
3. Help; support
4. Get ready
5. Sea's rise or fall
6. Connecting word
7. Brings up
8. Aluminum wrap
9. Self
10. Vase
11. Dinner ender
12. Home for 33-Down
13. Pilot pro
14. One who leases
15. Most honest
17. Story
19. Skillet
20. Sight or taste
23. Price label
27. Mimic
30. Classifieds
32. Halley's, for one
33. Flying mammal
34. Use a loom
35. Make less severe
36. Farm building
37. Mix
38. Feel concern
39. Deity
40. Poke fun at
41. Reef material
43. Trash container
44. Cattle marking
45. Loses brightness
47. Con's opposite
48. Task
49. Residences
50. Otherwise
51. Observed
52. Place to sit
54. Utilize
55. Prepares (ahead)
56. Chef's or tossed
59. Place for trials
60. Phones
62. Fill, as a truck
63. Poker stake
64. Adolescent

65. Quick (pace)
66. Types, kinds (of)
67. Forbid, outlaw
69. Use watercolors
70. Ice-cream holders
71. Buddy
74. Hornets, for example
75. Metal for 43-Down
76. Big, as a piano
77. Sole; only
78. Finishes
80. Fastens (a knot)

81. Lion's sound
82. Hill-dwelling pest
85. Kind of chicken
86. Solid water
87. Seasons for 86-Down
88. Lovers' tiffs
89. Makes even
90. Tooth coating
91. Turf
92. Sounds a warning siren
93. Brooch

96. Lyric poem
97. Shoe "fillers"
99. Retained
100. Tax bureau: abbr.
101. Gets older
102. Pompous person
103. 3-piece suit part
104. — and crafts
106. Pod vegetable
108. Exist
109. Clip, as a bud
110. Debtor's note
112. 22nd letter

Solution is on page 369

MEDIUM

ACROSS

1. Well-behaved
5. Earliest
10. Tangled mass
14. Do a butler's work
15. Boise's State
16. Regional
18. City road
19. Tailor
20. Expanded
22. Amateur radio operator
23. Snug places
25. Back of the neck
27. Word with "break" or "care"
28. Spoken
30. Distress signal
31. Gardener's item
33. At this point
34. Fine
36. Forays
37. Cautions
38. Affirmative vote
39. Word of greeting
40. And not

41. — down, made less harsh
44. Sample
45. Instigates
49. Copycat
50. Leases
51. Appraise
52. Be in debt
53. Church bench
54. In the —, likely to happen
55. Set of twelve
56. Compete
57. Poet's word
58. Show disapproval
59. Dealt (with problems)
60. Give temporarily
61. Small fish
63. Used asphalt
64. Auctions
65. Commissioned officer: abbr.
66. Wrinkles
67. Obese
68. Drops
71. Obeys
72. Cringed
70. Translucent gem
77. Sticky
78. Average
79. Perform a second time
80. Paddle
81. Sudden, quick movement
82. Muscular power
84. Dessert choice
85. Motorist
87. Fill with joy
90. Wooden shoes
92. Spoil
93. At no time
94. Rows of seats
95. Soviet news agency
96. Oozes
97. Editor's term

DOWN

1. Bonn native
2. Mine yield
3. Kiln
4. Hates
5. Boxing weapons
6. Roman date
7. Unprocessed
8. Pronoun
9. Whirlwind
10. Incline
11. Bob, of comedy
12. Expert
13. Silly fellow
14. Gape
17. Gain knowledge
18. Boutique
21. Tints
24. Sauce used in Chinese cooking
26. Public notices
29. Coat
31. Seasons
32. Heap
33. Jack rabbit
35. Guided
36. Takes a break
37. Females
39. Farm workers
40. Renowned
41. Uses an adhesive
42. "Aida," for one
43. More recent
44. Succinct
45. Disconcerted
46. John Updike creation
47. Interlace
48. Sows
50. Pours down
51. Uses a lasso
54. Does a gymnast's exercise
55. Peace symbols
59. Treat for Junior
60. Subsequently
62. Secluded valley
63. Half a quart
64. Adage
66. Takes advice
67. Woodlands
68. Sustenance

69. Separately
70. Rodeo item
71. Deface
72. Discharge: slang
73. Do a journalist's work

74. Prepares for publication
75. Accomplishes
77. Portions
78. Wharves
81. Lairs

82. Stage
83. Stay
86. By way of
88. Songstress, Peggy —
89. Hail!
91. Social insect

Solution is on page 369

HARD

ACROSS

1. Butter servings
5. Shade tree
10. Resist authority
15. Hawaiian island
19. Reverberate
20. Actor Flynn
21. Escape from
22. Czech river
23. Seed covering
24. New York county
25. "Key —," 1948 film
26. Thin
27. Happened as a consequence
29. Greek letter
31. Subscription extensions
33. Relate
34. Colorado city
36. Male parent
37. Experience again
40. Butcher's blade
42. Texas city
46. Metal mixture
47. "Barney Miller" actor, Jack —

48. At no time
50. Sticky matter
51. Baseballer Musial
52. Bee's "bite"
54. Seine, for one
56. Eastern European
57. Cannon sound
58. Black eyes: slang
60. Slackening
62. Ingested
63. Food fish
65. Totally: 2 wds.
67. B-complex member
69. Exclamation of sorrow
70. Sleep sound
71. Wild goat
72. Enthusiasm
75. Architecture style
76. Appreciative
80. Woodland deity
81. Massenet opera
83. Soup thickener
85. Summer: French
86. Troubles
88. — Flow, Scotland
90. Pipe part
91. Spouse
92. Golfing great
94. Construct
96. Elected ones
97. Sager
98. — system
100. Skilled gymnast
102. Food-storage room
103. Celebes ox
105. Alpine region
106. Spanish painter
107. "La —," Mona Lisa
111. Research room
112. Salve
116. Wander about
117. City of India
119. Tropical plant
121. Notion
122. Kentucky county
123. Of the eye
124. At right angles to a ship's keel
125. Nil
126. Armed conflicts
127. Halts
128. Earth: Latin
129. Seth's son

DOWN

1. Bosc, for one
2. Land measurement
3. "— Is the Army," 1943 film
4. Liquid mixture
5. Courage; fortitude
6. Asian gazelle
7. Poke
8. Fireplace fuel
9. Pass, as time
10. Baseball pitcher
11. High note
12. Actor, Raymond —
13. Margins
14. Autumn meteor-shower
15. Texas sights: 2 wds.
16. Cruising
17. Cure
18. Coffee servers
28. Impose (a tax)
30. Extend over
32. Important periods
34. Solo
35. English P.M. Chamberlain
37. Grating sounds
38. Rock singer John
39. Camel's cousin
40. Invents (a word)
41. Make merry
43. Pale purple
44. Violin designer
45. — Hills of Rome
47. Displaces
49. Soak (flax)
52. Sword cases
53. Pulverize
55. Football return
58. Divide into parts
59. Snubber
61. Michelangelo statuette
64. Average state
66. Tapestry
68. Cutting tool
70. Distrust
71. Clubs for Trevino
72. Muscular contraction
73. Patriot, Thomas —
74. Narrow waterway

75. Jeweled headdress
76. Huge being
77. Banquet
78. Complete; total
79. Wary
82. High card
84. Small bottle
87. Syrian nomads
89. Certain paints
91. Reduce

93. Flintstone's pet
95. The Pentateuch
97. Mr. Disney
99. Certain apartments, for short
101. Bay lynx
102. Colon's country
104. Highly skilled
106. Iraqi currency
107. Cultivate

108. Hawkeye State
109. Finished
110. Voice range
112. Unique person
113. Paradise
114. Roman emperor
115. New Mexico resort town
118. Aware: slang
120. Actor Vigoda

Solution is on page 369

SPECIAL CHALLENGER CROSSWORD

"CITY, STATE"   **by LOUIS SABIN**

Here is a real toughie for you. We have omitted giving you such helps
as "2 wds.," "hyph. wd.," and "slang"; but in the spirit of fair play,
all abbreviations and foreign words are so indicated.

ACROSS

1. Lhasa —
5. Cost-conscious shopper's concern
10. Play opener
14. Oil: comb. form
18. Alum
19. Showed twice
20. 1957 Cy Young Award winner
21. One of the Maverick brothers
22. "Silver State" city
24. "Buckeye State" city
26. Outermost point
27. But: Latin
28. Varied
29. "Reflections in a Golden —"
30. Sagacious
31. O'Hare abbreviation
32. Take heed!
33. — generis
34. Renews a CD
36. Make a choice
39. Syndicated sitcom
43. "West Side Story" actress
45. French number
46. Psychologist May
48. Declare invalid
50. Singer Cole
51. Samovars, e.g.
53. Loose overcoat
54. Lodger
56. Ms. Andrews
58. Toppling
60. Advisers to 53-Down
62. Noted seamstress
63. Oriental tea
64. Cartoon squeals

65. "Wolverine State" city
69. Italian winegrowing region
72. George Hamilton's trademark
73. Star of the silents
74. Greets
78. Soft-shell clams
80. Prevent by law
82. PBS series
83. Classified item
84. Corn spikes
86. Dowser's tool
88. Composer Erik
89. "A Lesson from —"
90. NHL great
91. Small eggs
94. "Big River" character, for short
95. Saul's grandfather
96. Carries on
99. Bog
101. Latin I word
102. Miner's quest
103. Liturgy
104. Bottle cap, for one
107. Took the leading role
111. Assam silkworm
112. California city
114. "Last Frontier" city
116. "Lone Star State" city
117. Change for a five
118. Iroquoian Indians
119. Castle or Dunne
120. Lodgings
121. "As cooks go she —" (Saki)
122. Watch over
123. North Sea sights
124. Dirk

DOWN

1. Come to terms
2. "Big wheel" on campus
3. À votre —, to your health
4. Scent
5. Bonus; reward
6. Change
7. Up in arms
8. Elizabeth — Stanton
9. Alfonso's queen
10. Footless animal
11. President Coolidge, to pals
12. Symbol of peace
13. Put in writing
14. Musette
15. Bolger-Garland costar
16. Goddess of discord
17. Sioux
20. Real bargain
23. Up-to-the-minute information
25. Exceeded the limits
27. "Show Me State" city
31. Cosmic cycle
32. Paragon: var. sp.
34. Taxpayer's form
35. Day of the week: abbr.
36. Stan's "sidekick"
37. Thick board
38. Blacksmith's tool
39. Antony to Cleo, perhaps
40. Celebes ox
41. Supercilious one
42. Mortify
44. Indian sovereignty

47. "Beehive State" city
49. Ms. Horne
52. Withstand
53. Bush's boss
55. Leased
57. Lumberjack
59. Greek letters
61. Emperor of Russia
66. Newspaper extras
67. Vocal group
68. Woe is me!
69. Dam site
70. "Old hat"
71. Member of 67-Down
75. Nobel Peace Prize recipient

76. Masculine name
77. Ask for
79. Cosmetic purchase
81. Country on the Baltic: abbr.
85. Noted Onassis, for short
87. Outlining
90. How certain challenges are met
92. Winner's sign
93. Posh benches
97. Brunch favorite
98. Bayes and namesakes

100. In apple-pie order
103. Less experienced
104. Poisonous compound
105. Siouan language
106. Out-of-date
107. Schusser's delight
108. Vocal pitch
109. May it be so!
110. Musical interval
111. — out, supplemented
112. Angry or aching
113. Beatty film
115. Sermon subject
116. Item for baby

Solution is on page 370

DIAGRAMLESS

EASY

This Diagramless is 15 boxes wide by 15 boxes deep.

ACROSS

1. Corn remnant
4. Saudi native
6. Snoop (into)
9. Challenge
10. Regret
11. Dairy animal
14. Units of instruction
16. — in, collapse
17. Command to Fido
18. Drilled (a hole) into
19. Hoover or Grand Coulee
21. Less polluted, as water
22. Spud bud
23. Shot (a gun)
24. Watches one's weight
26. Trap
28. Number "for tea"
31. Fence steps
32. Knight's title
33. Mournful sounds of pain
34. Boy
36. Great Lake
37. Provide refuge for
41. Word on a Hamilton bill
42. Ventilate (a room)
43. Foretelling sign
45. For each
46. Emulated a jockey
47. At this time

DOWN

1. Not-so-nice gent
2. By mouth
3. Reveals; discloses
5. Next to
6. — and con
7. Stocking mishap
8. Word of consent
11. Showed concern (for)
12. "Somewhere — the rainbow"
13. Marry
15. Don't go!
16. Apple center
18. Splits open
20. Olympics awards
21. Deep hole
23. Tuition charge
25. Dublin's country: abbr.
26. Blemish; blot
27. Shoe size
29. Humorist Rogers
30. Eloquent speaker
31. Painful to touch
33. Player at Shea Stadium
35. Fiend
37. Tree fluid
38. Hasten
39. Make a mistake
40. Make over
44. Modern

Solution is on page 370

1   2   3

DIAGRAMLESS

**This Diagramless is 15 boxes wide by 15 boxes deep.
Starting box is on page 377.**

ACROSS

1. Places for science experiments
5. Act in a theatrical manner
7. "Yes" vote
10. Burrowing creatures
11. Responds (to)
14. Mr. Preminger
16. — Picchu, Peru
17. Ms. Negri
21. Finely layered rocks
24. Novelist Murdoch
25. Very small creature
26. Knotty swelling
27. Well-timed; right for the purpose
31. Operatic melody
34. Indicator of wind direction
35. Immense
36. Prayer
39. Villa d' —, Italian fountains site
40. Different (than)
42. River of the Pharaohs
46. Store (green fodder)
47. Jeweler's measure
49. Shout of triumph (at a bullfight)
50. Eject (from an apartment)
51. Architectural pier

DOWN

1. Moon-trip vehicles: abbr.
2. I love: Latin
3. — tie, string tie with sliding clasp
4. Let it stand: printer's term
6. Superlative ending
7. Equip (with)
8. Cheers of encouragement
9. Apiece
12. Winner: slang
13. Famed Dutch flower
15. Express (an opinion)
18. Gold: Spanish
19. Cover
20. Enzyme suffix
22. Ike's area of command: abbr.
23. Automatic control system, for short
27. Made from a certain cereal grass
28. Paving substance
29. Labor organization
30. Hornets' dwellings
31. Wide street: abbr.
32. Ethiopian title
33. Ending for "left" or "art"
37. Akron's State
38. Actress Carter
41. Caddoan Indian
43. Word with "pick" or "cube"
44. Molten rock
45. Ireland, to Yeats
46. Kett, of the comics
48. Performance segment

Solution is on page 370

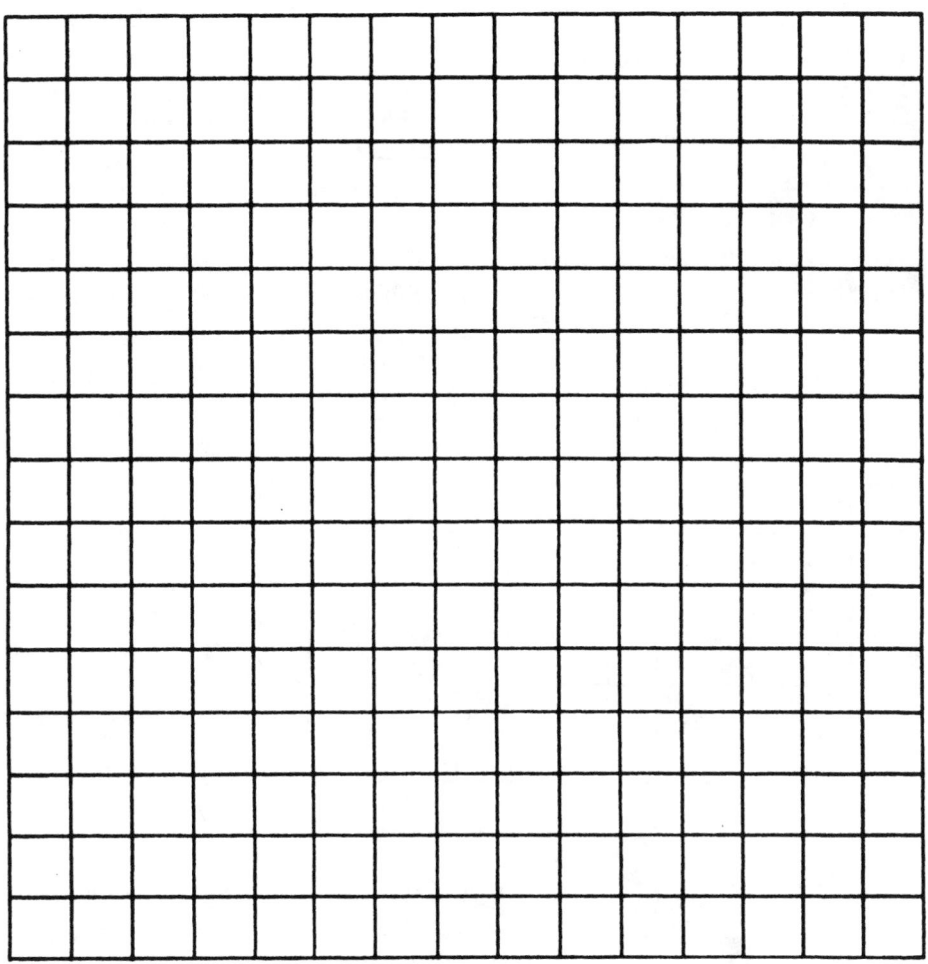

ACROSS

1. Acting company
5. Any
9. Sacrificial table
11. Employed
12. Blackboards
14. Buccaneer
15. Very warm
16. Dunces
18. Five pairs
19. Very moist
21. Deep in pitch, as a voice
22. Pea container
23. Does a jack-knife
25. Ventilate
26. Bring back to an original state
28. Gender
29. Avoid
31. Young man
32. Grow older
33. Transgression
35. Nothing
36. Legal property claims
38. Decay
40. Entertained
42. Composed; calm
44. Nibbles
45. Ocean movements
46. Goulash or ragout
47. Nuisance

DOWN

1. Money
2. Permit; let
3. Declared
4. Make lace
5. Knight's title
6. Public speaker
7. Allotted
8. Biblical garden
10. Bright color
11. That man's
13. Shoe bottoms
14. Church seat
17. Mailing cost
20. Weary
22. Wharves
24. Annoy; irritate
25. Exist
27. Baking chambers
28. Military greeting
30. Long, angry speech
31. Restrict (to)
32. Assist
34. Short letters
35. Arrests
36. Band leader Brown
37. Matching group
39. Quiz
41. Stitch
43. Short swim

MEDIUM

Solution is on page 370

66

ACROSS

1. Concealed
4. By oneself
9. Golfer Snead
12. Wedding vow: 2 wds.
13. Challenges
14. Hint
15. Tic- — -toe
16. Dollar bill
17. Indian groups
19. Grow weary (of)
21. Emulates an artist
22. Small rock
24. Idiots: slang
25. — a living, work
26. Relieved (a pain)
27. In the direction of
29. Overhead trains
30. Travel fees
31. Funnyman Caesar
32. Myself
33. Farm buildings
34. Ran away
35. Makes dirty, as linen
36. Homeowners' documents
37. Nickname for a very thin person
39. Walk in water
40. West Point student
41. Use a chair
42. Actor Johnson
45. Snacked
46. Wear away gradually
48. Adam's mate
49. Actor Danson
50. Ate in style
51. Stitch

DOWN

1. Wallop
2. "Apple cider" girl of song
3. Physicians
4. Idolize
5. Division of traffic
6. Raw metal
7. Compass point
8. Flees (from prison)
9. Reads (a page) quickly
10. Uncle's wife
11. Sloppy condition
18. Told a fib
20. Country lodge
21. Sits for an artist
22. Appear (to be)
23. Story
24. Mends (socks)
26. Ahead of time
27. Fastened
28. — and ends
30. Swooned
31. Shirt parts
33. Canine treat
34. Nourished
35. Agreed (with)
36. Old-fashioned
37. Shoo!
38. Actress Jackson
39. Broad
41. Junior, to Dad
43. Wide street: abbr.
44. Modern
47. Its capital is Providence: abbr.

EASY

Solution is on page 370

ACROSS

1. Umpire's call
5. L.A. team
9. Cut (hair) short
12. Ireland: poetic
13. Once more
14. Copy
15. Charm; lure
17. Support for a painting
19. Biblical boat
20. Yield
21. Journey segment
24. Palm fruits
25. Queue
26. Enjoys
27. Preposition
29. Tack on
30. Safe place
31. Vat
32. At
33. Arouses
34. Food
35. Whittles
36. Like some days or dispositions
37. Discolors
39. Caldron
40. "Product" of haste
41. Outcomes
45. Likely
46. — out, exclude
48. Rod's partner
49. Spelling contest
50. More or less
51. Whirlpool

DOWN

1. Word with "lion" or "dog"
2. Picasso's field
3. Suitable
4. Infuriate
5. — and ruin
6. Colonized insect
7. Eastern State: abbr.
8. Add honey to
9. "Bags" on a diamond
10. Candid
11. Hit hard: slang
16. Exist
18. Brewery output
20. Scours (through)
21. Thick slice
22. Shipshape
23. Plus
24. Nose —, sudden drops
26. Minnesota sights
27. Revolution
28. Do as told
30. Horse gear
31. Sunner's goal
33. Stay
34. Days to come
35. Adhesive
36. Plea at sea
37. Mop, aboard ship
38. Record, in a way
39. Rose or Rozelle
41. Island brew
42. Shepherded
43. Hall-of-Famer Williams
44. Stallone's nickname
47. Westward —!

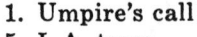

MEDIUM

Solution is on page 370

ACROSS

1. Bowlike curve
4. Turf
7. Youth
10. Indigent
12. Belonging to us
13. — dream, fantastic idea
14. Stubborness; grit
16. Prophetic sign
17. Small bottle
18. Group of stars
20. Brittle
22. Stockings
23. Ethnic group
24. Seeks out: 2 wds.
28. Garfunkel
29. Repairs
30. Put down
31. Communications
33. Lessen
34. Woeful cry
35. Yearns (for)
36. Tingle
39. Feline sound
40. Authentic
41. Flood
45. Rainbow
46. Decade
47. Hindrance
48. Males
49. Still
50. Even number

DOWN

1. Fitting
2. Fish eggs
3. Jailbirds
4. Stain
5. Away from home
6. Textile products: 2 wds.
7. Capital of Peru
8. Summit
9. Dispute
11. Boost
13. Krakow natives
15. Beret or tam
19. Inquires
20. Stuff
21. Unusual
22. Sharpens
24. Lawfulness
25. Glaringly bad
26. Pledge
27. Cereal grasses
29. Shaded walk
32. Schooner features
33. Aviary residents
35. Heavenly body
36. Well-proportioned
37. Hither
38. Precipitation
39. Football kick
42. Born: French
43. A marble
44. Self

HARD

Solution is on page 371

ACROSS

1. Wiggle, as a tail
4. Postage need
9. Southern State: abbr.
12. Ms. Gabor
13. Not the winner
14. For each
15. "Swan Lake" and "Giselle," for example
17. Likeness
19. Paid notices
20. Always
21. Portents
24. Exploded
27. Sit for an artist
28. Chairs
29. California city: abbr.
30. Actress Arden
31. Dinner dish
32. In favor of
33. Do, —, mi . . .
34. Mary Tyler —
35. Recording "ribbon"
36. Picasso and Van Gogh
38. Tardier
39. Picnic pests
40. Knight's title
41. Slip
43. Ceased
47. Actor Linden
48. Mature
50. Mine deposit
51. Sullivan and McMahon
52. Breaks suddenly
53. Cooking vessel

DOWN

1. Spider's creation
2. Ms. Gardner
3. "My — Sal"
4. Winter toys
5. Small children
6. Donkey's kin
7. Myself
8. Not public
9. Not together
10. Lower limb
11. Exist
16. Country road
18. Army meal
20. Make happy
21. "Aida" or "Carmen"
22. Furniture carrier
23. Compass point
24. Chicago team
25. Secretly wed
26. Challenger
28. Coin openings
31. Placards
32. Obese
34. Obey
35. Rainproof canvas cover
37. Follows
38. "Kings" of the jungle
40. Pace
41. The girl
42. Young boy
43. Health resort
44. Soda
45. Historical period
46. Cozy room
49. At home

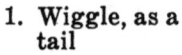

EASY

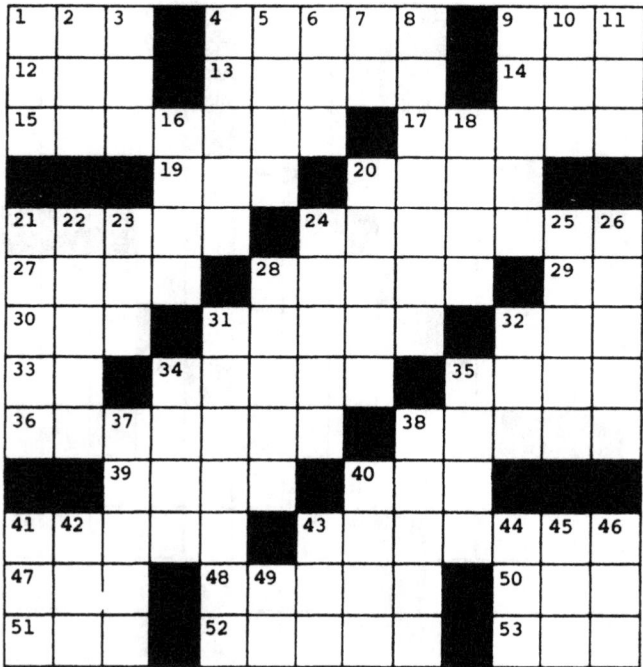

Solution is on page 371

ACROSS

1. House animal
4. Buddies
8. Trail
12. Mine output
13. Prepare for publication
14. Largest continent
15. Lubricate
16. Organ of scent
17. Drove too fast
18. Memento
20. Trial
22. Mouth part
24. Verselike
28. Cooled
32. Bread piece
33. Coal scuttle
34. Knock sharply
36. Guided
37. Let
40. Repel; drive off
43. Seesaw
45. Used to be
46. Make well
48. Lawful
52. Rural road
55. Medicine amount
57. Exist
58. Above
59. Sale condition: 2 wds.
60. Female sibling, for short
61. Obtains
62. Lease
63. Singer Boone

DOWN

1. Needy
2. A Great Lake
3. Narrate
4. Writing tool
5. Commotion
6. Shopping memo
7. Precipitous
8. Light shade
9. Cleopatra's viper
10. Dead heat
11. Possessed
19. Ailing
21. Distress signal
23. For each
25. Cash drawer
26. Sherbets
27. Relinquish
28. Short, friendly talk
29. Cavity
30. Inactive
31. Patriotic organization: abbr.
35. Church seat
38. "Do unto —..."
39. Tiny
41. Most wan
42. Utilize
44. Plane detector
47. Misplace
49. Pant
50. Operatic solo
51. For fear that
52. Fireplace fuel
53. Hail!
54. Tennis court feature
56. Transgression

MEDIUM

Solution is on page 371

BIBLE CROSSWORD

MEDIUM

by RUSS CARLEY

Bible references in this puzzle are from the King James Version. You'll find it stimulating to solve, and may discover you know more about the Bible than you think you do.

ACROSS

1. These men were bound in their coats . . . and their —. *Dan. 3:21*
5. O c— your hands. *Ps. 47:1*
8. Consider the lilies how they —. *Luke 12:27*
12. He shall rule them with a rod of —. *Rev. 2:27*
13. Ye do —, not knowing the scriptures. *Matt. 22:29*
14. He maketh his sun to — on the evil and on the good. *Matt. 5:45*
15. He shall — them one from another. *Matt. 25:32*
17. Cain and —.
18. I will — you out of their bondage. *Ex. 6:6*
19. Those . . . have their — exercised to discern both good and evil. *Heb. 5:14*
21. All creeping things that — . . . shall shake. *Ezek. 38:20*
24. Jesus — the multitude away. *Matt. 13:36*
25. Abraham obeyed my . . . statutes, and my —. *Gen. 26:5*
26. When Moses saw it, he — at the sight. *Acts 7:31*
30. The . . . — of Jacob was an hundred forty and seven years. *Gen. 47:28*
31. He . . . ministered to my —. *Phil. 2:25*
32. High priest of Israel
33. Events such as between Jacob and Leah and Jacob and Rachel
35. The axletrees of the wheels were joined to the —. *I Ki. 7:32*
36. He shall make am— for the harm that he hath done. *Lev. 5:16*
37. The mariners . . . cast forth the — that were in the ship. *Jonah 1:5*

38. I have been a stranger in a s— land. *Ex. 2:22*
41. Of a truth thou art the — of God. *Matt. 14:33*
42. Father of Abihail
43. They — at the preaching of Jonas. *Luke 11:32*
48. Thy garments smell of myrrh, and —, and cassia. *Ps. 45:8*
49. —, the family of the Erites
50. It is —er for a camel to go through the eye of a needle. *Mark 10:25*
51. The thoughts of the diligent — only to plenteousness. *Prov. 21:5*
52. They brought Daniel, and cast him into the — of lions. *Dan. 6:16*
53. W— thee all the words that I have spoken . . . in a book. *Jer. 30:2*

DOWN

1. — name was called JESUS. *Luke 2:21*
2. Blessed — the meek. *Matt. 5:5*
3. I will stand on the — of the hill. *Ex. 17:9*
4. They shall be — and traps unto you. *Josh. 23:13*
5. — us not into temptation. *Matt. 6:13*
6. Thou — my beloved Son. *Mark 1:11*
7. They despised him, and brought him no —. *I Sam. 10:27*
8. God —d him that which he requested. *I Chr. 4:10*
9. Adam . . . slept: and he (the Lord) took one of his —. *Gen. 2:21*
10. Variant spelling of Hosea

72

11. The servant brought forth je— of silver. *Gen. 24:53*
16. The harvest of the earth is —e. *Rev. 14:15*
20. All the — of the earth shall fear him. *Ps. 67:7*
21. His hairs were grown like eagles' feathers, and his nails like birds' —s. *Dan. 4:33*
22. Jealousy is the — of a man. *Prov. 6:34*
23. They s— fig leaves together, and made themselves aprons. *Gen. 3:7*
24. Sing us one of the — of Zion. *Ps. 137:3*
26. They — through the wilderness. *Isa. 16:8*
27. Go up, — an alter unto the Lord. *II Sam. 24:18*
28. Give me children, or — I die. *Gen. 30:1*
29. Where thou —t, will I die. *Ruth 1:17*
31. Oh that I had —s like a dove! *Ps. 55:6*

34. Jesus answered him ... The cock shall not crow, till thou hast — me thrice. *St. John 13:38*
35. Lift ye up a — upon the high mountain. *Isa. 13:2*
37. — is me now! *Jer. 4:31*
38. Every one — asketh receiveth; and he that seeketh findeth. *Matt. 7:8*
39. A fierce king shall — over them, saith the Lord. *Isa. 19:4*
40. The Lord spake unto Moses and A— in the land of Egypt. *Ex. 12:1*
41. Consider the lilies of the field ... they toil not, neither do they —. *Matt. 6:28*
44. How long will it be — they believe me? *Num. 14:11*
45. There were stings in their —ls. *Rev. 9:10*
46. I say unto you, That many shall come from the east and w—. *Matt. 8:11*
47. A time to be born, and a time to —. *Eccles. 3:2*

Solution is on page 371

73

HARD

ACROSS

1. African antelope
4. Boohoos
8. Recipe word
12. A Howard
13. Having a piece of the action: 2 wds.
14. Ogee
15. "Comment" from a comic-strip canine
16. Do a senatorial task
18. Shade of purple
20. Cronies
21. Laundry cycle
24. Acts
27. Chose
30. Reliable
31. "I think, therefore I —"
32. Like some pitchers
34. Family member
35. Sediment
38. "The Gay —"
41. Weasel
43. Spirit lamps
44. Algonquian Indian
46. Leers
49. Breathless awe
53. 100 sq. meters
54. Beverage choice
55. Pouting grimace, in Paris
56. Compass point
57. "East of —"
58. Formicary residents
59. Retreat

DOWN

1. Metric weight unit
2. Writer Ephron
3. Open out
4. Quiet!
5. Undivided
6. Marsh
7. Impudent youth
8. Balanchine creation
9. Classroom item
10. Function
11. Article
17. Downcast
19. Enter into competition
22. Mr. Musial
23. Creepy
25. Cheat
26. Oceans
27. Act like 7-Down
28. Send out
29. Toothlike projection
33. Signifies
36. Site
37. Edgar Rice Burroughs character
39. Follow close behind
40. Manhattan, e.g.
42. To a —
45. Flaubert heroine
47. Sea eagle
48. Observed
49. Expert
50. Up-to-date: abbr.
51. Long, long time
52. Devotee: slang

Solution is on page 371

74

ACROSS

1. Existed
4. Word with "code" or "rug"
8. Flat, thick piece
12. Female sheep
13. Chair, for one
14. Become weary
15. Educator
17. From then till now
18. Scarlet
19. Not coarse
20. Foundation
23. Mayflower passenger
26. "A" in U.A.R.
27. Helper; associate
28. Myself
29. Stitch
30. Cash
32. Feline
33. "Just — Time"
34. Expect
35. Book leaf
36. With no additives
38. Cavalry sword
39. Spoken
40. Was victorious
41. Oyster's product
43. Freedom
47. Famous lioness
48. Assistant
49. Be in debt
50. "— this ring, I thee wed"
51. Doe or buck
52. Tiny speck

DOWN

1. Moist
2. Great wonder
3. Ocean
4. Fire residue
5. Critic, Rex —
6. Corn spike
7. Near
8. Miserly
9. Steamship
10. Circle segment
11. Hive dweller
16. Baby's bed
17. Foolish
19. Rasp
20. Washbowl
21. Stadium
22. Carpenter's tool
23. Jury
24. Picture
25. Verse rhythm
30. A fable has one
31. October gem
32. Taxi
34. Shout of joy
35. Window glass
37. Browned bread
38. Serious
40. Broad
41. Church bench
42. Actor Wallach
43. Falsehood
44. Fishing pole
45. Couple
46. As of now
48. Classified

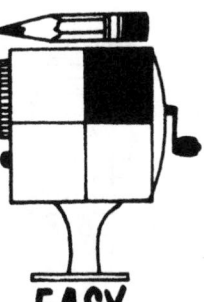

EASY

Solution is on page 371

ACROSS

1. Ibex
5. Hardwood tree
8. Friends
12. Ballerina Pavlova
13. U.S. architect
14. "Burn" plant
15. Term of farewell
17. Yield
18. Levy
19. Medicine show cure-all
21. Nomad, e.g.
24. Come out ahead
25. Secondhand
26. Ranch hands
30. ——-de-France, French region
31. Soft drinks
32. Ms. Gardner
33. D-Day beach
35. Mulligan's dish
36. City in Utah
37. Scoundrels
38. Wrought-iron grating
41. Sprinted
42. Give temporarily
43. Farewell performance: 2 wds.
48. Formerly
49. Cover
50. Bread spread
51. Take (baby) off the bottle
52. Deposit
53. Make over

DOWN

1. Joke
2. Yoko ——
3. Conjunction
4. Sampled
5. High point
6. Bishopric
7. Place to retreat to
8. "Scarface" star
9. Author Haley
10. California city
11. Prophet
16. Average
20. Facial features
21. Impoverish
22. European capital
23. Swerve
24. Mrs. Meir
26. Competitive events
27. Petruchio's beloved
28. Knievel
29. Carpentry tools
31. Summon
34. Actor, Karl ——
35. Smoke-detector part
37. Chinese dynasty
38. Shine softly
39. Descartes
40. Peruvian Indian
41. Engrossed
44. Great sorrow
45. Chemistry suffix
46. Actor Beatty
47. Sticky stuff: slang

Solution is on page 372

76

ACROSS

1. Foot digit
4. Outbuilding
8. Film about a shark
12. Treat a floor, in a way
13. Long (for)
14. Region
15. Fruit or nut tree groves
17. Medicine tablet
18. Rabbit's kin
19. Baby bed on rockers
21. Use a razor
23. Smile
24. Melody
25. Comedian Wilson
26. Fruit seed
29. Omelet need
30. Sphere
31. "Happy Days — Here Again"
32. Very small
33. Rant
34. Budge
35. Location
36. Scarlett O'Hara's was 17 inches
37. Receive willingly
40. Fury
41. Tribe
42. Proof
46. Feel a lack
47. Ceremony
48. Coquettishly shy
49. Fencing sword
50. Oceans
51. Ram's mate

DOWN

1. Couple
2. Boat paddle
3. Trade
4. Extra tire
5. Employ
6. Conclude
7. Give an account of
8. Asiatic country
9. Desertlike
10. Healthy
11. Store event
16. Possess
20. Ready to be picked
21. Mulligan, for one
22. Enormous
23. Baseball mitt
25. Praises extravagantly
26. Calm endurance
27. Spring flower
28. Saucy
30. Tight hold
34. Wise man
35. Perceive
36. Walks in water
37. Summit
38. Snip
39. Instance
40. Actress Moreno
43. Compete
44. Dairy animal
45. Look over

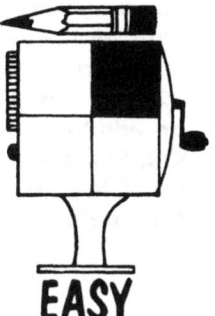

EASY

Solution is on page 372

PUNANAGRAMS

by MEL TAUB

Punanagrams are tricky but fun to solve. Definitions may be jokes or puns on the word wanted, or an anagram of the word itself. Generally there's a straight definition as a clue, too. For example, the answer to 32-Across is ENERVATE. *Never eat* is the anagram, with "get weak" as an additional clue. Roman numerals may be used; the words YOU, ARE, EYE, SEE, etc., might stand for U, R, I and C, respectively; "energy" could stand for the letters N, R, G, or "any" for N E. Consider the definitions from all angles and you will find they do make definite sense. And, have fun!

ACROSS

1. Basset is one of them
7. Stable females?
12. Is to entreat so legitimate?
13. N. Miami's belief in spirits
16. Yield in favor of Mussolini?
17. Work hard by doing it
18. Caught Pedro
19. Expert gets one thing out of cheating
21. Begin as artist? Not I!
22. Hanimal skins
23. Sign of Emil's sunny disposition
25. Note during blue-pencil test
26. Kind of ade
27. May diet before dark
29. Kind of ax
30. Pursued U.S. need
32. Never eat and get weak
34. Beer for Yank from Sandusky
36. Eastern Siberia
37. They'd rarely caress an old Crusader
41. Grammarian's need: Gr.
45. Miss Stevens' middle name
46. They'd like to see me in trouble
48. Man with a retirement account?
49. Will adherents not enter race?

51. Appears to take a look at manuscript briefly
52. Is he seventy? Not yet
53. Olaf gains nothing by being reserved
55. Kind of lace
56. 'Taint bushel
57. Creamy dessert, like it or not
59. Who Phoenicians treat as goddess
61. At ten, Nero may begin
62. See hand, e.g., when transformed
63. 'Taint auld or syne
64. Nested and got jittery

DOWN

1. Composer who would brood in Russia
2. They'll sleep or get married
3. They assist Sadie
4. S'what Bossy chews
5. What Fran needs to become wild
6. Like my seat in Turkish bath
7. She's looking for ideal men
8. Spanish heart
9. Vehicles in which U.N. sent off insurgents
10. Sends out for the Times

11. A star in his own right
12. Sp. ceremony depicts pixie
14. Where stray setter is found
15. Streak for Mel Ott
20. — seer (give a fortune-teller a summons)
23. Unhappy groups of cub scouts?
24. Comes out to see germ
27. Exclude sixty in Rome, leaving two
28. The ones I see are Indians
31. Sausage center
33. Vehicle at the front?
35. Showing contempt for sinner, e.g.
37. Serious when seated

38. Gardner-Chaney island locale
39. Places where one plays or rests
40. 'Taint you, ducky
42. Deviate when grieved
43. Set up for deer, etc.
44. Rated Dr. Kane
47. Shock produced by deed of mischievous fellow?
50. The ol' Ritz
52. Keep G.I. from passing bridges
54. In favor of a group of Roman marketplaces
56. He hangs around station
58. Why does band become bad? (2 wds.)
60. With whom he's mixed up

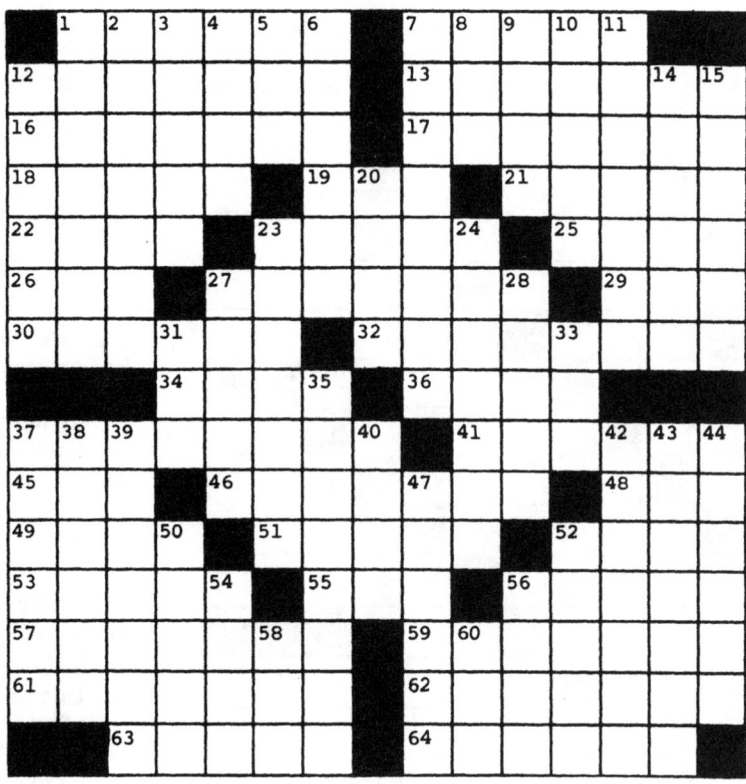

Solution is on page 372

ACROSS

1. Brisk energy
4. Thick slices
9. Carpenter's tool
12. Canoe paddle
13. Traveler's stop
14. Even (the score)
15. Vow
17. Wear away
19. Picnic pest
20. Gave a sly look
21. Tent peg
24. Memory slip
25. Frilly fabric
26. Mechanical man
27. Public prosecutor: abbr.
29. Gorilla
30. Poe's bird
31. Pot cover
32. Myself
33. Even
34. Evergreen tree
35. Covers with asphalt
36. Puts in order of preference
37. Pebbles
39. Hunter's companion
40. — of London, prison
41. Surrenders: 2 wds.
45. Half a pair
46. Captive worker
48. Put in service
49. For each
50. "— beaver"
51. Gym cushion

DOWN

1. Mom's mate
2. Corn unit
3. Paid athlete, for short
4. Brightness
5. Misplaced
6. Had lunch
7. Exist
8. — it, think about something overnight: 2 wds.
9. Pack away
10. Assistant
11. Unwanted plant
16. Manufacture
18. Relax
20. Tag
21. Shut violently, as a door
22. Record (music)
23. High card
24. Is mad about
26. Speaks irrationally
27. Eat in style
28. Fruit drinks
30. Gearshift position
31. Ignited
33. Highway division
34. Book feature
35. Strength
36. Dog's name
37. Halt
38. Musical sound
39. Plunge (into)
41. Actor's joke
42. Total
43. Our nation: abbr.
44. Favorite
47. Creole State: abbr.

EASY

Solution is on page 372

80

ACROSS

1. Building top
5. — and board
9. Recompense
12. Spoken
13. Therefore
14. First-rate
15. Choir voice
16. Aria performers
18. Snuggle
20. A Fitzgerald
21. Fly high
23. Birch tree
26. Essay division
30. Guido's note
31. Detail
32. Financial professional: abbr.
33. At the very least
34. Seaver or Mix
35. Between second and home: 2 wds.
37. Mennonite sect
39. Laraine and Doris
40. Ibsen character
42. Caretaker
46. Piece of furniture: 2 wds.
49. Actress Gam
50. Oh, my!: slang
51. Wild plum
52. Air passage
53. Above: poetic
54. Preliminary contest
55. Geological periods

DOWN

1. Horse color
2. Heraldic border
3. Feedbag treats
4. — and jetsam
5. Scholarly investigation
6. Gold: Spanish
7. Stare at impertinently
8. Money: slang
9. Rose Bowl site
10. Play segment
11. Affirmative!
17. Not well
19. Ship's record
22. Swift
24. Building wings
25. Comedienne Martha
26. Pocket bread
27. Jot
28. String around a finger, for one
29. Pet bird
33. Remark
35. Defeat overwhelmingly
36. Coloring solution
38. Tosspot
41. Skilled
43. Wharf
44. Sicilian volcano
45. Cry of disappointment: slang
46. Conceit
47. Born: French
48. Mauna —

MEDIUM

Solution is on page 372

81

ACROSS

1. Tease: slang
4. One-dish meal
8. Back talk
12. Summer drink
13. Story
14. Factual
15. Whatever the meal may be
17. Flat or enamel
18. Armored vehicle
19. Towel word
20. '60s dance, with "The"
22. Pays attention (to)
25. Talk wildly
26. Strongholds
27. Cry of surprise
28. — on, encourage
29. Bowling alleys
30. Disapproval sound
31. Thus
32. — with, supports
33. Instance
34. Gym shoe
36. Military installations
37. Falsehoods
38. Speak
39. Matinee —, popular actors
41. Gather
44. Sleeveless garment
45. Dangerous challenge
46. Also
47. Watched closely
48. Dollar bills
49. Male heir

DOWN

1. Knock sharply
2. Marriage vow words
3. Wagering
4. Trick, as on a trapeze
5. Carpet nail
6. Mooselike deer
7. You and I
8. Begins
9. Get up
10. Light source
11. Adjust, as a clock
16. Endure
17. Nuisances
19. Puts on the payroll
20. Ringlet
21. Child's cart
22. Independent one
23. Lariat loop
24. Footwear
26. Loses coloring
29. Prefers
30. Wicker containers
32. Went by ship
33. Summon
35. Wed secretly
36. Cotton bundles
38. Ripped (apart)
39. Frost, as a cake
40. Time period
41. Metal container
42. Dove's sound
43. Cargo unit
45. Perform (a deed)

Solution is on page 372

ACROSS

1. Bric-a- —, knickknacks
5. Exclamation
8. Church part
12. A Turner
13. Name
14. Theater award
15. *Huevos rancheros*, e.g.
16. Responding to each other: literary term
18. Bundled, as cotton
20. Slant
21. A Muse
23. Actress Terry
26. Comforts
28. "To's" partner
29. Secure
30. Predecessor of HST
31. Newcastle product
32. Hockey great
33. Overcome by cleverness
35. Relieve
37. Sculptor, Richard —
38. Biblical patriarch
40. Car style
43. Pungent
46. Countenance
47. Tableland
48. Farm-address abbreviation
49. Do — others . . .
50. Candid
51. Caesar's "ands"
52. Collect IOU's

DOWN

1. Air bubble
2. Ravi Shankar piece
3. Stegner novel: 3 wds.
4. Barracks, in a fortified town
5. Harem room
6. Bellow novel: 2 wds.
7. Woodwind
8. Kind of prize
9. Hersey novel: 4 wds.
10. By way of
11. Poet's abbr.
17. Pre-holiday times
19. — Rheingold, Wagnerian work
22. Bean curd
24. Part of QED
25. Lon —, former Cambodian official
26. Goldfish
27. Gaelic
29. Call for help
31. Prudent
33. Clay pot
34. Feminine title
36. Geneva's lake
39. To be: French
41. — *Sanctorum*
42. Kind of light
43. —, *amas, amat*
44. Tie fabric
45. Record albums' kin: abbr.

HARD

Solution is on page 373

EASY

ACROSS

1. Find the sum
4. To's partner
7. Take a plane
10. In favor of
13. Black bird
15. Move smoothly
17. More cunning
19. Fly high
20. Comfort
21. Orange skins
22. Baggy
23. Unblemished
24. — willow tree
26. Royal headpiece
28. Steeple
30. Royal ruler
31. Western footwear
32. Dime or nickel
33. Use up, as money
35. Jacks and fours
36. Ex-President Jimmy and family
39. Unaccompanied
40. Adhesive; glue
41. Stockades

42. Be in debt (to)
44. Grasped
45. Factions
46. Taxi fees
47. Hide away
48. Caspian, for one
49. Drive too fast
50. Tease
51. Seaside
52. Defend
54. Parrot's nickname
55. Listened to
56. Step
57. Hen's perch
58. Musical group
59. "Jaws," for one
61. Sample (food)
62. Loads
65. Fur wrap
66. Husbands' mates
67. Turns, as pancakes
68. Cereal grain
70. Tool sets
71. Ten-cent pieces
72. Aims; objects
73. Cavity
74. Wrath
75. Ambulance's warning signal
76. Explode
77. "It" makes waste
78. Cinderella's shoe
80. Vote into office
81. Forest hazards
82. Tears
83. Reason
84. Magician's stick
85. Pebble
87. Book leaves
88. "The Three Little Kittens" lost them
91. Tattered
92. Elevate
94. Elude
96. Make airtight
98. Woe is me!
99. Guide, as a car
100. Challenges
101. Domesticate
102. Energy
103. Curved letter
104. Decimal base
105. A bright color

DOWN

1. Highest card
2. Sketch
3. Medicine portion
4. Hurl
5. Wedding band, for one
6. Strange
7. Runs, as a river
8. Jungle cat
9. Sure!
10. Serve tea
11. Unusual
12. Raw metal
14. Saturday and Sunday
15. Pulverize
16. Ushers
17. Mailbox openings
18. Health spas
19. Backbone
25. Evergreen tree
27. Took a cab
29. Cherry seeds
31. Founded
32. Insertion mark
33. Snooze
34. — bear, arctic mammal
35. West Point student
36. Hackneyed; trite
37. Helicopter blade
38. Saber
39. Sighs of satisfaction
40. Portion
41. Blame
43. Female sheep
45. Dot
46. Untrue
47. Shutter; blind
49. Gaze; gape
50. Sounds (a whistle)
51. Transmits
53. Iridescent gems
54. Sits for the camera
55. Angels' instruments
57. Poe's bird
58. Constructed
59. Agitates

60. Traveler's "home"
61. Race official
62. Explosion
63. Slip knot
64. Seasons
65. Snow runner
66. Telegrams
67. Power; might
69. Golf gadget
71. Ladles

72. Surmised; supposed
73. Most difficult
75. Twirl
76. Sky color
77. Cue
79. Presses (clothes)
80. Anxious
81. Destinies
83. Packing boxes
84. Make broader

85. Shoe bottom
86. Snare
87. Baked desserts
88. Female horse
89. Close by
90. Identical
91. Faucet
93. Had lunch
95. Large tub
97. Guided

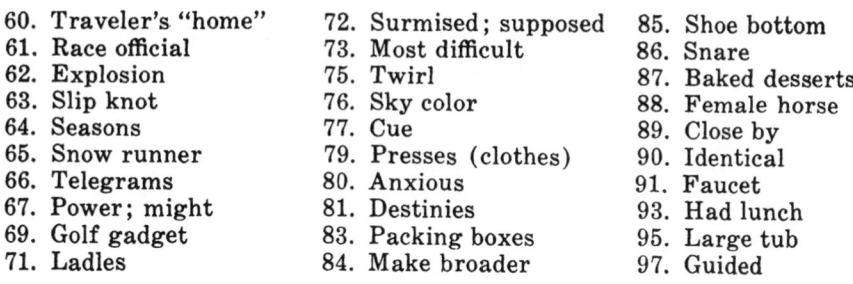

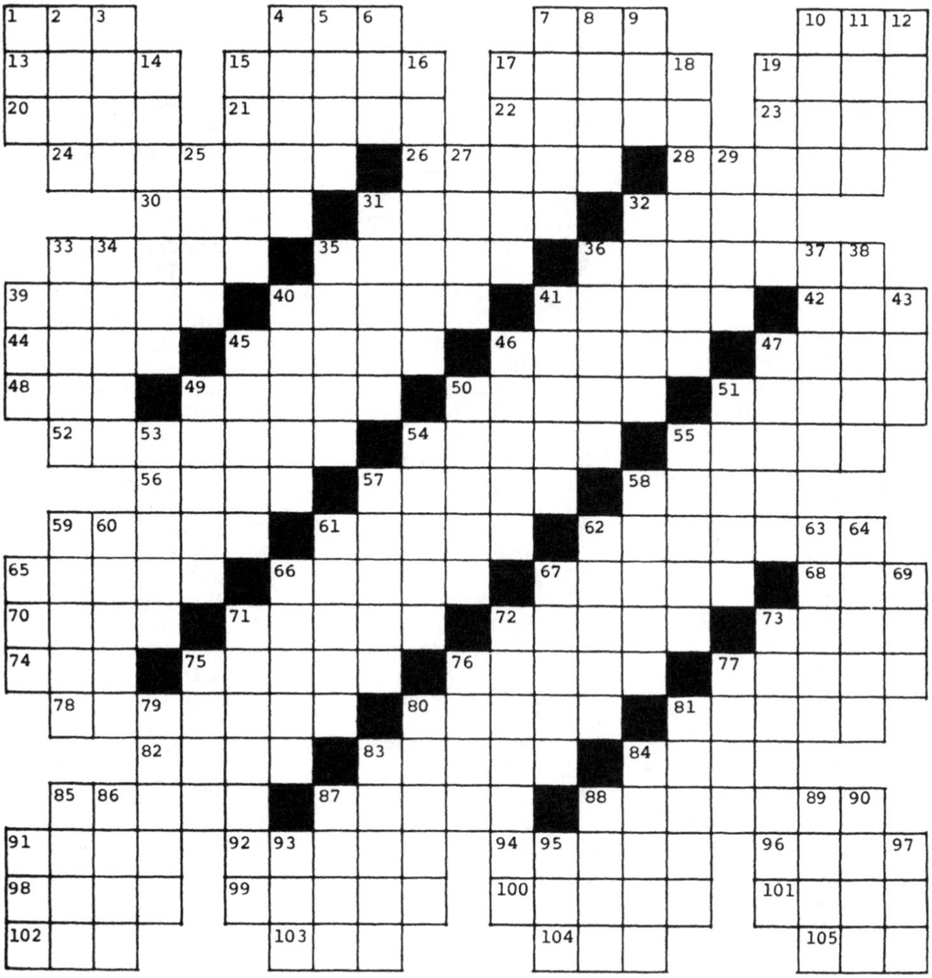

Solution is on page 373

MEDIUM

ACROSS

1. Bounder
4. Photograph
8. Garment fold
12. Blushing
15. Cab
16. Cavity
17. Always
18. A Great Lake
20. Peels
21. So be it!
22. Chilean coin
23. Part of USNA
25. Mimic
26. Docile
28. Article
30. Musical quality
32. Miss Arden
33. Part of some sand-
wich orders
35. Country stopover
37. Motor-driven
39. Metal source
40. Slim
44. Marry
45. Azalea, e.g.
48. Concise
49. Adage
51. Likewise

55. Rip
56. Backbone
57. Pigpens
59. Certain sibling
60. Circle segment
61. Ireland: poetic
62. Support
64. Anger
65. Exude, as fumes
67. Old-timer
68. Hand-to-hand
struggle
69. Stretches
71. Watches closely
73. Like some jackets
74. Splendid!
75. Vocalist
78. Does a house-
painter's work
79. Also
80. Word in some
recipes
84. Commotion
85. Pays respect to
87. Lima's country
88. Fruit drink
89. Lost
91. Theater boxes
92. Armored vehicles
93. Sword handle
94. Slumber
96. Average
97. Pulls apart
98. Worries
99. Ship's journal
101. Gorges
103. Deface
104. "— are the
meek . . ."
108. Allow
109. Car features
113. Ventilate
114. Mets or Padres
116. Snare
118. Catcher's need
119. Stadium cheer
120. See 48-Across
122. Praise
124. At a distance, to
poets
126. Call forth
128. Sullen
129. Otherwise
130. Overlook
131. Go by horse
132. Mansion: abbr.
133. Do a farming chore

134. Nuisance
135. Understand

DOWN

1. Editor's mark
2. Lumberjack's item
3. Interrupt
4. Disgrace
5. It's "where the
heart is"
6. *Corrida* cry
7. Canvas shelter
8. Rely
9. Hail!
10. "Take five"
11. Boy scout's unit
12. Took up again
13. Historic age
14. Lifeguard, at times
15. An adhesive
19. Roof edge
20. Buddy
24. Guided
27. Expert
29. Suggestion
31. At this time
34. Sightseeing trip
36. Snuggled
38. Blue-pencil
40. Man's garment
41. Solitary
42. Poet's word
43. Lift
45. Luminary
46. — and now
47. Marathon
48. 007, and others
50. Moist
52. Slender branch
53. Become weary
54. Singles
56. A few
57. Repairs, as shoes
58. Solemn
62. Curves
63. Managed
66. Small barrel
68. Digs, as for coal
70. Novel
72. Absolutely!
73. Sideways
74. Silverware items
75. Droops
76. Object of adulation
77. No part
78. Baker's need

79. Takes care of
81. Word with "cut" or "net"
82. Inactive
83. Favorites
86. Cut (off)
87. Window section
90. Congers
92. "Sawbuck"
93. Difficult
95. Placards
97. Ceremony
98. Moves at an easy pace
100. Command to Dobbin
102. Sold (merchandise)
103. Encountered
104. Right off the —, immediately
105. Was deceptive
106. "Boner"
107. Valleys
109. Primary
110. Wear away
111. Lawn tool
112. A pronoun
115. Masculine
117. Pound (down)
118. Bulk; size
121. Take to court
123. Employ
125. For shame!
127. Compete

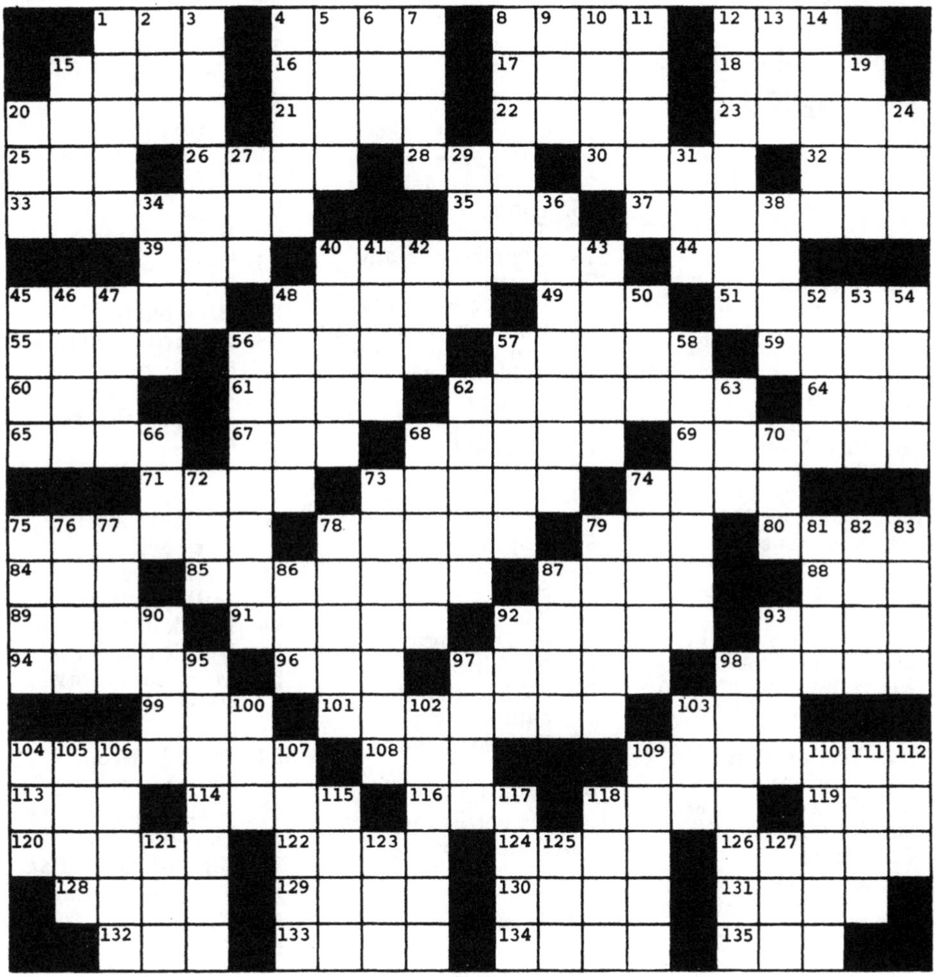

Solution is on page 373

HARD

ACROSS

1. Vile
5. Girdle
9. Hex
14. Uttered
19. Author Paton
20. "Kon- —," 1951 film
21. Doctrine
22. Bridle path
23. Sediment
24. Blue-pencil
25. Corporal O'Reilly
26. Derby "prize"
27. Hungers (for)
29. Shopper's plus
31. Hindu incantation
32. *Affaire d'honneur*
33. Ghost
34. Trot or canter
35. Originated
37. Kissed, in a way
38. English painter
42. Abide
43. Draw back
44. Total confusion
45. Men's nicknames
46. Conger
47. Diminish
48. Gather (fabric)
49. Suffrage
50. New Jersey city
51. Loose change
52. Chess piece
53. Terrier
56. Cotton fabric
57. Car-lot transaction
60. Certain mineral deposits
61. Tows
62. Becomes irate: 2 wds.
63. Wagered
64. U.S. concert pianist
65. Textile pattern: 2 wds.
66. Headwear
67. Pan-fry
68. Sword
69. — Khayyám, Persian poet
71. "Old hat"
72. RV owner
73. Settle (a debt)
76. King: French
77. Turn aside
78. Grumbles: slang
79. Defy
80. Hotel employees
82. Like a baby who can drink from a cup
83. Gobbles (down)
84. Creepy
85. Exchange
86. Get out!
87. Spirit
90. Convertible couch
91. Raged
94. Topple
95. Passageway
96. Slick
98. Speck
99. — Domingo
100. Turbine
101. USSR mountain range
102. Before: prefix
103. Singer John
104. Coliseum
105. Head: French
106. Amphibian

DOWN

1. Game fish
2. Landed
3. Italian dressing ingredient: 2 wds.
4. Consign
5. Tough metal
6. Furthers
7. Schuss
8. "Psycho" director
9. Pastry
10. Legume container: 2 wds.
11. Fund
12. Spare
13. Piece of correspondence: abbr.
14. Overtaxes
15. Right away!: slang
16. Furnace
17. Vat
18. Feminine name
28. Letter
30. Actor, Jack —
31. Ed Koch's title
33. Safe
34. Cogs
35. Veneration
36. "Norma —," 1979 film
37. Bike parts
38. Horned animal, for short
39. See 77-Down
40. An insecticide: abbr.
41. Compass point
43. Bonus
44. Gossips: slang
47. Get back
48. Besmears
49. Millay's alma mater
50. Drink of the gods
51. Vertical trough
52. More submissive
53. Police dispatch: abbr.
54. Island: French
55. Grenadier
56. Malicious, in a way
57. Depends (on)
58. Sign of the zodiac
59. Time zone: abbr.
61. Frequent
62. Took up (liquid)
64. Cautions
65. Mollycoddle

67. Watery
68. Canceled, in a way: 2 wds.
69. Sphere
70. One of the Three Stooges
71. Assignment
72. "Clunker": slang
73. Golden horse
74. Comment from Fido

75. Okay
77. With 39-Down, actor-director
78. African flower
79. Front-porch item
81. Shed: hyph. wd.
82. Singer Jennings
83. One of the 5 W's
85. Stitch
86. Vogue

87. Cogitate
88. Gem
89. Fissure
90. Noted designer
91. Louver
92. Ms. Kett, of the comics
93. Exploit
95. Physicians' group: abbr.
97. Anger

Solution is on page 373

SPECIAL CHALLENGER CROSSWORD

by LOUIS SABIN

Here is a real toughie for you. We have omitted giving you such helps as "2 wds.," "hyph. wd.," and "slang"; but in the spirit of fair play, all abbreviations and foreign words are so indicated.

ACROSS

1. Record
5. Raccoon's kin
10. Stradivari's teacher
15. Hollow
19. Ham's sign-off
20. Oak nut
21. "Gigi" ingénue
22. A Great Lake
23. Knowledge passed on from generation to generation
24. Airport staff
26. Out of —, impertinent
27. Very good: French
29. Speedy Jesse
30. Brightly colored bird
32. Beach-goer's "souvenir"
33. Cicerone
34. Praise
35. Andretti's sport
38. Slight coloring
39. Abstract notions
43. Deteriorate
44. Deciduous tree
45. Mary, of the comics
46. Boring place to be in
47. Robin Cook thriller
48. "Ammo" for a BB gun
49. Bauxite and cesium
50. Israeli dance
51. Audiophile's purchase, for short
52. Roof rims
53. Energetic one
55. Implied
56. "Shane" costar
58. Deadly Sin count
59. Peaceful
60. World-peace advocates
64. Mutual agreement
66. Obliterate, as from the mind
67. Declares to be true
70. Grind into shreds
71. Actress, Janis —
72. Domesticates
74. Borrower's chit
75. Some learn by this
76. Stable equipment
77. Spread (a rumor) about
79. Little lake
80. Lamb's mom
81. Home of a brave
82. August weather report
83. Devilfish
84. Check casher
86. Specks of dust
87. "Mrs. Miniver" star
88. Takes the odds
89. Ed Norton's workplace
90. Sicilian resort
91. Placard
94. Invitation from a butler
95. Yukon district
99. Nanook's house
100. Break in the action
103. March date
104. Rueful remark
105. Perseus' mother
106. Positive pole
107. Stein's nickname
108. Gala
109. "Wow!," once
110. Bumpkins
111. Lion's "ruff"

DOWN

1. Blockhead
2. Mr. Novello
3. All dried up
4. "Troilus and —"
5. Calling, in a way
6. Like an estate
7. High time, in the old West
8. Joanne of film fame
9. Declare
10. Give in
11. Seine feeder
12. Son of Zeus
13. Haul
14. Split seconds
15. Fool, as by false promises
16. Viking explorer
17. Certain 15th-century vessel
18. Menudo fan
25. Past President
28. Poison
31. Toe-stubber's cry
33. Young ladies
34. 1961's Oscar-winning actress
35. Summarize
36. Bouquet
37. Hard to analyze
38. Grimm creation
39. Cigar
40. Religious parades
41. City on the Po River
42. D.C. department
44. Pry
45. Aunts and moms
48. Waited, in a restless sort of way
50. "The Luck of Roaring Camp" author
52. — nous
54. Bacchanals' bellow

55. Midterms and finals
57. Make — of, observe
58. Gamecock
59. Located
61. More fastidious
62. Greet the day
63. 12th Hebrew letter
64. Come to terms
65. Tower of London item
68. Scout's rider
69. Chad neighbor
71. Emulates Pan
72. Chef's aid
73. Sale condition
76. Straddle
78. Otolaryngologist's concern
79. Pattern, example or model
81. Shea, roka or lin
83. Noted U.S. educator
85. Dull
86. British measurements
87. Fairy-tale creatures
89. "Slamming Sammy"
90. Sidestep
91. Edith Giovanna Gassion, to fans
92. Eye
93. Venetian-blind component
94. Spirit lamp
95. Handle
96. Concept
97. "Ol' Man River" composer
98. Town near Padua
101. Carp
102. Shaggy beast

Solution is on page 373

DIAGRAMLESS

EASY

This Diagramless is 15 boxes wide by 15 boxes deep.

ACROSS

1. Pea casing
4. Opposite of "girl"
7. Factual
8. — and get it!
9. Clipped, as wool from sheep
10. Apple or orange
11. Injures
12. Slope
13. Margarine
14. Shell out
15. Molars, bicuspids, etc.
17. Playground fixture
18. Have a snack
20. Lightish-brown
21. Movie house
24. Cloth for dusting
25. Unhappy
27. "Silly" birds
29. Iron, as clothes
33. Postpone
34. Great Lake
35. Children's tale, "Beauty and the —"
36. A la —, by the piece
37. Signal light
38. Styles; fashions
39. Stocking mishaps
40. Mimicked
41. Aye!
42. Funnyman Skelton

DOWN

1. Advance to a higher grade
2. Belonging to us
3. Lion's retreat
4. Leap; jump
5. Leave out
6. Still; however
7. "— Blind Mice"
8. Hoisting device
9. Store event
10. Escaped (from prison)
11. Peppery
12. Backbones
14. Ventian-blind part
16. Sombrero or bonnet
17. Theater platform
19. Menace
22. Simple to do
23. Knock sharply
26. Feared greatly
27. Shifting mechanisms on cars
28. Otherwise
30. Made a mistake
31. Convenes
32. Visualize
33. College heads
35. Color of some eyes
36. Deal (with)
37. Sauté
38. Deface

Solution is on page 373

CHALLENGER DIAGRAMLESS

As in the Special Challenger Crossword (21), we have not given you such helps as "2 wds.," "hyph. wd.," or "slang"; but in the spirit of fair play, all foreign words and abbreviations are so indicated. This Diagramless is 21 boxes wide by 21 boxes deep. Starting box is on page 377.

ACROSS

1. Military crime: abbr.
5. De —, star of "The Deer Hunter"
6. Melville character
10. Sir Joseph or Ernie
11. Iraqi town on the Tigris
12. Convinced
13. Like some recordings
15. Word with "squash"
17. A Gemayel of Lebanon
18. Backus's "Mr."
19. Celtic paradise
21. *Canis lupus*
24. Marceau's art
25. Edible roots
29. Criterion: abbr.
32. Cancelled (a news story)
34. Actor Estrada
35. Stag
37. Money
38. Ceramic square
39. Endorse
40. Originate
41. Monte Rosa peaks
43. Rates of activity
46. Join (to)
48. Vex
51. Glaze for cloth
52. Medieval tales in verse
56. Abadán's land
57. Hit on the head
59. Great expanse
60. Either of two Roman statesmen
61. Latin "year"
62. Hickok, e.g.
64. Affirmative reply
65. A wife of Jacob
66. Make bankrupt
68. Climbing iron
70. Examine
72. Soprano, Nellie —
76. Sanction
77. Scottish "child"
78. Like some baths
81. Spare; thin
82. Pallid
83. Adjust, in a way
85. Inert gas
86. Seeger or Rose
87. Trifles (with)

DOWN

1. Word with "computer"
2. Line of raked hay
3. Mork's planet
4. Spanish article
6. — acids, organic compounds
7. Boater, e.g.
8. Southern constellation
9. Formal dance: French
10. — Raton
11. Nimble
12. Actor Waterston
13. Biblical foes
14. Mosque prayer leader
16. Small recess
19. Aviator Earhart
20. No: Russian
22. Branch
23. Ice field
26. "Unit" suffix
27. Thousand: French
28. Doubter
29. Worn out
30. Snare or catch
31. 60-grain units
33. Record of occurrences
36. Characteristic
42. Go wrong
44. Water-purifying gas
45. Medicinal plant
47. Pour wine, in a way
49. Dilatory
50. Baseball's Slaughter

53. Stitch
54. Beret's "kin"
55. Give way suddenly
58. Eye cosmetic
63. Insensible
66. Actor Williams
67. Fretted instruments, for short
69. Fact
71. Like some buckets
73. Feudal lords
74. Giant king of Britain
75. Actress Jillian
78. Tawny
79. Exploit
80. Greek letter
83. Appropriate
84. Author Rosten

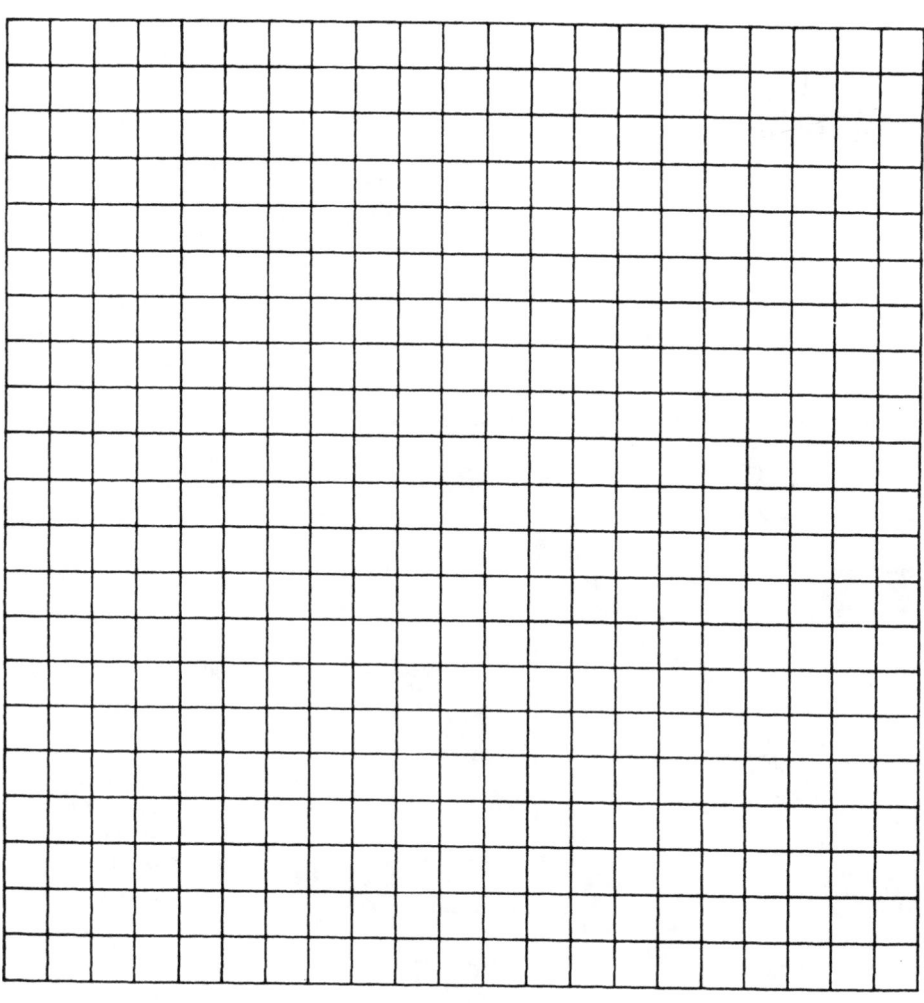

Solution is on page 374

ACROSS

1. Average
4. Man's garment
9. Soft drink
12. Cain's mother
13. Provide food
14. Reverent wonder
15. Clergymen
17. Change
19. Center
20. Quarrel
21. Galway's instrument
23. Exceptional
26. Deceptions
27. Grab
28. — and behold!
29. Outcome
30. Risk; gamble
31. Mr. Ameche
32. Asner or McMahon
33. A famous Dinah
34. Splendid
35. Skillful methods
37. Scrooge, e.g.
38. Slab
39. Segment
40. Excuse
42. "A — to India," E. M. Forster work
45. Chum
46. Make a choice
48. Recent
49. Watch carefully
50. Raves
51. Golf gadget

DOWN

1. Energy
2. Miss Gardner
3. Saved
4. Make a point
5. Jack rabbit
6. Possessive pronoun
7. Football player: abbr.
8. Circus sight
9. Miss Page
10. Be in the red
11. For each
16. Kindergarteners
18. Ornamental trim
20. Heavy nail
21. Armada
22. Evans or Lavin
23. Chars
24. Unaccompanied
25. Reclusive sort
27. Inventory
30. Brighter
31. Far
33. Theater-goer's receipt
34. Evergreens
36. Santiago's country
37. Sail supports
39. Treaty
40. Mimic
41. Prefix with "over" or "away"
42. Small enclosure
43. "Turn to the right"
44. Ram's mate
47. California city: abbr.

MEDIUM

Solution is on page 374

ACROSS

1. Family member
4. Identical
8. Be absorbent
12. Lyric poem
13. Much-admired person
14. Word with "guard" or "admiral"
15. Toothpaste type
16. Ewe's mate
17. Coronet
18. Article
20. Skillets
21. Large crow
23. Glove parts
26. Kiln
27. Forty —, brief sleep
28. In operation
29. For each
30. Claret and chablis
31. Past
32. Vocal pause
33. Rescued
34. Finished
35. Bee feature
37. "On the ball"
38. Understands
39. Songbird
40. More ashen
42. Part of some breakfast orders
43. Employ
46. Baker, at times
47. It "makes the world go round"
48. Corn spike
49. Common suffix
50. Grew older
51. Health resort

DOWN

1. Lassie, e.g.
2. Summer cooler
3. Do a postal worker's job
4. Warning device
5. First man
6. Mother
7. — Paso, TX
8. Fetches
9. Rental contract
10. Rowing need
11. —la-la
17. Army vehicles
19. "Sawbuck"
20. Yearned
21. Lassoes
22. Prevent
23. More elegant
24. A Moore
25. Harsh sound
27. Spouses
30. Bet
31. Pathways
33. Scoffs
34. Spanish cheer
36. Capri and Man
37. Prepared to do battle
39. Brandish
40. Brooch
41. High card
42. Gluttonous sort
44. Tree fluid
45. Notable period
47. Where Baton Rouge is: abbr.

Solution is on page 374

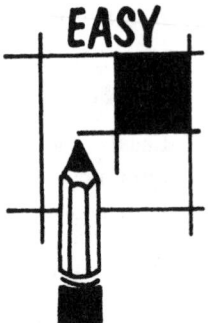

EASY

ACROSS

1. Impertinent talk: slang
4. Dodge; evade
9. — Angeles
12. Pitching statistic: abbr.
13. Stop
14. TV series, "— House"
15. "Sal" of song
16. Annoy; vex
17. "Dukes"
19. Actor Griffith
21. Crop of China
22. Mexican treats
24. MacArthur was one
27. Elderly
28. Released; liberated
29. You and I
30. Bandleader Brown
31. Posts (a letter)
32. Food tin
33. — route, on the way
34. Quiets
35. Election district
36. Alarm suddenly
38. Parking penalties
39. Decays
40. Stiff breeze
41. Incline
43. Petroleum
44. Land parcel
47. Skirt edge
48. Wash cycle
50. Corn spike
51. Nay's opposite
52. Scoff (at)
53. Pigpen

DOWN

1. Turkey drumstick
2. Lyricist Gershwin
3. Royal abodes
4. Caustic substances
5. Extremely
6. Hardwood tree
7. Exists
8. Gives the meaning of (a word)
9. Opposite of "winner"
10. Umpire's call
11. Former juniors: abbr.
18. Frosted (a cake)
20. Show drowsiness
21. Film holders
22. Stories
23. Actor's representative
24. Sooty dirt
25. Conscious (of)
26. — an ear, listens
28. Niagara sight
31. Is of importance
32. Wax lights
34. Farmland product
35. Earn the blue ribbon
37. Scent
38. Office worker
40. Knowledgeable
41. Timid
42. Actor Marvin
43. Dollar bill
45. Grain morsel
46. Attempt
49. At home

Solution is on page 374

ACROSS

1. Existed
4. Reckless
8. Energy
11. Expert
12. Choir member
13. Taxi fee
14. Wrath
15. Liz Taylor role
17. Brief
19. Charged particle
20. Dry
22. Pie portion
26. Drink in great gulps
29. Do secretarial work
31. Mr. Bolger
32. Villain of the seas
34. Reach one's destination
36. Commotion
37. Leave out
39. Mimics
40. Restore
42. Napped rug
44. Bambi, e.g.
46. Discourage
50. Take turns
54. Crude metal
55. Observed
56. Profound
57. Be victorious
58. Writing need
59. Wooden strip
60. Snare

DOWN

1. Stay
2. Land measure
3. Prophet
4. Certain contestant
5. Every one of
6. Constant
7. Owl's sound
8. Gentle touch
9. Blunder
10. Legume
13. Renown
16. Might
18. Norse legend
21. Article
23. Faucet problem
24. Donated
25. Potato buds
26. Shadowbox
27. Broad
28. Golf club
30. Trail
33. Lighthouse, for one
35. Fury
38. Tel Aviv's nation
41. Paradise
43. Skilled
45. Concludes
47. Word with "crier" or "hall"
48. A Great Lake
49. What tenants pay
50. Viper
51. Mr. Majors
52. "Sawbuck"
53. Oolong, for one

Solution is on page 374

MEDIUM

ACROSS

1. Male sheep
4. Cain's brother
8. Furtive glance
12. Self
13. Ms. Ephron
14. — Stanley Gardner
15. Lorne Greene western
17. Ballesteros' homeland
18. Peter, Paul and Mary
19. Drinks slowly
20. Dish
22. Thoroughfares
25. Female chickens
26. Transparent
27. "— The Waterfront," Brando classic
28. Ms. Gardner
29. Peels
30. Had dinner
31. Opposite of NW
32. Break, as ties
33. Region
34. Built
36. Lab container
37. Stone Age "Flintstone"
38. Young 1-Across
39. More uncommon
41. West Indies island
44. Took a plane
45. Memo
46. Goal
47. Becomes less distinct
48. Rank in a tournament
49. Snooze

DOWN

1. Jewish title
2. Past
3. Treasure State
4. Ms. Oakley
5. Uncouth fellow: slang
6. Historic period
7. Musical tone
8. Condiment
9. Wipe out
10. Whitney or Wallach
11. Actor Berry
16. Garfunkel and Carney
17. Kingly titles
19. Guide
20. Moon stage
21. Prying tool
22. Torn off strip
23. Carryalls
24. Underhanded person
26. Rescued
29. Actor Ustinov
30. Bedouin
32. Threaded nails
33. — mater
35. — Zimbalist, Jr.
36. Well-known
38. Overdue
39. Country address: abbr.
40. Actress MacGraw
41. Namath, of football
42. U.S. security group: abbr.
43. Electrical unit
45. Canadian province: abbr.

Solution is on page 374

100

ACROSS

1. Punctual
7. Hard times
13. Animosity
14. Bicycle built for two
15. "— Human Bondage"
16. Fissure
18. New England state: abbr.
19. Rare sight: abbr.
21. A Brontë
22. Coniferous tree
23. Lingerie item
25. Autumn month: abbr.
26. Arrange (passage)
27. Oppenheimer's colleague at Los Alamos
29. Rises
31. Low island
32. Football position
33. Mover's boxes
36. Young soarer
39. Gambling city
40. Roman goddess of peace
42. Third son of Adam
43. Ninny
44. Kind of beer
46. Timorous
47. A Greek letter
48. Large artery
50. Printer's measure
51. Burstyn and namesakes
53. Fit for consumption
55. Took long steps
56. Negligent

DOWN

1. French novelist, Marcel —
2. Lottery
3. "Who's — first?"
4. 1200, to Nero
5. Study carefully (with "over")
6. Quake
7. Marsh birds
8. Like tatted material
9. One: French
10. Doctor: abbr.
11. Interval
12. Snobby smiles
17. Actor Morrow
20. Lubricant dispensers
22. Caresses
24. Aristotle's teacher
26. Loud noises
28. Storm center
30. Hot drink
33. Derricks
34. Consequence
35. Meager
36. English cathedral town
37. Barrymore and Merman
38. Certain herbs
41. Past
44. Turf; earth
45. Tease unmercifully
48. Head of a company: abbr.
49. Not bright
52. Place for a TV: abbr.
54. Two: prefix

HARD

Solution is on page 375

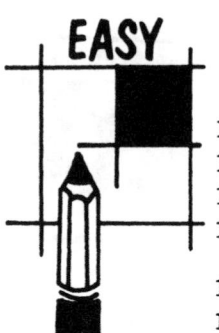

ACROSS

1. Jelly's kin
4. Pillow cover
8. Strike with the palm
12. Actress Arden
13. Short letter
14. Book leaf
15. Paving substance
16. Large monkey
17. Mistake: slang
18. Gather leaves
20. Stickum
21. Bangor's State
23. School groups
26. Associate with a common purpose
27. Glassy finish
28. Scale note
29. Great happiness
30. Not poetry
31. Writing tool
32. Atop
33. Gives up
34. True statement
35. Comes back
37. Linguini is one kind
38. Corn spikes
39. Desire
40. NY baseball club, for short
42. On a — with, equal to
43. This land: abbr.
46. Otherwise
47. Pepper's "pal"
48. Actor Steiger
49. Connections
50. Sole; mere
51. Terminate

DOWN

1. Fast plane
2. Actress Gardner
3. Cheerfully
4. Viper, for one
5. Word with "faith" and "charity"
6. Dined
7. Myself
8. Husband or wife
9. Country roads
10. Grow older
11. For each
17. Fire
19. Some
20. Drinking vessel
21. Student's field of study
22. Unaccompanied
23. Coagulates
24. Put in office
25. Dasher's driver
27. Smiles
30. Cat sounds
31. Meadow
33. Trembles
34. Summer cooler
36. On edge
37. Gala occasion
39. Barrier
40. Up to now
41. — Baba
42. Skillet, for one
44. Male heir
45. Do sums
47. Consequently

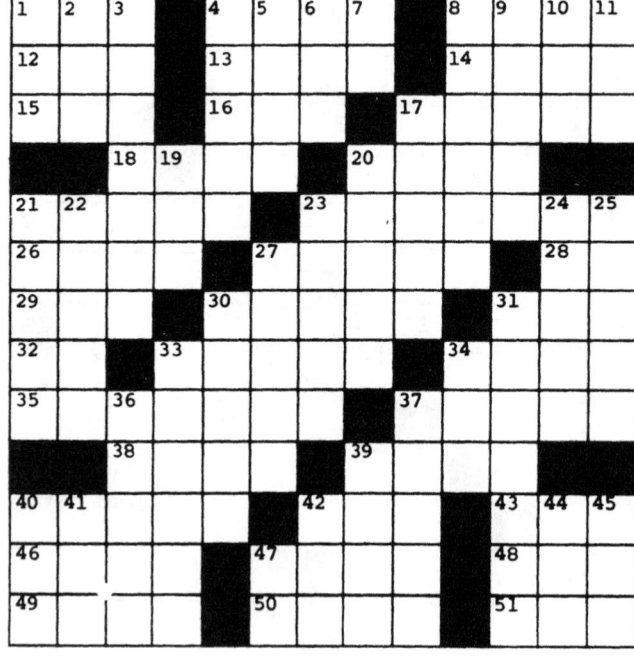

Solution is on page 375

ACROSS

1. Alack
5. Holliday or Severinsen
8. Resolve (with "out")
12. Seethe
13. Lyricist Gershwin
14. Grand Canyon phenomenon
15. Party decoration
17. Rainbow
18. Geological era, the — age
19. University boardmember
21. Theater area
24. Desire
25. Luxuriant
26. Breaks into pieces
30. Distinct part (of a whole)
31. Toupee
32. Spicy stew
33. Type of fuel
35. FDR's pet
36. Excellent
37. "— Hours," Scorsese film
38. Talked effusively
41. Wedding words
42. Opera solo
43. Concern of a palm reader
48. Sew, in a way
49. Tolkien character
50. Cut of meat
51. Coaster
52. Clever; foxy
53. Christmastime

DOWN

1. Not present: abbr.
2. Part of a movie studio
3. Make public
4. Quick magic trick: 3 wds.
5. Nickel and —, petty
6. Mine product
7. Bearing
8. Completely unwise: 3 wds.
9. Land measure
10. Lower leg part
11. Holy wafer
16. Part of a royal flush
20. Judge (cost): abbr.
21. Punch
22. Albacore
23. Condition of some sales: 2 wds.
24. Complaining tone of voice
26. Flimflams
27. Israeli port
28. Anger
29. Fly high
34. Falsehood
37. Summer cooler
38. Roams (about)
39. U.S.S.R. mountains
40. Royal form of address
41. Questionable
44. Under the weather
45. Debtor's paper: abbr.
46. Nothing
47. Chemical ending

HARD

Solution is on page 375

103

BIBLE CROSSWORD   MEDIUM

by RUSS CARLEY

Bible references in this puzzle are from the King James Version. You'll find it stimulating to solve, and may discover you know more about the Bible than you think you do.

ACROSS

1. Thou shalt call — name John. *Luke 1:13*
4. The Son of man hath — . . . to forgive sins. *Mark 2:10*
9. — brought forth her firstborn son. *Luke 2:7*
12. Lead us not —o temptation. *Matt. 6:13*
13. There — a great tempest. *Matt. 8:24*
14. Their — calveth. *Job 21:10*
15. Laban went to — his sheep. *Gen. 31:19*
17. The — Commandments
18. I — no pleasant bread. *Dan. 10:3*
19. I saw . . . a book . . . — with seven seals. *Rev. 5:1*
21. I have — the faith. *II Tim. 4:7*
23. Go out quickly into the streets and — of the city. *Luke 14:21*
25. He took —, and washed his hands. *Matt. 27:24*
28. The Lord — my shepherd. *Ps. 23:1*
30. The king . . . died, and his son reigned in his —. *I Chr. 19:1*
32. There — giants in the earth in those days. *Gen. 6:4*
33. Set them in two rows, six on a —. *Lev. 24:6*
35. The man . . . spake roughly to us, and took us for —. *Gen. 42:30*
37. They — the ship aground. *Acts 27:41*
38. They have taken cedars . . . to make masts for thee. Of the oaks of Bashan have they made thine —. *Ezek. 27:5, 6*
40. I did cast them out as the dirt in the —ts. *Ps. 18:42*
42. — man can serve two masters. *Matt. 6:24*
43. John came neither eating nor dri—. *Matt. 11:18*
45. His truth shall be thy s— and buckler. *Ps. 91:4*
47. I have — you that I am he. *St. John 18:8*
49. The rough ways shall be made —. *Luke 3:5*
52. They are — with the showers of the mountains. *Job 24:8*
54. Birds of the — have nests. *Luke 9:58*
56. — ye in at the strait gate. *Matt. 7:13*
57. Blessed — the meek. *Matt. 5:5*
58. As a jewel of gold in a swine's —, so is a fair woman . . . without discretion. *Prov. 11:22*
60. How long will it be — they believe me? *Num. 14:11*
61. He that committeth — is of the devil. *I John 3:8*
62. He that — me seeth him that sent me. *St. John 12:45*
63. His favour is as — upon the grass. *Prov. 19:12*

DOWN

1. They — and gnash the teeth. *Lam. 2:16*
2. The meek shall —rit the earth. *Ps. 37:11*
3. Thou shalt not —. *Ex. 20:15*
4. Children, obey your —. *Eph. 6:1*
5. To day — to morrow we will go. *James 4:13*
6. — ye not what the scripture saith? *Rom. 11:2*
7. He called the name of the well —. *Gen. 26:20*
8. They that wait upon the Lord shall — their strength. *Isa. 40:31*
9. I will — your bones round about. *Ezek. 6:5*
10. Thou art neither cold nor —. *Rev. 3:15*

11. What mean these seven — lambs? *Gen. 21:29*
16. —, my daughter! thou hast brought me very low. *Judg. 11:35*
20. Thou hast laid me in the lowest pit, in darkness, in the —. *Ps. 88:6*
22. The Lord . . . delivered me . . . out of the — of the bear. *I Sam. 17:37*
24. He — to his disciples, Sit ye here. *Mark 14:32*
26. —, family of the Eranites
27. We . . . have —unced . . . dishonesty. *II Cor. 4:1, 2*
28. He shall rule them with a rod of —. *Rev. 2:27*
29. Their land shall be —ed with blood. *Isa. 34:7*
31. I am in —ion daily, every one mocketh me. *Jer. 20:7*

34. What I have — I have written. *St. John 19:22*
36. Do what — good unto thee. *I Sam. 14:40*
39. His hairs were . . . as white as —w. *Rev. 1:14*
41. —, family of the Elonites
44. There was a sea of — like unto crystal. *Rev. 4:6*
46. She — on her lovers. *Ezek. 23:5*
48. These men shall — with me at noon. *Gen. 43:16*
50. I feared thee, because thou art an aus— man. *Luke 19:21*
51. They t— her down. *II Ki. 9:33*
52. Jesus — born in Bethlehem. *Matt. 2:1*
53. —, family of the Erites
55. My beloved is like a — or a young hart. *Song 2:9*
59. My lips shall —ter praise. *Ps. 119:171*

Solution is on page 375

105

HARD

ACROSS

1. Luncheon entree
6. Lugged
12. Regal abode
13. Eight-note span
14. Panacea
15. Born
16. Elected
17. Tear
18. Small change
20. Social insect
21. Leg joint
23. Time period
24. Biotite
25. Burdened, in a way
27. Paragon
28. Vapor
29. Blemish
30. Atomizer's output
33. Card game
37. God of war
38. Descendant
39. Thin
40. Inexperienced
41. Grooves
43. Probe
44. Has being
45. Soup morsel
46. Place
48. Edward Teach's crime
50. Beetle
51. Perfumes
52. Planted

DOWN

1. Salt marsh
2. Web-footed
3. Careless
4. Sour
5. Mocks
6. Certain sweetener
7. Deck members
8. Western Indian
9. Scale syllable
10. Indicate
11. Of teeth
12. — up, rallies
19. Demented
20. Succor
22. Bergen
24. Ethical
26. Minstrel's song
27. Homo sapiens
29. Flowing cloaks
30. Denudes
31. Periodic
32. Argument
33. Murmur
34. Decorous
35. Followed: slang
36. Ire
38. Murders
41. Breakaway group
42. Alone
45. Prospecting vessel
47. Crow's call
49. Concerning

Solution is on page 375

ACROSS

1. Drink bit by bit
4. Indian boat
9. Spider's home
12. Mine product
13. Detroit football players
14. Fruit drink
15. Harbor town
17. Bakery products
19. Frosty
20. Natural ability
21. Pile, as of hay
24. Cassettes' contents
25. Cut roughly, as with a hatchet
26. Floor pieces
27. And — on, et cetera
29. Single item
30. Everything
31. Young man
32. All right
33. Christmas plant
35. Angel's "hat"
36. Peels
37. Strength
38. Crushes, as coffee beans
40. Dove's sound
41. Cookstove
42. Puddinglike dessert
46. Carney of "The Honeymooners"
47. Way
49. Billiard stick
50. Affirmative reply
51. Torn off strip (of cloth)
52. "— Little Indians"

DOWN

1. Distress signal
2. Anger
3. Tiny "veggie"
4. Big Ben is one
5. Breezy
6. Negative word
7. Atop
8. Get away from
9. Rouses from sleep
10. Paradise
11. Superior
16. Choose
18. Beery beverages
20. Score; add (up)
21. Scat!
22. Water-storing receptacle
23. Playing card
24. Plows, as a field
26. Stories
27. Auction
28. Aroma
31. Rule
33. Dangle
34. Commands
35. Owl's sound
36. Half-quarts
37. Sat for an artist
38. Grandma's hair color
39. Very uncommon
40. — as a button, pretty
42. Mongrel; mutt
43. Perform
44. Regret
45. Cozy room
48. Cry of surprise

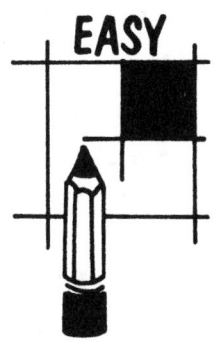

Solution is on page 375

107

by JOHN GREENMAN

This special crossword is solved in the same way as a regular crossword, except that the words are written into the diagram either from right to left (for the ACROSS words) or from bottom to top (for the UP words). The answers to definitions 1-Across and 1-Up have been entered to help you get started.   Solution is on page 376.

ACROSS

1. Fiftieth State
7. Coronet
12. Emulating James Galway
13. Devise; invent
15. It gauges electrical currents
16. Rabbit food
17. Filing aid
18. Notice
19. Feel under the weather
20. Wine cask
21. Medical student's course: abbr.
23. Admit: 2 wds.
25. Overlook
26. Pub brew
28. Grand Coulee, e.g.
29. Comedy-writer Taylor
30. Enciphered
32. Processors, of a sort
34. Environment: prefix
36. Statesman Hammarskjold
37. Part of a Caesar quote: 2 wds. (Latin)
42. Family member
46. Infirm
47. "— the season . . ."
49. Handled
51. Baseball-team number
52. Go off the —, take a detour
54. Goad
55. Native: suffix
56. Mr. Turpin
57. Priest's robe
59. Ms. Lupino
60. Locate
62. Spoiled
64. Milliners
65. Makes well-liked
66. Suspicious
67. Toughens

UP

1. Reference book
2. Back problem
3. "Noshed"
4. Perches
5. Show deference
6. Acquiesced
7. Assume a dancer's position: 2 wds.
8. Universal: abbr.
9. Insincere display
10. Commonplace
11. One who points the finger
12. Lethal
13. Asserted a right to
14. Tightens

22. Danson or Turner
24. Paving material
25. Chess pieces
27. "Superman" actor
29. Stiff
31. 601, to Lucullus
33. Devotee
35. Hydrocarbons found in gasoline
37. Disappear
38. Part of a monogram
39. Eating alcove
40. — -de-France

41. Trio, in Old Rome
43. Some technical-school graduates: abbr.
44. Principal
45. Escape artists, e.g.
48. Designates
50. Established customs: abbr.
52. Put to the proof a second time
53. Incline
56. Max, of boxing fame
58. — one's time
61. Shoshonean
62. Society-page word

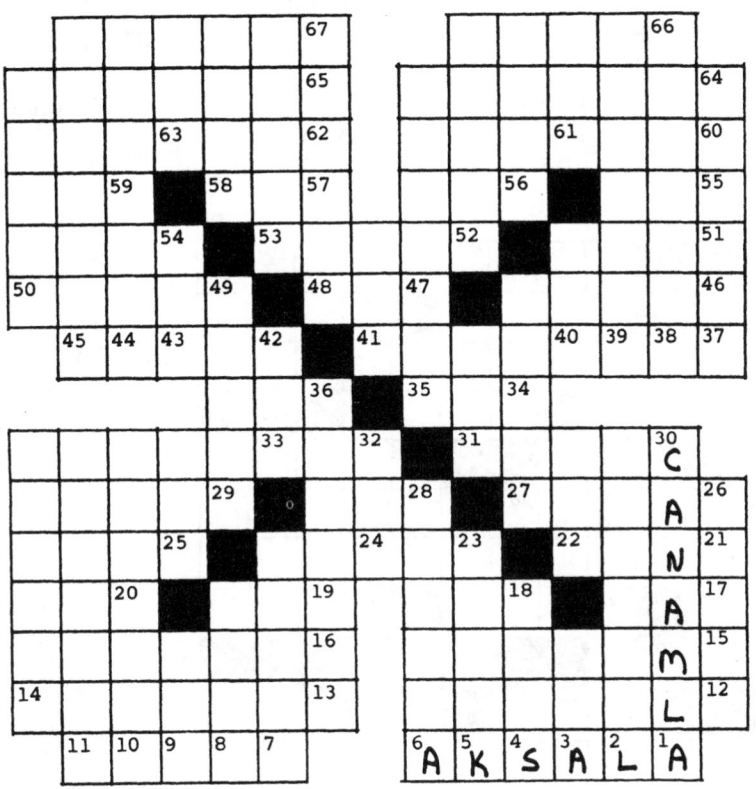

HARD

ACROSS

1. Golf score
4. Tree fluids
8. Candid
12. Expert
13. Threesome
14. Body of laws
15. Ashen: 4 wds.
18. Mister: Spanish
19. Mimic
20. Teachers' group: abbr.
22. Happen again
26. Jai —
29. Son of Jacob
32. — *pro nobis*
33. Speedy: 4 wds.
36. *Sturm — Drang*
37. Pianist, Dame Myra —
38. Word of woe
39. Old World lizard
41. Half a score
43. Related (to)
46. Endures
50. Sleeping heavily: 4 wds. (slang)
54. Entreaty
55. Roof part
56. As well
57. Rend
58. Reach across
59. Eat dinner

DOWN

1. Animal's "hands"
2. Dull, steady pain
3. Harness restraint
4. Cubic meter
5. Southern constellation
6. Galileo's home
7. Washing need
8. Earth color
9. He wrote "The Gold Bug"
10. Dutch city
11. Seine
16. Restorative
17. Letter part
21. Wings: Latin
23. Kind of fuel
24. Bear in the sky
25. Stadium sounds
26. Bluish-green
27. Respiratory organ
28. Verdi heroine
30. Kind of curve
31. Extensive
34. Uniform color
35. Hawaiian veranda
40. Of the cheek
42. Actress Terry
44. DDE namesakes
45. Kind of tide
47. NCOs: abbr.
48. Biblical pronoun
49. Halt!
50. Make a choice (for)
51. Suffix meaning "little"
52. Pekoe, for one
53. A Gardner

Solution is on page 376

ACROSS

1. Sear
5. Streak of lightning
9. Courageous
10. Worship
12. Playground chutes
13. Duplicated
15. Sunbath's result
16. Hearsay
18. In favor of
19. Compulsion
21. Person
22. Use a letter opener
23. Prodded
25. Escapes
26. Wander restlessly
27. For shame!
28. Anticipates
31. Woodlands
35. Frosts a cake
36. Fuel
37. Use a peeler
38. Depot: abbr.
39. Trousers
41. Falsehood
42. Rarely
44. Overjoyed
46. Poke fun at
47. Speed contests
48. Coloring agents
49. Drove recklessly

DOWN

1. Cower
2. Possessed
3. Assert
4. Began again
5. Breakfast meat
6. Aroma
7. Cut off, as branches
8. "Three-bagger"
9. Play loudly
11. Weird
12. Daze
14. Polka followers
17. Angry
20. Borders
22. Slumber
24. — Vegas
25. Evergreen tree
27. Promotes
28. Sound of disapproval
29. Group of eight
30. Resounded, as bells
31. Admirer
32. Seasoned
33. Attempts
34. Plant starter
36. Fun contests
39. Model's stance
40. Openhanded blow
43. 24 hours
45. Expert

EASY

Solution is on page 376

111

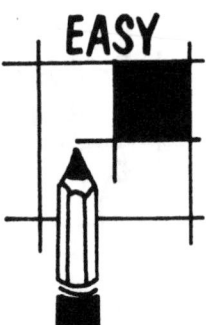

EASY

ACROSS

1. Butter square
4. Paper fastener
8. Wound mark
12. Gone by
13. Actress Turner
14. Story
15. Disappointment
17. Renowned
18. Possess
19. Canary home
20. Blemish
23. Leave: 2 wds.
26. Ripped (apart)
27. Rescues
28. Creole State: abbr.
29. Had lunch
30. Titles
31. Distant
32. Pa's mate
33. Vaulting aids
34. — across, find by chance
35. Gratifies
37. Jackrabbits
38. Practices deception
39. Saucer's edge
40. Stupefies
42. Conceal: 2 wds.
46. General's assistant
47. Change positions
48. Yankeeland: abbr.
49. Unwanted plant
50. Performs (a deed)
51. Not used

DOWN

1. Chum
2. Stone or Iron —
3. Youngster
4. Circus performer
5. Grassy area
6. Traveler's stop
7. Keystone State: abbr.
8. Old West transports
9. Portrait-bearing gem
10. Pub brew
11. Carmine
16. Kill: 2 wds. (slang)
17. Counterfeits
19. Grottos
20. Postal seal
21. Add up
22. "You — My Sunshine"
23. Domesticates
24. Sweetheart
25. Travel costs
27. Bargain events
30. Pries inquisitively
31. Favoring
33. Ached
34. Sleeveless garment
36. Dodge artfully
37. Busy places
39. Valentine word
40. Carpenter's tool
41. Bind (up)
42. Dove sound
43. Sprint
44. Put in service
45. Lion's foot
47. Physician: abbr.

Solution is on page 376

ACROSS

1. Harangue
7. Tiffs
12. Mrs. deHavilland
13. Falcon's claw
14. Kingly substitute
15. Jockey, Eddie —
16. Concise
18. Scatter seeds
19. Loud, saucer-shaped bell
23. Lasso and lariat
25. Love: Spanish
26. Pioneer
30. Actress Thompson
31. Moynihan's title: abbr.
32. Rant
33. Gift
35. Frosts
36. Coin grooves
38. Beaver skin
39. Health resort
42. Groans
44. Put up (fruit)
46. Clothing
51. Aquatic mammal
52. Annoyed
53. Dandelions
54. Chimney cleaners, for short

DOWN

1. Moor hill
2. Island: French
3. Gear
4. Hail!
5. Drive in with force
6. Gourmand
7. Public road
8. Insulated boot
9. Woe is me!
10. Matador's contender: Spanish
11. TV-screen spots
15. Ski resort
17. — stone, hieroglyphic tablet
19. Inhale suddenly
20. General Bradley
21. Knob
22. Lawn cover
24. Dispossess, as of honors
27. Doily openwork
28. Stuntman Knievel
29. Pause
31. Hair covering
34. Fudd and Gantry
37. Ginger cookies
39. Flat-bottomed boat
40. — de foie gras
41. Casino stake
43. Fret; worry
45. Actor Beatty
47. Alphabet letter
48. Contraction
49. Agent, for short
50. Sullivan and Begley

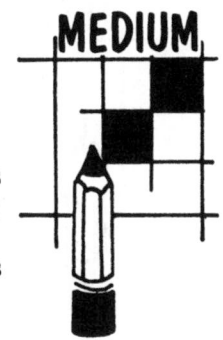

MEDIUM

Solution is on page 376

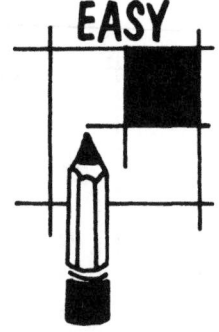

EASY

ACROSS

1. Plane's personnel
5. Give a smack to
9. In addition
13. Cabbage salad
17. Musical, "A Chorus —"
18. Bees' shelter
19. Sign of faulty plumbing
20. Cavity
21. Tack on
22. Leaving
24. Medicine portions
25. Wishes for
27. As a matter of —, really
28. Most deep, as a voice
29. Mouser
30. Gigantic
31. Eat
32. Scatter, as seed
35. Hoover and Grand Coulee
36. Day after today
40. Urge into action
41. Identical
42. Thames or Nile
43. DDE's nickname
44. Intention
45. Stitches
46. Apple centers
47. Land measure
48. Summit
49. Biddy
50. Foundations
51. Staff of life
52. Hobo
53. Window glasses
54. Dress border
55. Heavenly body
58. Rouses from sleep
59. Sunner's reward
60. Villain's cry
63. "Once — a time . . ."
64. Valleys
65. Sudden jerk
66. Small, seedy fruit
67. Asphalting
68. Zoo compartments
69. Do a household chore
70. Tahoe or Huron
71. Replacement for stairs
73. Not as much
74. Jack rabbits
75. Shop sign
76. Corrode
77. Uncooked
78. Schedules
81. Healthy
82. Baseball flag
86. Domesticates
87. Putting back , as funds
89. Court
90. Always
91. Employ
92. Melody
93. Dad, to mom
94. — out, succeeds
95. Mimics
96. One-dish meal
97. Changes the color of

DOWN

1. Dressed
2. Motor trip
3. Finishes
4. You and I
5. Article of bedding
6. "Your — were sweeter than julep . . ."
7. Actress Gardner
8. Filler for an atomizer
9. "Wonderland" girl
10. Penitent time
11. Droop
12. All right
13. Rainfall
14. Misplace
15. Pub beverages
16. Compass heading
22. Sketch
23. Price labels
24. Giver
26. Frosted (a cake)
28. Lemons' kin
30. Overacting actors: slang
31. Cooing birds
32. Petty quarrel
33. Threesome
34. Frolic (about)
35. Daybreak
36. Whitewalls or retreads
37. Crop of China
38. Gumbo ingredient
39. Crab grass is one
41. Appear (to be)
42. Corsage favorites
45. Close (a door)
46. Walking sticks
47. Provide with weapons
50. Oven-cooks
51. Crooked
52. Vereen or Gazzara
53. Less colorful
54. Sentry's shout
55. Adorable
56. October gem
57. Greater amount
58. Child's four-wheeler
59. Throw
60. From a distance
61. Long walk
62. Grows older
64. Fruitcake fruits

65. Fair; even
68. Sleeveless garments
69. Sahara and Gobi
70. Yard grass
72. Those who cast ballots
73. "Humdinger": slang
74. Dangle (from)

76. Fixed charges
77. Continue a subscription
78. Short distance
79. Volcanic overflow
80. So be it!
81. Roll-call reply
82. Evergreen tree

83. On vacation
84. Memo
85. Baby's discovery
87. Tear
88. Pecan or almond
91. Laugh sound
93. Baltimore's State: abbr.

Solution is on page 376

115

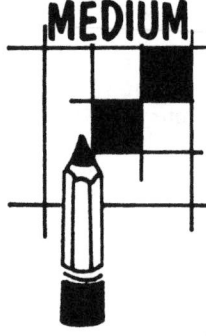

MEDIUM

ACROSS

1. Mast
5. Pace
9. "Red Planet"
13. Parker House specialty
17. Healthy
18. Wide-mouthed pitcher
19. Biblical garden
20. Great Lake
21. Historic periods
22. Depend (on)
23. Roman garment
24. Penny
25. Merit
27. Takes into custody
29. Requires
31. Walk on; trample
32. Seasons
35. Plant fluid
37. Scoundrel
38. Air holes
42. Has faith in
44. Irrigate
46. Want
47. Intention
48. Drink slowly
50. Show drowsiness
51. Passing fancy
52. Pod vegetable
53. Siesta
54. At this time
56. Called for publicly
58. Group of like things
59. Wag
61. Uncooked
62. Favorite
65. Gentleman's title: Spanish
67. Wager
69. Steal from
72. Malt brew
73. Knight's title
74. Money roll
76. Wield oars
78. Part of a military address: abbr.
79. Embraces
81. Metric yard
83. English equivalent of 65-Across
85. Try the flavor of
86. Chum
87. Used to be
89. View
90. Receive and pass on
92. With less color
94. Walked proudly
97. Professions
101. Presently, to poets
102. Totals
105. Detroit products
107. Biblical brother
108. Male deer
109. Entreaty
110. Assist in wrongdoing
111. Method
112. Lateral surface
113. Transmitted
114. Four-posters
115. Winter forecast word

DOWN

1. Hut
2. Peel
3. Oh, woe!
4. Feels indignation about
5. Wait on
6. Certain woolens
7. Snakelike fish
8. Snoop
9. Encountered
10. Commotion
11. Consider
12. Trap
13. Moves out, as the tide
14. Metal sources
15. Tiny bits of cloth
16. Allows
26. Reposes
28. Ranted
30. Carpenter's tool
31. Asphaltlike substance
32. Man's nickname
33. Operatic solo
34. Shapeless mass
36. Cooking utensil
37. Aromatic wood
39. Bites lightly
40. Dogwood, for one
41. Chair
43. Transgression
45. Spinning toy
46. Father
49. Strength
51. Not as many
55. Be victorious
57. Talk a lot
60. Drying cloth
62. Agreement
63. Woman's name
64. Afternoon socials
65. Family member, for short
66. Rodent
68. Male cat
69. Be important

70. Ready for business
71. Use a drill
73. Drive fast
75. Moisture on the lawn
77. Smarter
80. Odd
81. "Merry" month

82. Knock sharply
84. Shrieks
86. Oar
88. Holy
91. Jumps
93. Endures
94. Go by
95. Against: prefix

96. Thoroughfare
98. Black, to poets
99. Redecorate
100. Killed
103. Lair
104. Had a chair
105. Taxi
106. Man's nickname

Solution is on page 377

ACROSS

1. Soup ingredient, perhaps
6. Overwhelmed, in a way
10. Hindu god
14. Oklahoma Indian
15. Location
16. Time periods, to Pablo
17. Exaggerate: 3 wds.
20. Whitney, et al.
21. Hidden fence
22. Street show
23. Capitol Hill VIP: abbr.
24. Urchin
25. Maples
26. Banjolike instrument
28. Asner and Begley
29. Under the covers
30. Federal agents: hyph. wd.

33. Acted servilely
36. Greet
37. Glib
40. Medicinal plants
41. TV bulletin: 2 wds.
43. Malicious talk
44. Picnic sites
45. Whale
46. Purpose
47. Transport by air
48. Discover: 2 wds.
49. Besmirched
51. Dainty
52. College exams
53. International actress
54. Barbers' items, in the old days
56. Develops
59. Suburban sights
60. Spelunkers' finds
62. Dallas institution: abbr.
63. Woodwind
64. Cylinders
65. Send via carrier
66. In mourning
68. Intact
69. Mason's aid
70. Fissure
71. Moon feature
72. Tipplers
73. Very small margin
74. Director's command
76. Dispute
79. Promontories
81. Nobles
82. Word with "art"
84. Social brotherhood
85. Type of hairdo
86. Prank
87. Speechless: 5 wds.
90. Head: French
91. Consumer
92. Weak
93. Luge
94. Negatives
95. Exits

DOWN

1. Comes in last
2. Basket fibers
3. Small harbor
4. Ripens
5. Hardened
6. Feeling humiliated
7. Inside
8. Allen or Frome
9. Scottish river
10. Arab
11. Habituated
12. Electorate
13. Ruins
18. Pursued
19. Musical syllable
24. Jeers
27. French painter
30. Ungainly
31. Overlook
32. Sprite
33. Waned
34. Straighten
35. Verbatim: 3 wds.
36. German title
37. Remark made upon departing: 2 wds.
38. Necktie
39. Clan chief
41. Fragrant perennials
42. Dawdle
44. Rinds
47. Flutters
48. "— Johnny!"
50. Laundry employee
51. Apples and pears
53. Demolish
54. Splash about
55. *Verboten*
57. Mr. Zola
58. Great!
60. Slaps
61. Border on
64. Tease
65. Be generous
67. Gold, in Madrid
68. Legal documents

71. Frankness
72. Made tough
73. How terrible!
74. Monopoly
75. Modernize

76. "Java"
77. Panache
78. Walk with uncertainty
79. Layers

80. Hit sign: abbr.
81. Riata
83. Acts the model
86. Spanish title
88. Heat source
89. Joker

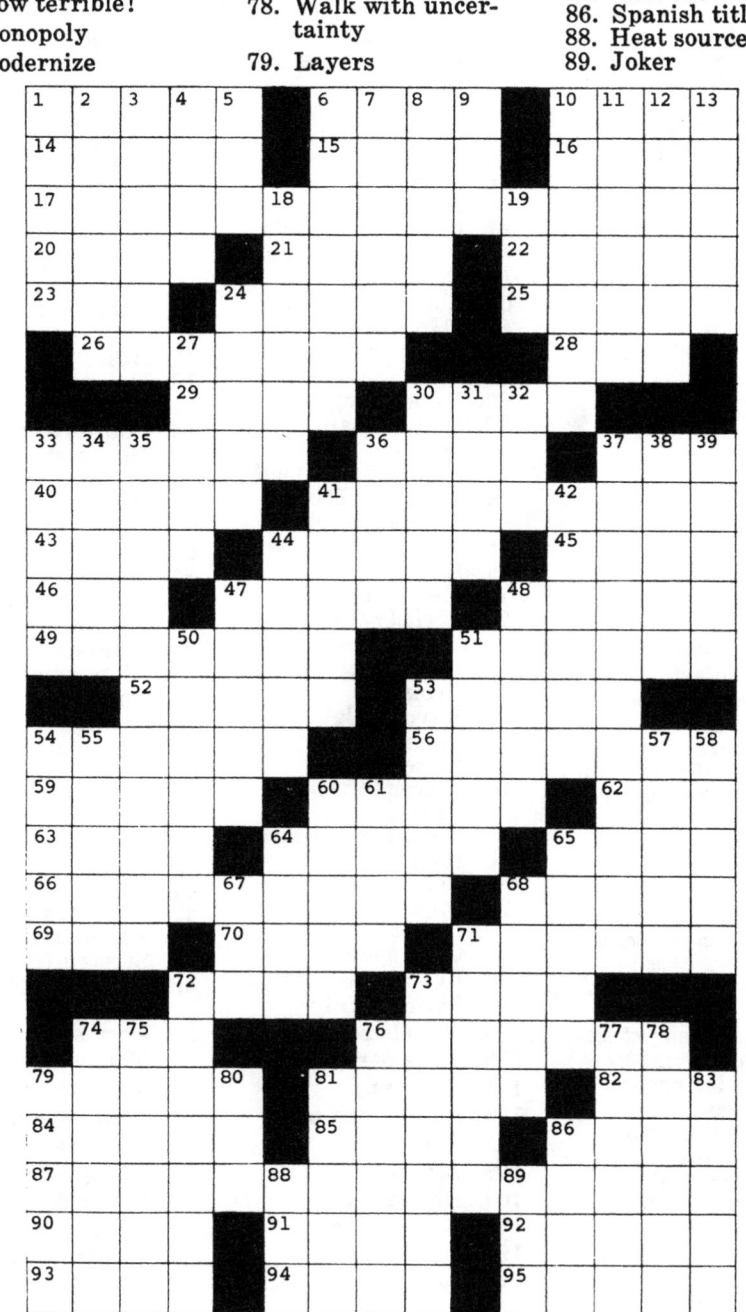

Solution is on page 377

HARD

ACROSS

1. Movie-studio locale
4. 5,280 feet
8. Theatrical performer
13. Mature
17. Type of foil: abbr.
19. One who sits for an artist
20. Lamp cover
21. Opera solo
22. Tiny insect
23. Eskimo house
24. Tobacco holders
25. Cans
26. Small specialty shop
28. Gleam
30. Beginning; start
32. Drag along
33. Jeweled crown
34. Ringlet
35. Raised platform
37. "— Were the Days"
38. York's rank
42. Cotton cloth for work clothes
43. Popular house plant
44. Posture
46. Dove sound
47. Tardy
48. Apple center
49. Ceremonial act
50. United Kingdom inhabitant
51. Building wing
52. Red gem
54. Sports followers
55. The ones here
56. Emotion
58. Public decree
60. Mr. Ed is one
61. Crowd (of people)
62. Pretended attack
63. Festivals
64. Christmas plant
65. "Home on the —"
66. Begin (with): 2 wds.
69. Prison rooms
70. Watch-chain ornaments
71. Roll of parchment
74. — de Janeiro
75. Gambler's term
76. Beak
77. Not more
78. Medicinal tablet
79. Period; era
80. "Swan Lake" or "The Sleeping Beauty"
82. Sweet rolls
83. "Norma Rae" actress
84. Places for barbecues
86. Irritated, western style
88. Conjecture
89. Inquires
90. Optical adjustment
91. Cat's sound
92. Red root vegetable
95. Satisfies fully
96. Upholstered stools
100. Time periods
101. Grown up
103. Frequented place
105. Departed
106. Against
107. Doctor's aide
108. Borders
109. Notion
110. Bank transaction
111. Postpone
112. Film holder
113. Snaky fish

DOWN

1. Mary's pet
2. Medley
3. Ballet skirt
4. Hollywood bigshot
5. Wight or Man
6. Lion constellation
7. Ecologist's concern
8. Has lofty ambitions
9. Peking's country
10. Recording ribbon
11. Lyric poem
12. Asset
13. Noisy toy
14. Eye part
15. Coniferous tree
16. Not west
18. Gaseous fuel
19. Ruffled pride
27. "Othello" villain
29. Possesses
31. Entreat
33. Number of blind mice
34. Pennies
35. Thin, layered rock
36. Champion, as in boxing
37. Sea swallow
38. New Orleans football player
39. Belts and scarves
40. Loop made with a slipknot
41. Carry
42. Musical sign
43. Form (metal)
45. Stretch (of land)
48. Lollipops and gumdrops
50. Torn strip
52. Young ladies
53. Adolescents
54. Penalty sums
55. Entire amount
57. Lounges (about)
59. Excavate
60. Shoe parts
62. Children's story
63. Dental thread
64. Bordering shrub

65. Buns
67. Completely occupies
68. Pleat; crease
69. Winter garment
70. Office cabinets
72. Holmes looks for these
73. Tear or rip
76. Kind of tennis stroke
78. Meat- or cheese-filled dough

80. Low singing voice
81. One who jogs
82. Rouge
83. Mink or sable garments
85. Dried grape
87. Frost
88. Blasts (of wind)
90. Opposite of 92-Down
91. Quiz-show group

92. Genuine
93. Central Italian river
94. Information
95. Breaking waves
96. Very large
97. Morse —
98. Leg joint
99. Hermetic closure
102. Payable
104. Fruit drink

Solution is on page 377

SPECIAL CHALLENGER CROSSWORD

"SWEETLY"

by LOUIS SABIN

Here is a real toughie for you. We have omitted giving you such helps as "2 wds.," "hyph. wd.," and "slang"; but in the spirit of fair play, all abbreviations and foreign words are so indicated.

ACROSS

1. Meat-curers
8. Pollux's twin
14. Son of Tantalus
20. Unfortunate commuter
21. Canny
22. Consecutively
23. Survivor's share
24. Sweet stuff
26. Resort
27. Spread to dry, as hay
28. Snatch
29. Adam's grandson
30. Nickname for Edgar
31. Pastor
33. Star of "Brian's Song"
34. Giant of folklore
35. Complains
38. Recent
39. Fleet
40. Curl
41. Harpsichordist Kipnis
42. Supporters
53. Fabric with a glossy finish
44. Intrepid
45. Behind
47. Fleshy underground stem
48. Over-the-phone purchaser
51. Fervent
52. Portioned out sparingly
54. Wrath
55. Narrow channel for ships
56. More polite and elegant
57. Fragment
58. Curved
61. Exchanging teasing remarks
62. Long-haired lap dogs
63. Expressions of disgust
64. Axiom
65. Interdiction
66. Observe
67. Say over and over
68. Castigated
72. UNC player
74. Liturgy
75. One in custody
76. Agitate
77. Manumit
78. Hazard to river boats
79. Seine tributary
80. "Captain Blood" star
82. Row of seats
83. Extremely long time: var. sp.
84. Sudden bursts
85. Appraise
86. Fishing boat
87. Agreeable
89. Spanish demonstrative pronoun
90. Circus unit
91. Hollywood's "Cowardly Lion"
92. In the past
93. Camp bed
96. Sweet stuff
99. Calm (oneself)
101. "Ditz"
102. Conger-catchers
103. Molasses, in Manchester
104. Beginnings
105. Puts forth energetically
106. Poet Siegfried

DOWN

1. Swift aircraft: abbr.
2. Crowning
3. Singer Cantrell
4. Blasting material: abbr.
5. Sitwell and Head
6. Name meaning "born again"
7. One of a large botannical group
8. Marks of distinction
9. To land
10. Tolerated
11. Fit (into)
12. Siouan Indian
13. Deliverance
14. Climber's spike
15. Once upon a time, of old
16. Resin
17. Sweet stuff
18. Fireplace tools
19. Men of Malmö
25. Art student's course: abbr.
31. Partridge snares
32. Be contingent (on)
33. Nun
34. Heraldic wreath
35. Name
36. Taj Mahal site
37. Outraged reaction
39. Top-notch
40. Sondheim musical, "Sweeney —"
42. Pugilist's weapon
43. Connect systematically
44. Fictional rabbit's "title"
46. Be in the vanguard of
47. Man of fashion

48. Designer Cassini
49. Pennsylvania port
50. Members of a house of Congress: abbr.
52. City in northeastern Mexico
53. Cord
56. Tinge; shade
57. Emits
58. Sanction
59. East Indian broad-bill
60. Sweet stuff
61. Be furious
62. Drained of color
64. Orange skin
65. Court great
67. Check

68. Carries on, as business
69. Singer Redding
70. Happy gathering: comb. form
71. Charges
73. Sharpen
75. Wild ox of the Celebes
77. Landscaper's choice
78. Cassandra of Troy
80. City in the San Joaquin valley
81. First out, sometimes
82. Vocal quality
83. Notable trumpet player

84. Fabled earth-dwellers
86. Obligations
87. Monograph
88. Marketplace of old Athens
90. Taunt
91. 1977 Cy Young Award winner (AL)
93. Chanel of Paris
94. Scandinavian capital
95. Adolescent
97. Overwhelm
98. Critic Reed
100. Series of steps, in dancing

Solution is on page 377

DIAGRAMLESS

MEDIUM

This Diagramless is 17 boxes wide by 17 boxes deep.

ACROSS

1. Cork's sound
4. Enemy
7. Molten rock
8. Smack
9. Warning device
10. Soul
12. Purify
13. Double
14. Chilly
17. Dyes
18. Leap
20. Also
21. Bettor's advantage
22. Crease
23. Blackboard material
25. Absolutely!
26. Destiny
27. Puddle
28. Countenance
29. Sketch
30. Discharge
31. Toothed wheel
32. Accomplished
33. Harsh cry
34. Unadulterated
35. Smile
36. Blemish
39. Playground feature

41. Fall in drops
42. Dunce: slang
43. Lubricate
44. Exchanges
46. Resided
47. Require
49. Sharpen
50. Followed the course of
52. Mum
54. Marathons
55. Uncommon
56. Ripe, as cheese
57. Lamb's mom
58. Marry

DOWN

1. French capital
2. Baking chamber
3. Window sections
4. Hurl
5. Rowing need
6. Homeric work
7. Raises
8. Backbone
9. Dispatches
10. Pigs and hogs
11. Entire
12. Roller coaster
13. Hackneyed

15. Land parcel
16. Buck's mate
17. Plaything
19. Position
23. What eagles do
24. Deep
26. Taxi passenger
27. Beseech
28. Splendid
29. College official
30. Golfer's cry
31. Complain: slang
32. Failure
33. Star of the wedding
34. Heaps
35. Cary or Lee
36. Relocates
37. Mimicked
38. Blushing
39. Male heir
40. Falsehood
41. Monotonous buzzing
42. Cut into cubes
44. At that place
45. Soda sipper
46. Streaked, as with color
48. Dreadful
51. Fury
53. Statute

Solution is on page 377

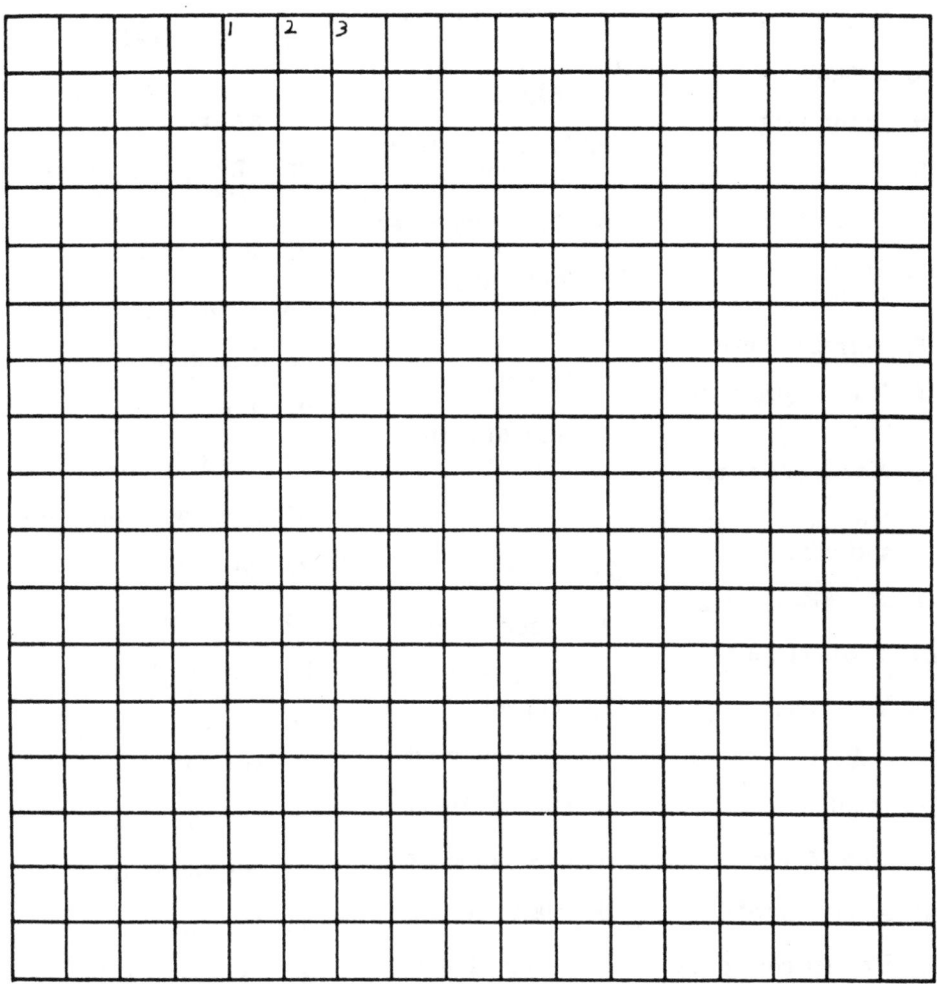

DIAGRAMLESS　　　　HARD

This Diagramless is 15 boxes wide by 15 boxes deep.
Starting box is on page 377.

ACROSS

1. Island east of Java
5. Dregs
9. Actor Jannings
10. Other
11. River duck
12. Government agency: abbr.
13. Actress Sheridan
14. Freshwater minnow
16. North Sea port
21. Numbers expert, of a kind: abbr.
24. Achieve success
25. Those people
26. Tried out
27. Sub
28. Foolish
31. July 15, e.g.
32. Anent: 2 wds.
33. Private college in Poughkeepsie, N.Y.
38. Smith, of tennis
39. Noble principles
40. Poulard
41. Stretch
43. Tricky rascals
46. Jewish title of respect
49. Mother of Helen and Pollux
50. Yorkshire river
51. Made angry
52. Get!
53. Proboscis
54. Gap, of a kind

DOWN

1. Greek letter
2. Word with "corner"
3. Tropical vine
4. Unpropitious
5. Russian leader
6. Flair; style
7. Being: Latin
8. Looked for
14. Golfer Ballesteros
15. Pay close attention to
17. Sawed strip of wood
18. Poetic "before"
19. Transportation systems: abbr.
20. Morse code character
22. Father: French
23. Hebrew prophet
25. Strong desire
28. Bowl
29. Feed the kitty
30. Actress, Bonnie —
33. Depraved
34. Big fusses
35. Coin of 1-Across
36. Droop
37. Winglike part
41. Elude
42. Writer Jong
44. Roman emperor
45. Dog days drinks
47. Notable periods
48. Wagers
50. Horned viper

Solution is on page 378

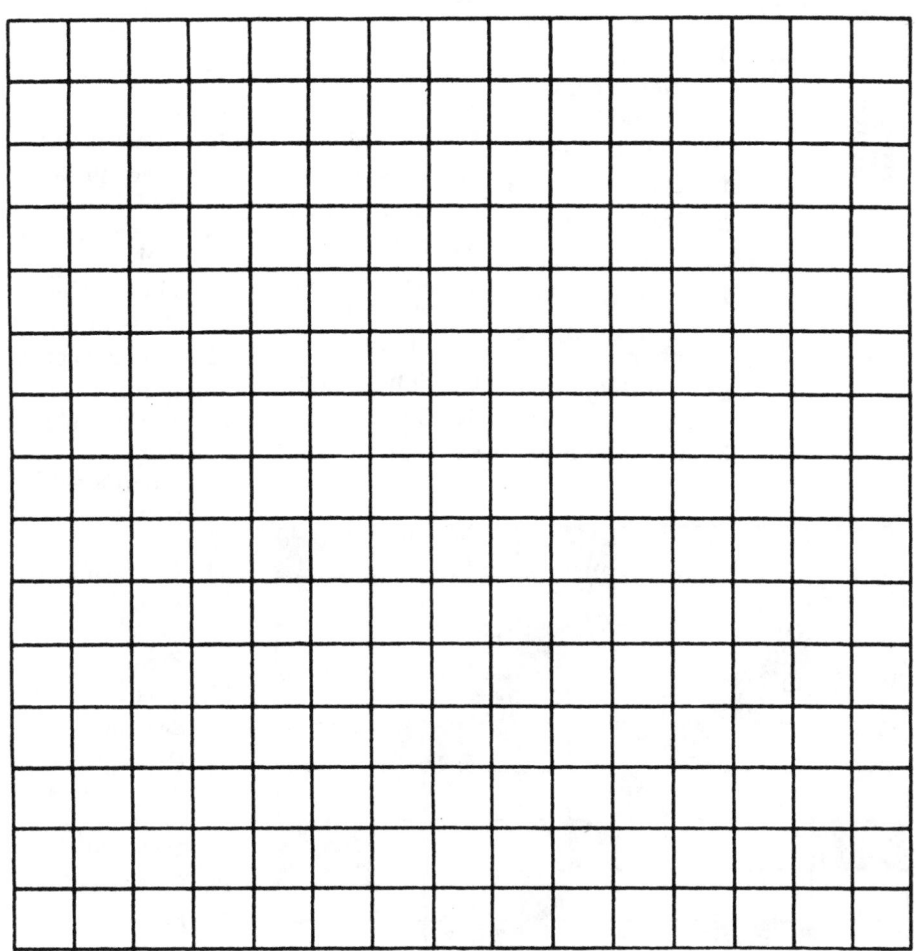

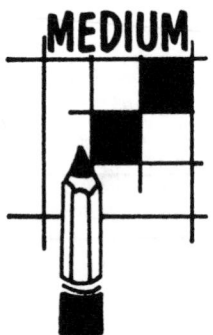

MEDIUM

ACROSS

1. Renowned
7. "...the shot — round the world"
12. Unwilling
13. Raid
15. This: French
16. Flock
18. Newsperson Sawyer
19. Compass point
21. Bambi, for one
23. Defeat soundly
24. Large casks
26. Tenpenny item
28. College degree: abbr.
29. Establish: 2 wds.
31. Crowing bird
34. Cleveland's lake
36. Not false
37. High-pitched cry
40. Southern States
43. Else
44. Avoid
46. Earth colors
47. Fewer
50. Burden
52. Weaken
53. Gem State
55. Oak
57. Amtrak, for one: abbr.
58. Share
60. Sandwich meat
62. Creed
63. Sign up

DOWN

1. Gem surfaces
2. Street
3. Myself
4. Globe
5. Second-hand
6. Lucky number
7. Hello!
8. Terminate
9. Dry
10. Lion's sound
11. River in Germany
14. Prevent; prohibit
17. Time period
20. Come in
22. Public disorder
25. Certain
27. Nobleman's title
30. Baker's products
32. Befit
33. Western State
35. Reverberated sound
37. Firm
38. Account entry
39. Search
41. Up —, ready to fight: 2 wds.
42. — de corps, group spirit
45. Doctor's aide
48. Rescue
49. Leg part
51. Actor Connery
54. Lyric poem
56. Building wing
59. And: Latin
61. Three-toed sloth

Solution is on page 378

ACROSS

1. Orangutan
4. Ink spots
9. Tear
12. Mesh fabric
13. Word with "pot" or "rib"
14. Historical period
15. Follow the trail of
17. Paver's need
18. "My Gal —"
19. Cries of pain
21. Rave
23. Painters
27. Mean
30. Banister
31. Man's nickname
33. Laugh sound
34. Bible woman
35. Becomes less important
36. Evergreen tree
37. Compass direction: abbr.
38. Catholic church leaders
39. Discover
40. South American mountains
42. Orchestra section
44. Dines
46. Male offspring
47. Sickly pale
49. Building wing
51. Lucky number
55. Deed
56. Hoist, as a flag
58. Wonder
59. Surely!
60. Plant stalks
61. Golf peg

DOWN

1. Picnic pest
2. For each
3. Airport sign: abbr.
4. Steeps (tea)
5. — and behold!
6. Cereal grain
7. Russian ruler: var. sp.
8. Ropelike lengths, as of pearls
9. Takes a nap
10. Mr. Gershwin
11. Buddy
16. Wind around, as a rope
20. Leather binding strip
22. Negative vote
23. Stadium
24. Black bird
25. Popular Father's Day gift
26. Bargains
28. Item
29. Fabric measurements
32. Bird homes
35. Teen-ager's pinups
36. Fish wing
38. Green vegetable
39. OK
41. Fender benders
43. Fragrant flowers
45. Thin, wood strip
47. Route
48. High card
50. Fib
52. Large tank
53. Ram's mate
54. Born
57. Dress size: abbr.

Solution is on page 378

EASY

ACROSS

1. Game, tic- — -
   toe
4. Strikebreaker
8. Avoid
12. Miss Lupino
13. Bats' home
14. Mexican dollar
15. For each
16. Dollar bill
17. Portioned
    (out)
18. Jogging gait
20. Swimming
    tank
21. Single-masted
    sailing vessel
23. Inflatable
    party favor
26. Whistle sound
27. Fender nicks
28. Canada's con-
    tinent: abbr.
29. Pitcher Dar-
    ling
30. Shoe bottoms
31. Family mem-
    ber, for short
32. While
33. Leopard mark-
    ings
34. Resident of
    Glasgow
35. Annoys
37. Crazy: slang
38. Swindles:
    slang
39. Perform alone
40. Fire (a gun)
42. Overly
43. Faucet
46. Medicinal tab-
    let
47. Chicken shelter
48. Self-esteem
49. Totals (up)
50. Picnic pests
51. Bright color

DOWN

1. Waiter's re-
   ward
2. Lemony drink
3. Animated —,
   Disney spe-
   cialty
4. Ice-cream por-
   tion
5. Play, "You —
   Take It With
   You"
6. Wide street:
   abbr.
7. Take place
8. Thread holders
9. Greeting word
10. Utilize
11. Show sleepi-
    ness
17. Blockheads
19. Decay
20. Window sec-
    tions
21. Watchband
22. Wiggly, as a
    tooth
23. What suspend-
    ers replace
24. Stew vegetable
25. Mean; ornery
27. Room en-
    trances
30. Shelled out
31. Child's vehicle
33. Counter seats
34. Scale tone
36. Rebuke; chide
37. Airplane ma-
    neuvers
39. Chimney grime
40. Health resort
41. Concealed
42. Coal weight
44. Grow older
45. Pea casing
47. Sacramento's
    State: abbr.

Solution is on page 378

ACROSS

1. Aromatic wood
6. Informal language
11. King's chair
12. Works hard
14. James Taylor song, "Fire and —"
15. Barter; swap
17. Exclamation of surprise
18. Expend, with "up"
19. Songs for two
20. Payable
21. Myself
22. Fathers
23. Discover
24. Make believe
26. Time indicators on a clock
27. Dyeing vessels
28. Vigorous and healthy
29. Petty quarrels
31. Large rock
34. Secret message system
35. Room separators
36. "So" follower
37. Pub brew
38. Thin ropes
39. Gym pad
40. Providence's State: abbr.
41. Bull's "weapons"
42. Fence opening
43. Group of fish
45. Unlocked
47. Give the right of way
48. Identified

DOWN

1. Pursuer
2. A Great Lake
3. Comedian Rickles
4. For each; per
5. Comes back
6. Wood strips
7. Young boys
8. President Lincoln, to friends
9. Negative vote
10. Earth; land
11. Outdo
13. Lean-tos
16. Oboe, for one
19. Counts calories, perhaps
20. Ate supper
22. Declare
23. Tourist spot, Niagara —
25. Avoid; escape
26. Transports by truck
28. Continues clutching; 2 wds.
29. Lasting marks
30. Insurance contract
31. Farm building
32. Overjoyed
33. Estimated
35. "We Are the —"
38. Composed
39. Lion's "collar"
41. Gardening tool
42. Opal or emerald
44. Hello!
46. Ma's mate

MEDIUM

Solution is on page 378

HARD

ACROSS

1. Alphabet members
4. Mrs. Robert Schumann
9. Medical group: abbr.
12. Perched
13. Leverets
14. Neon, for one
15. Preclude
17. Jibs
19. Relaxation
20. Correspondence
21. Baked items
23. Remittance
26. Spumescent drinks
27. Fees
28. Cry of surprise
29. Owned
30. Abhorred
31. "C'est la —"
32. Word of choice
33. Gluts
34. Instance
35. Feeling
37. Apples, e.g.
38. Farm building
39. Fight for air
40. Oak fruit
42. Cracker
45. Fish eggs
46. Gladden
48. Singer Clark
49. Romaine
50. Diminish
51. Summer: French

DOWN

1. Psychic sense: abbr.
2. Scratch
3. Guided
4. Board game
5. Narrow way
6. Gallery display
7. Scale tone
8. Examined ore
9. Nimble
10. Badly: prefix
11. Beast of burden
16. Brewing tubs
18. Intentions
20. Spouses
21. Nevada-California lake
22. Warning device
23. Church plate
24. Din
25. Quaker pronouns
27. Boca —, Florida
30. Coif preserver
31. Count Dracula, e.g.
33. Vedette
34. Price
36. Woodwind instruments
37. More wan
39. Slalom opening
40. Circle segment
41. Columbary sound
42. Fool: slang
43. Negative particle
44. Hurricane center
47. CA city: abbr.

Solution is on page 378

132

ACROSS

1. Masculine
5. Stage backdrop
8. Tiff
12. Ireland: poetic
13. Pub drink
14. Wan
15. Intelligent
17. Inactive
18. Took a chair
19. List of names
21. Ignited
22. Occurrences
26. Shows concern
29. Exist
30. Metallic rock
31. Leave out
32. Madison Avenue products
33. Skier's need
34. Ballpoint, for one
35. Aged
36. Food regimens
37. Railroad locomotive
39. Pleasure
40. Gets on one's —, exasperates
42. Unhappy
45. Most important
48. Octopus arm
50. Rural land measure
51. And so forth: abbr.
52. Conceited
53. Person of equal rank
54. Female deer
55. Hill dwellers

DOWN

1. Untidy condition
2. Region
3. Fluff
4. USNA grad: abbr.
5. Wooden shoe
6. Building additions
7. Seesaws, for short
8. Steeple
9. Tablet
10. Everyone
11. Golf peg
16. Colored eyepart
20. Night before a holiday
21. Allow
23. Not any
24. Fox —, ballroom dance
25. Stitches
26. Contend successfully (with)
27. Prayer ending
28. Telephone, with "up"
29. Use an abacus
32. Put on one's guard
33. Transgression
35. Smallest number
36. Clean the furniture
38. Interior
39. On the —, uncommitted
41. Prohibition
42. Examine with care
43. Dismounted
44. Lairs
45. Chart
46. Expert
47. Anger
49. Actress Gardner

MEDIUM

Solution is on page 379

HARD

ACROSS

1. Malt beverage
4. "— There Eyes," oldie
8. Manual-training course
12. King
13. The Orient
14. Window section
15. Advises earnestly
17. Flinch
18. Weapons
19. Impede
20. Cudgel
22. Wither
23. Towel word
24. Second lieutenant: slang
29. Emmet, today
30. Wretched hut
31. — and con
32. Deposition
34. Hog
35. In excess of
36. Satisfy requirements
37. Draftsman
40. Have on
42. Sell down the —, betray
43. Jargon
46. Heathen deity
47. Pie plates
48. At once
49. Enclosures
50. Dark black
51. Furthermore

DOWN

1. Exist
2. Roman law
3. Makes very weary
4. Semester
5. Berets
6. Curve
7. Treasure State: abbr.
8. Small harpsichord
9. Worker
10. Formerly
11. Legal equal
16. Sphere
17. Over a large area
19. Harbor
20. Cat: French
21. Cord
22. Kind act
24. Tremble
25. "Iliad" creator
26. Evident
27. Rainbow goddess
28. Pilot's records
33. Absorbents
36. Chum
37. Faucet problem
38. Go on horseback
39. English river
40. Eye signal
41. Effortless
43. Confused clamor
44. Dove sound
45. A pair of
47. Palmlily

Solution is on page 379

ACROSS

1. Friend
4. Glide high
8. Box in an exhibition
12. Mining find
13. Ocean force
14. Child's fiier
15. Tease playfully
16. Ancient
17. Went out with
18. Lawn-trimming tools
20. — out, begin (on) a journey
21. First woman
22. More sugary
26. Ruler measure: abbr.
28. Magazine chief
30. Be in debt
31. Persia, today
33. Spoil, as beauty
34. Start a lawn
35. Guided
36. Vegetable spot
38. Thus
39. Memo
41. Dyeing tub
43. Robin Hood's drink
44. Say again
47. Range
50. Take first place
51. Perfect serve
52. Assistant
53. Not straight
54. Wrongdoing
55. Realty title
56. — and ends

57. Asner and Sullivan

DOWN

1. Prod
2. Very dry
3. Shelf
4. Put away for later
5. Lubricates
6. State further
7. Scale tone
8. Use a rink
9. Cherry seed
10. Devoured
11. Autumnal foliage hue
17. Doe or buck
19. Smooth (out)
20. Saber
22. Prolonged look
23. Boot end
24. Rams' mates
25. Change the decor of
26. Movie
27. Maple or elm
29. Reflection
32. Paid announcements, for short
34. Break sharply
36. Strong wind
37. Happenings
40. Rescued
42. Poke fun at
44. Orange's skin
45. Citric, for one
46. "Sawbucks"
47. Blue
48. Neckwear item
49. Lyric poem
50. Marry
53. Actress Derek

EASY

Solution is on page 379

BIBLE CROSSWORD MEDIUM

by RUSS CARLEY

Bible references in this puzzle are from the King James Version. You'll find it stimulating to solve, and may discover you know more about the Bible than you think you do.

ACROSS

1. Biblical high priest
4. And he — to them a parable. *Luke 21:29*
9. Father, . . . —ect our way unto you. *I Thess. 3:11*
12. The —n hath roared. *Amos 3:8*
13. Master, —t thou not that we perish? *Mark 4:38*
14. It is large —ugh for them. *Gen. 34:21*
15. Get thee out, and — hence. *Luke 13:31*
17. I have a secret — unto thee. *Judg. 3:19*
19. Chief officer of David
20. Blessed are the — in spirit. *Matt. 5:3*
21. Iron —eth iron; so a man sharpeneth the countenance of his friend. *Prov. 27:17*
25. A man shall cast his idols . . . to the — and to the bats. *Isa. 2:20*
28. He lodgeth with one Simon a —ner. *Acts 10:6*
29. Son of Seth
31. Hiram king of — sent messengers to David. *II Sam. 5:11*
32. — I my brother's keeper? *Gen. 4:9*
33. — ye not yet understand? *Matt. 16:9*
34. Forgive us our debts, — we forgive our debtors. *Matt. 6:12*
36. They sow not, neither do they —ap. *Matt. 6:26*
37. An he— cried aloud. *Dan. 3:4*
40. There — wise men from the east to Jerusalem. *Matt. 2:1*
42. Aaron . . . died in mount —. *Num. 33:39*
43. The —ing of his horses was heard. *Jer. 8:16*

45. A superscription also was written over him in — of Greek and Latin. *Luke 23:38*
47. Jesus . . . was a prophet mighty in — and word. *Luke 24:19*
49. Judas Iscariot . . . was the trai—. *Luke 6:16*
50. There was a certain — named Lazarus. *Luke 16:20*
52. The rain descended, and the — came. *Matt. 7:25*
55. — no man any thing, but to love one another. *Rom. 13:8*
56. They —d upon the Lord God. *II Chr. 13:18*
58. The second row shall be an emerald, a sapphire, and a —mond. *Ex. 28:18*
59. Thou camest but —terday. *II Sam. 15:20*
60. Put up thy — into the sheath. *St. John 18:11*
61. Moses sent them to — out the land. *Num. 13:17*

DOWN

1. The —er shall serve the younger. *Gen. 25:23*
2. He maketh me to — down in green pastures. *Ps. 23:2*
3. He had married an Eth— woman. *Num. 12:1*
4. He shall cause the house to be — within. *Lev. 14:41*
5. Thy word is . . . a light unto my —h. *Ps. 119:105*
6. Make thee an —k of gopher wood. *Gen. 6:14*
7. If ye love me, — my commandments. *St. John 14:15*
8. Phares begat Esrom; and — begat Aram. *Matt. 1:3*

9. — beloved, avenge not your-selves. *Rom. 12:19*
10. There was no room for them in the —. *Luke 2:7*
11. Thy — and thy staff they com-fort me. *Ps. 23:4*
16. Take bow and —ows. *II Ki. 13:15*
18. The love of money is the — of all evil. *I Tim. 6:10*
21. The — shall fall from heaven. *Matt. 24:29*
22. Esther set Mordecai over the house of —. *Esth. 8:2*
23. —h son of Cain
24. — man can serve two masters. *Matt. 6:24*
26. He . . . converteth the sinner from the — of his way. *James 5:20*
27. The Lord testified . . . by all the prophets, and by all the —. *II Ki. 17:13*
30. And there were in the — country shepherds. *Luke 2:8*
35. Before the mountains were —, before the hills was I brought forth. *Prov. 8:25*

38. Where thou —t, I will lodge. *Ruth 1:16*
39. Thou hast drunken the —s of the cup. *Isa. 51:17*
41. Love the Lord thy God with —l thy heart. *Mark 12:30*
42. As soon as he knew that he be-longed unto — jurisdiction, he sent him to Herod. *Luke 23:7*
44. They that sow in — shall reap in joy. *Ps. 126:5*
46. Is any thing — hard for the Lord? *Gen. 18:14*
48. One of them . . . — his sword. *Matt. 26:51*
50. The streets . . . shall be full of —s and girls. *Zech. 8:5*
51. What mean these seven — lambs? *Gen. 21:29*
52. The angel . . . appeared unto him in a flame of —e. *Ex. 3:2*
53. The priest shall — his finger in the blood. *Lev. 4:6*
54. I — to this man, Go, and he goeth. *Matt. 8:9*
57. —, I am with you alway, even unto the end of the world. *Matt. 28:20*

Solution is on page 379

137

MEDIUM

ACROSS

1. Existed
4. Men
9. Weep
12. Intention
13. Idolize
14. Female sheep
15. Sketches
17. Awarded; agreed to fulfill
19. Rodents
21. Coin opening
22. Doctor's "client"
25. Capital of Oregon
28. Actor Pacino
29. Blazed path
31. In this place
32. Actor Marvin
34. Divide
36. Newsman Rather
37. Notable times
39. Tempest
41. McGovern's State: abbr.
42. Swaggering walk
44. Cold symptoms
46. Tidy
48. Rational
49. Conjectured
52. Large brass instruments
55. Curvy letter
56. Taunt
58. River: Spanish
59. Encountered
60. Concluded
61. Say further

DOWN

1. Roll of money
2. Broadcast
3. Clever
4. Becomes expert in
5. Paid notice
6. Ship's diary
7. Makes mistakes
8. Closes tightly
9. Colonized
10. Be in debt
11. Cot, for one
16. Remain in readiness
18. Ark builder
20. Breaks suddenly
22. Fades
23. Watchful and ready
24. Slants
26. Rub out
27. Repairs
30. Zoo animals
33. Sincere; serious
35. Picked up the tab
38. Takes to court
40. Bill of fare
43. Sample; savor
45. Striped animal
47. Adolescent
49. Jewel
50. Employ
51. Father
53. Assist
54. Turf
57. Direction: abbr.

Solution is on page 379

ACROSS

1. Faucet
4. Bathing need
9. Shade tree
12. Chicago's State: abbr.
13. Nebraska city
14. Pay to court
15. Pod vegetable
16. Broadcast
17. Frock
19. Throw; hurl
21. Idolizes
22. Put into —, publish
24. Snow vehicles
25. Real estate
26. Mixes with a spoon
27. Up —, as far as
29. Hen product
30. Saturates
31. Brooch
32. While
33. Burn slightly
34. Medicine pellet
35. Protrude; swell outward
36. Score
37. Frightens
39. Autumn
40. Grasped
41. Water barrier
42. Do sums
45. Grow older
46. Household task
48. Cereal grass
49. Affirmative reply
50. Avid
51. Stitch

DOWN

1. Pointed end
2. Pub brew
3. Finding employment for
4. Browned bread
5. Fail to include
6. Armed conflict
7. Huh?
8. Eloper's needs
9. Pitchers
10. Fail to win
11. Playwright Hart
18. Fishing poles
20. Also
21. Similar
22. Entreaty
23. Tatters
24. Theater platform
26. Melodies; tunes
27. Work the soil
28. Merely
30. Quietness
31. Columns
33. Certain
34. Chum
35. Cooks in an oven
36. More docile
37. Remain
38. Canary's "house"
39. Transportation fee
41. Canine
43. Coloring agent
44. Garden moisture
47. Laughter sound

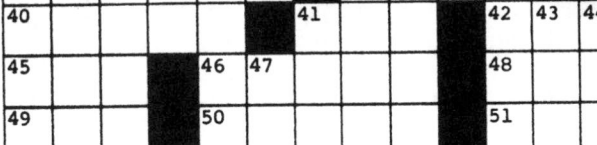

Solution is on page 379

PUNANAGRAMS

HARD

by MEL TAUB

Punanagrams are tricky but fun to solve. Definitions may be jokes or puns on the word wanted, or an anagram of the word itself. Generally there's a straight definition as a clue, too. For example, the answer to 31-Across is NARRATE. A ranter is the anagram, with "Give an account of" as an additional clue. Roman numerals may be used; the words YOU, ARE, EYE, SEE, etc., might stand for U, R, I and C, respectively; "energy" could stand for the letters N, R, G, or "any" for N E. Consider the definitions from all angles and you will find they do make definite sense. And, have fun!

ACROSS

1. They provide drama, as in battle
8. L' 27-Down, by the year
13. Where Bahamans provide wine gratis
14. What I misdo in some languages
16. What the decorous fellow said is incorrect
17. Friend of Mike and Artie
18. The color of 100 Eries
19. It gives me no idea of what's ahead
21. Pedro's year in the manor
22. — -wit (waggish fellow with a yarn)
23. Eager to have diva return
24. Did she see Mr. Durocher?
25. He's no lout
26. Ebsen portrays Czech statesman
28. What passengers on gig are doing
29. Why wet articles corrode
31. Give an account of a ranter
33. In passing, no sin should sound shocking
34. He's mixed up with Lana
35. With Ellen he can wind up in gutter
38. Keeping mum ain't the way to free slaves
42. A shoe for a prophet
43. State of nuclear experimentation
45. Expert who, with 49-Across, becomes a threat
46. Caesar's bird vanishes as hens disappear
47. Publisher who manages article out of chaos
48. Alien without a claim
49. See 45-Across
50. Kind of bargain that's beyond the pale
51. Tamiroff-Derek position at arms
53. At 1 P.M. Red is prepared
55. Ivan, Omar, a Czech, perhaps
57. Where any seat is an elective one
58. Rare sign at the jeweler's
59. Kind of mine
60. Glass at P.O.W. camps

DOWN

1. It may remain a part of U.S.S.R.
2. New edition of old book about inept R.R.
3. How to make "maid" into 'mermaid"
4. Mil. addresses in Eastern El Paso
5. Produced no curd for dummy
6. Karen's midriff
7. Tried hard to get voters
8. Was fond of elk, 500-1

9. Did they need an apple here?
10. Hit covers the top of the 'ead
11. I am also from Africa
12. Describing nine Met players
13. For Casey, life is capricious
15. He goes to work as straight man
20. Mistakenly says one of the men is Sam
23. No particular spot, but a Big Apple location
24. Horn found on cur
26. Sir around Botswana
27. See a way to comfort
28. Gr. insect
30. Miss Egan's given name
32. Western Alaska

35. Munches on ham. See?: Sp.
36. What her dove did overhead
37. Describing one who is inane
39. 1,000 pointing guns?
40. Use these for big case of tennis elbow
41. On on on on on on on on on
44. River that has met the North Sea
47. One who 'as something in 'is grasp
48. At 57, a lady
50. He sounds rather mossy
51. Farrar's middle name
52. He's out on a lark
54. Kind of tress
56. Name given to a cereal

Solution is on page 380

ACROSS

1. Pale
4. School, in Paris
9. Curve
12. Ms. Gardner
13. Serving item
14. Vast amount
15. Usual
17. A Ford
19. Force into place
20. Problem student
21. Concede
24. "Dough"
25. Toupees: slang
26. Jeweler's unit
27. Meteorologist's term: abbr.
29. Pub order
30. Trite
31. Presidential nickname
32. New England State: abbr.
33. Skirmish
34. Tough task: slang
35. Web-footed friend
36. Does a laundry task
37. King of Denmark
39. Golf pole
40. Unwilling
41. Showing affection
45. Formicid
46. Noteworthy period
48. Data-gathering group: abbr.
49. — Moines
50. Lariats
51. Shade tree

DOWN

1. Conflict
2. Hail!
3. Scold incessantly
4. Renown
5. Stuff
6. Possessive
7. Football player: abbr.
8. Everlasting
9. Scholarly product
10. Observed
11. A condiment
16. Vases
18. Musical composition
20. The Scripture, the Talmud, etc.
21. Metrical unit
22. Govern
23. Mature
24. Parsonage
26. Bring about
27. Pause
28. Favorable thing
30. Tommy Smothers, to Dick
31. Contemptible one
33. Struggle
34. Tedious
35. Two-winged insects
36. Expresses relief
37. Dressed
38. Superior: 2 wds.
39. Brownish purple
41. Get aboard
42. On thin —
43. Nothing
44. School of whales
47. River in Italy

Solution is on page 380

ACROSS

1. Boast
5. Certain time periods
9. For each
12. Folk knowledge
13. Biblical spot
14. Mine find
15. Get rid of
17. "— Abner," comic strip
18. Marry
19. Cup feature
20. Black
22. Intention
23. In favor of
24. Dens
27. What you pay to send a letter
31. Aroma
32. Cushion
33. Hastens
34. Grant, e.g.
36. Cap, for Pierre
37. Stitch
38. Mink or ermine
39. Hurls
42. Brooch
43. Knight's title
46. Museum display
47. Do an interpreter's job
50. Falsehood
51. Merit
52. Old
53. Drink, cat-style
54. Tints
55. Water barriers

DOWN

1. Bungled and failed in: slang
2. Function
3. Like the Sahara
4. Opal, e.g.
5. Sturdy fabric
6. First man
7. Still
8. Scoffs
9. Horseback game
10. Ireland: poetic
11. Depend
16. Eye part
21. Annoy
22. Do a sheriff's task
23. Seed container
24. Ship's journal
25. Fruit drink
26. Electrically charged atom
27. Buddy
28. Ventilate
29. Command to dobbin
30. Suffix with "great"
32. Handle roughly
35. Took a break
36. Bakery products
38. Helsinki natives
39. Shout
40. Operatic solo
41. Pace
42. Peel
43. Heroic tale
44. Article
45. Ohio team
48. Beam of light
49. Young man

MEDIUM

Solution is on page 380

ACROSS

1. Gibbon
4. "Able — I ere . . ."
7. Humble
12. Loose; slack
13. Wrath
14. Neck backs
15. Actress Lupino
16. Teachers' group: abbr.
17. Uses a keyboard
18. Curved
20. Bring up
22. Matched groups
23. Play division
24. Reverence
27. Express relief
29. Claw
31. Decorous
34. Calm; serene
35. Three-spots
36. Derelicts
37. Tree fluid
38. New York baseballer
39. Conduct
43. Hermit
46. Nervous excitement
47. Run away to marry
49. MacGraw or Baba
51. Gershwin, the lyricist
52. Bogs
53. — Aviv
54. 102, in Roman numerals
55. Used, as money
56. Lamb's mom
57. "Sawbuck"

DOWN

1. Assumed name
2. Father: Spanish
3. To a tee
4. Curve, as a road
5. Exist
6. Delve
7. Con
8. Howls at the moon
9. Takes to a higher court
10. Behold
11. "R" follower
19. Short composition
21. To
23. Years since birth
25. Alas!
26. Finish
28. Possessive pronoun
29. Mr. Selleck
30. Usher's domain
31. Roads: abbr.
32. Historical period
33. Regret
34. Place; set
36. Scold
38. Myself
40. Force out; expel
41. High nest
42. Down the —, gone
44. Unlock (the door)
45. Cozy place
46. Nail implement
47. Printer's measures
48. Rim
50. Actor Ayres

Solution is on page 380

ACROSS

1. Li'l Abner cartoonist
5. May
8. Cola, for example
12. Elliptical
13. Mimic
14. Legal document
15. Actress Eichhorn
16. This moment
17. Move very slowly
18. Endured
20. Property; capital
22. Wore away (at)
23. Fauna's "partner"
25. Large cask
26. "Important" carpet color
27. Nourished
28. Swarms
30. Sold door-to-door, perhaps
32. Subject
35. Mr. Majors
36. Cries of pain
39. Gold: Spanish
40. Use the fitting room: 2 wds.
42. Chat: slang
43. Silk tree
45. Hitchcock classic
47. Seaweed
48. Resort
50. Buckeye State
51. Flood or ebb, for example
52. For: Spanish
53. Spasm; cramp
54. Single units
55. New York Mets pitcher, — Fernandez
56. Lyric poems

DOWN

1. Harness part
2. Fly a plane
3. Got above an "F"
4. Map out
5. Examined (eggs)
6. Part of a military address: abbr.
7. Fresher
8. MASH actress, Loretta —
9. Showy
10. Pronouncement
11. Greece's capital
19. Results
21. Lustrous fabrics
24. Peculiarly
29. Wynn or Begley
30. Mathematical ratio
31. Jaguar
32. Garden fruit
33. Darwin's "— of Species"
34. Hair ointment
36. Corsage flower
37. Polynesian woman
38. Ghosts
41. Irritates
44. Swedish coins
46. — Ono
49. Hawaiian food

HARD

Solution is on page 380

MEDIUM

ACROSS

1. In this place
5. Bat (a fly)
9. Cinema lioness
13. Haughty person
17. Wicked
18. Fork prong
19. Tidy
20. Own
21. Gibson or Brooks
22. Week divider
24. Sulked
25. Ready (oneself)
27. Connected in a certain way
28. Funnylady Joan
29. Vase
30. Repair
31. Cotton bundle
32. Agitate
35. Yelp
36. Negligent
40. Mature

41. Battles
42. American Beauties
43. Low
44. Tumult
45. Bowling necessity
46. Enticer
47. Money drawer
48. Stooping
50. Acts the flirt
51. Governed
52. Also
53. Trousers
54. Lie
55. Idolize
58. Garden implements
59. Rummy variation
63. Holmes trademark
64. Rabbits' kin
65. Fenway —
66. Witch
67. Actress Gabor
68. Rescues
69. Still
70. Stupid person
71. Chosen (one)
73. Trevino's game
74. Planted seeds
75. Lively dance
76. Corn bread
77. Sticky stuff: slang
78. String of pearls
81. Waste time
82. Mallets
86. Stood up
87. Lucky
89. Stadium cheer
90. Citrus fruit
91. Ponder
92. Sensible
93. Recipe direction
94. Spinning toys
95. Social insects
96. Souffle needs
97. Donna or Lou

DOWN

1. Rope fiber
2. Always
3. Anger
4. City train
5. Strict
6. Vast
7. Actress Jillian
8. Seesaws
9. Concluded
10. Guide
11. Declare
12. By
13. Spade
14. Back of the neck
15. Across
16. Rollaways
22. Caution
23. Kitchen basin
24. Mr. Standish
26. Unmixed
28. More uncommon
30. Planet
31. Foundations
32. Grouch
33. Conceal
34. "Once — a time . . ."
35. Loud noise
36. Bottle stoppers
37. Actor Jannings
38. Flatfish
39. Auctioneer's call
41. Zephyr
42. Tiniest ones of the litter
45. Evergreen tree
46. Rows
47. Large brass instrument
49. Venture
50. Rouses from sleep
51. Skating arena
53. Peeled
54. Raise crops
55. Monkeys

56. Emulate Mr. Louganis
57. Iridescent gem
58. Fray
59. Baby whale
60. Display
61. Narrow band
62. Grown old
64. Detested
65. Lose color
68. Play division

69. Mix up
70. Gloom's partner
72. Rubs out
73. Capricorn symbol
74. Indefinite amount
76. Skin openings
77. Yard entrances
78. Seasoning
79. The Andrews Sisters, for example

80. Frolic
81. Missing
82. Dangle
83. A Great Lake
84. Speed contest
85. Lean-to
87. Merriment
88. Badger; complain
91. Mother
93. Ben Casey: abbr.

Solution is on page 380

HARD

FORE!

ACROSS

1. Political division of a city
5. Stable bedding
10. Ice-cream treats
15. Crafty
19. Wings
20. Antelope
21. Love: Italian
22. Okinawa town
23. LPGA VIP: 2 wds.
25. LPGA VIP: 2 wds.
27. Petitions
28. Irregular
30. Fastening, in a way
31. Every
32. Nocturnal sound
33. Cad
34. Lower
37. Counts calories
38. Placed in the wrong role
41. That is: 2 wds. (Latin)
42. 38th U.S. President and family
43. Relatives

44. Sedate
46. Sand hill
47. Confront
48. Malay Archipelago islands
50. Mariners' saint
51. Government bureau: abbr.
52. PGA VIP: 2 wds.
55. Part of a journey
56. Destructive insects
58. Valuable beans
59. Sylvan deities
62. Cardinal number
63. Husk, as corn
64. Assayer's vessel
65. Woolly
67. *La* —, Milan's "Met"
68. Sporadic
71. Curved letter
72. PGA VIP: 2 wds.
75. Golfer Weiskopf
76. German exclamations
78. Factotum: hyph. wd.
79. Club fees
80. Ticket part
81. Certain horses
83. Military supplies: abbr.
84. Garment
86. Throb
87. Double-cross: hyph. wd.
89. Vessels
90. Used the blender
91. Cautious
92. Repairs, in a way
93. TV's Griffin
94. Saudi —
97. Word with "dined"
98. Pardons
102. Beloved duo in golf lore: 3 wds.
104. PGA VIP: 2 wds.
106. Golfer's purchase
107. Atelier item
108. Poetry muse
109. Perfume
110. Starch
111. Cubic meter
112. Boca —, FL
113. Remainder

DOWN

1. Diminish
2. Alda
3. Talk wildly
4. Lessen
5. Consolation
6. Loyalty
7. Tears
8. Vigoda
9. Withered
10. Military officers
11. Divert
12. Ore source
13. Essay
14. Suit fabrics
15. Ringed
16. Near-Eastern liquor
17. Facial feature
18. Pend
24. Baker's need
26. Guinness, et al.
29. Spoils
32. Lorelei
33. — Kush, Afghanistan range
34. "...I — my way...": 2 wds.
35. Elicit
36. PGA VIP: 2 wds.
37. Waterfront sights
38. Weights of ancient Greece
39. LPGA VIP: 2 wds.
40. Kitchen gadget
42. Aspect
43. Wealthy Russian farmer
45. AKC listings
47. "Meatball": slang
48. Airport porter
49. Takes for granted
52. Lively dances
53. Part of a famous MacArthur promise: 2 wds.
54. Was able to
57. My: Italian
60. Copycat
61. Asian holiday
63. Berate
64. One of Santa's team
65. Shakespearean king

66. British horse-racing meet
67. Trap
68. Insults
69. Timid person
70. Set in firmly
73. Spacious
74. Accesses to mines
77. Increase rapidly
80. Durable person
82. Blot
84. Painful
85. Horse trainer
86. Get rid of, in a way
88. Decrees
89. Charm bracelet item
90. Outdoor stairway
92. Trucker's stop
93. Guiding principle
94. Rock music group
95. Wander about
96. Competently
97. Sage
98. Daring act
99. See: Latin
100. Son of Seth
101. Classify
103. Night mammal
105. Notable period

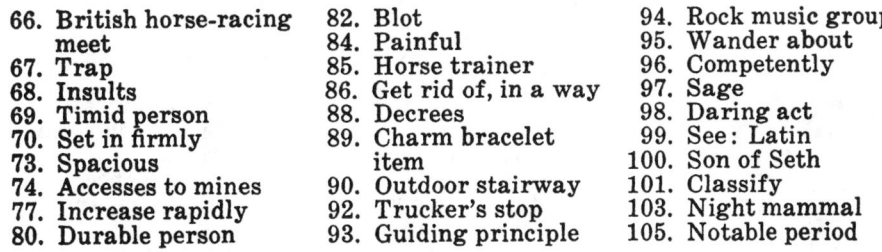

Solution is on page 381

EASY

ACROSS

1. Ale's kin
5. Frog leap
8. Unhappy
11. Folklore monster
15. Tremendous
16. Tavern order
17. Pastry delight
18. Magnificent
20. Pattern
21. Fixes
23. Spearlike weapons
25. Garden tool
26. Shade tree
28. Brooch
29. Lean-to
31. Singleton
32. Utilize
33. Be in the red
34. Nourished
35. Guide
36. Diva's solo
37. Measuring device
39. Urge
41. Section
42. Articles
43. Abate
45. Small wagon
46. — and con
47. Tree's "skin"

50. Child
51. Slipped
52. Raise in rank
56. Frosty cubes
57. Male
58. Equipment
59. Like fatless meat
60. Fish eggs
61. More than good
63. Cover in paper
64. Pink and healthy
65. Scent
66. Feel poorly
67. Swimming spot
68. Sign of disuse
69. Color
70. Slender
72. Shine
73. Treat for Rover
74. Weasel's relative
77. Heavy weight
78. TV's Flintstone
79. Common seasoning
80. Mug
81. Ms. Gabor
82. Vienna is there
84. Pickling herb
85. Sighs of delight
86. Adam's garden
87. Skirt edge
88. Musical combo
89. Crawls
91. Concur
94. Investment spot
95. Rounded roof
96. Chef's protection
100. Jungle "king"
101. Nip; snap
102. Turf
103. Mother pig
105. Citrus drink
106. Height: abbr.
107. Desire
108. Lair
109. Barnyard biddy
110. Conceal
111. Drudges
113. Teach
116. Swapped
118. Not fresh
119. Regret
120. Paving substance
121. Different
122. Terminates
123. Still
124. Id's partner
125. Bosc or Anjou

DOWN

1. Wicker vessel
2. Great Lake
3. Omelet ingredient
4. Make fresh again
5. Injure
6. Spanish cheer
7. Salt's companion
8. Twirl
9. Broadcast
10. Sweet course
11. Eyed
12. Alum, for short
13. Did a marathon
14. Audience's cry
15. Rent
19. Jeans material
20. Tom-tom, for one
22. Assist
24. Oceans
27. Learning unit
30. Head topper
33. Raw metal
34. Merriment
35. Cooking fat
36. Tiny particle
38. Moose's cousin
40. Household animal
41. Two of a kind
42. Press
44. Celebrity
45. Applaud
46. Entreat
47. Baby's "apron"
48. Highest card
49. Keeps
51. Water mammal
52. Nuisance
53. Commanded
54. Also
55. Always, to a poet
57. Torme or Brooks
58. Get bigger
59. Misplace
62. Comedian Conway
63. Lumber
64. Litter's smallest
65. Your and my
67. Beg
68. Bun's kin
69. "With it": slang
70. Depot: abbr.
71. Baseball's Gehrig
72. Serious

73. Hairless
74. Join by melting
75. Actress Arden
76. Earth tone
78. Liberate
79. Basin
80. Gouda, for one
83. At that time
84. Copenhagen native
85. Give weapons to
86. Sixth sense letters
88. Power source
89. Food fish
90. Fido's foot
91. Woe!
92. Fish features
93. Turn
94. Storage container
95. Give
97. Ambush member
98. More unusual
99. Require
101. Foundations
102. Part of a minute: abbr.
104. Upon: 2 wds.
107. Unite by heat
108. Song for two
109. Courageous guy
110. Laughter sound: 2 wds.
112. Movers' truck
114. Payable now
115. Label
117. Highway: abbr.

Solution is on page 381

151

EASY

ACROSS

1. Estimate
5. High playing cards
9. Land parcel
13. Filled with wonder
14. Lightning flash
15. Chases off
16. "Play It Again, —"
17. Fragrant wood
18. Sets down, as a plane
19. Fife players
21. Neat
23. Alphabet letter
24. Small rock
25. Chablis
26. Certain siblings: abbr.
27. Open-mouthed
29. Dove's call
30. Wrongdoing
33. Sharp taste
34. Ammo unit
37. — board, presser's need
39. Ostrich
40. Accomplish
41. Terraces
42. Use the phone
43. Set of tools
44. Traveler's stop
45. Building side
46. Wagers
47. Loafer, for one
49. Lend a —, aid
50. Pub brew
51. Sardine can
52. Deuce or joker
53. Uses up, as money
56. Public notice
57. Allowed
59. "So" follower
60. Jog one's memory
62. Exit
63. Storage vessel
64. Play a part
65. Angel's instrument
66. Great lake
67. Knife's partner
69. Fence door
70. Brazil State, — Paulo
71. Mature
72. Cover with asphalt
73. Cooks' smocks
76. Chicago's State: abbr.
77. Labyrinth
78. King's sons
79. Go to bed
81. Espied
82. Very warm
83. Social insect
84. Seas
86. Election district
88. Object of worship
89. Consuming one
93. Actor Carney
94. Disassemble
95. Sock pattern
96. Land documents
98. Schoolboy collars
100. Diaper fastener
101. Follow
102. Shipped
103. Most suitable
104. Appointment
105. Willow
106. Lyric poems

DOWN

1. Grating sounds
2. Anticipate
3. Musical pace
4. Actor Asner
5. Vigoda and Beame
6. Food fish
7. Making joyful
8. Thin cord
9. Cry of discovery
10. Manipulate
11. Cowboy event
12. Snaking curves
15. Crafty
17. Genesis
20. School subject: abbr.
22. Ponce — Leon
25. Ell
26. Brazen
28. Skillets
29. Coil
30. Use a straw
31. Mr. Gershwin
32. Thought
34. Beak
35. Correct copy
36. Toddlers
38. Baseball team
39. Like Telly or Yul
42. Election hopeful
43. Sharp
45. Toasty
46. Ran, as dye
47. Play the lead
48. Keep from view
49. Firm
50. Copycat
52. Penny
53. Halt!
54. 552, in Roman numerals
55. Rational
57. Choose
58. Ripped
61. Foal's mama
63. Ornamental pin
65. Own
66. Receive, as wages
67. So-so
68. Leer
69. Look fixedly (at)
70. Yarn makers
72. Piece
73. Locale
74. New: comb. form
75. Fast jet
77. Tend to
78. Rind
80. Most acidic
81. Two-wheeled vehicle

84. Most strange
85. Droop
86. Walked through water
87. Bout site
88. Enclosed by
90. Used a keyboard
91. Beethoven's "Für ___"
92. Leases (out)
94. Employ
95. Poker stake
97. Owing
99. Single
103. Ms. Derek

Solution is on page 381

SPECIAL CHALLENGER CROSSWORD

by WILLIAM A. LEWIS, JR.

Here is a real toughie for you. We have omitted giving you such helps as "2 wds.," "hyph. wd.," and "slang"; but in the spirit of fair play, all abbreviations and foreign words are so indicated.

ACROSS

1. Fly-caster, often
6. Actor's goof
11. Recycling material
16. Mummers' New Year's event
17. Hermit
18. King of the Visigoths
20. Hotly contested fight
22. Cockpit assistant
24. Porter
25. "High-hat"
26. Her cow started the Chicago fire
28. Belly dancer
29. Cheese substance
31. Catches a "pipeline"
33. Stogies and pattens
34. Sound of impact
35. Inventor Howe
37. Attach
39. Together with
40. Porker: var. sp.
42. Legume plants
44. QE 2 route
46. Cajoled
47. Dressy affairs
49. Floated in the neap
50. A lot
51. Meerschaum part
54. An envelope abbreviation
55. Unlikely winner
59. Needing TLC
60. Bitter
62. Fabler
64. Splash about
65. Chulalongkorn's land
67. Continental custom

70. Present-day Fort Presque Isle site
71. — Beach, Florida
73. Word with "point" or "four"
74. Dig for dirt
76. Work as a fitter
77. Henny Youngman forte
79. Professorial degree, usually: abbr.
81. Naked: British
83. Pindaric poetry
84. Aficionados
86. Thomas Cook novel
87. Vote of assent
90. Well liked
92. "Mooch"
95. Plaster framework
96. "Easy come, easy go," e.g.
97. Subsequently
99. Lowest Hindu caste
100. Vesuvius output
101. City of France
103. Squeezable packaging
105. Part of "TWTWTW"
106. "Gimme a Break" star, — Carter
108. Realm
110. Take another look
112. Cockney's expectation
113. Forester
115. Progeny
118. Famish
119. Hebrew prophet
120. Except
121. Henry's only child
122. Wooded
123. Kid

DOWN

1. Spa
2. Curved line
3. Morse dashes
4. Perfect places
5. Half swoon
6. Policemen
7. Piece of land
8. "For — us a child is born . . ."
9. "Decks"
10. Latitude
11. Inviolate
12. Surfeits
13. Thump
14. "Un bel dí," e.g.
15. Container for 16-Down
16. Little tablet
19. Hairy: Bot.
20. Walks the floor
21. "Boom-Boom" Becker
23. Under control
27. Tops
30. Mother of Perseus
32. Single step
36. Sauce: Spanish
38. Yellowstone sight
40. Chansons
41. Fuss
43. Louis Armstrong nickname
45. Yellow fever carrier
46. Fool
48. Señor's shawls
50. Singer's upper range
51. Brandy from Peru
52. Troy: Greek
53. UMW member
55. Cuts of beef
56. All even

57. Wickerwork branch
58. Muscular power
61. Banned insecticide
63. Draft board: abbr.
66. Australian lizard
68. Tumbling routine
69. NHL stats
72. One's staff
75. Studies for college
78. Aerialist's safety device
80. One half step above "C"

82. Whip
84. Ship headlamp
85. Sammy Cahn's "loneliest night"
87. Factory
88. Optical masers
89. Letterman
90. Feeler
91. Precursor of the violin
93. Concord, et al.
94. Consumed, with "up"

96. English fruitcake
98. Close again
101. Clear out
102. Faux pas
104. Fish, in a way
107. Principal role
109. Relax
111. Ms. Raines
114. Paul Simon's "— Robinson"
116. Formerly named
117. French article

Solution is on page 381

155

DIAGRAMLESS

MEDIUM

This Diagramless is 15 boxes wide by 15 boxes deep.

ACROSS

1. — the question, propose marriage
4. Historymaking ages
6. Suitcase
9. Heathen
11. Buckets
13. Lawful
15. Eyes are often called "the — of the soul"
17. Knighted woman's title
18. Occupied a chair
19. Wallop (a housefly)
20. Go into (a room)
22. Secret agent
23. Press for payment
24. Took the bait
26. Lubricate
28. Golfing average
31. Staff of life
33. October birthstone

35. Word of consent
36. Goad (on)
39. Made up one's mind
41. Enjoy (food) with appreciation
43. Send money due
44. Subsides; ebbs
46. Bright color
47. Solitary
48. Decay

DOWN

1. Get-up-and-go
2. Spoken
3. Summoned, bellhop style
5. Long tale of adventure
6. Prohibit
7. Assists
8. Shines; radiates
10. Identify
11. Deep hole

12. Exchange
14. — an ear, listen
15. Declaration of Dec. 8, 1941
16. Pigpen
18. 12th-graders
21. Bath fixture
25. Cause of extra innings
27. Licks up
28. Pea casing
29. Copycat
30. Indy 500 participant
31. Cradle or four-poster
32. Sketch
34. Lemon-like fruit
35. However
37. Egg-shaped
38. Welcome person at a blood bank
40. Accomplished
42. Nevada city
45. Harden, as cement

Solution is on page 381

DIAGRAMLESS   MEDIUM

**This Diagramless is 15 boxes wide by 15 boxes deep.
Starting box is on page 393.**

ACROSS

1. Bowl or plate
5. Craze
6. Measurement
10. Contestant
11. Lawn menace
12. Cry of dismay : German
13. Indigent
14. Foot digit
17. See 13-Across
20. "Do — others"
21. Assembly room
23. "Gidget" star
25. Book of maps
27. Points of debate
29. Forerunner of bridge
30. Biblical vessel
31. Like an ocean liner, sometimes : 2 wds.
34. Guides
36. Climb, as a mountain
37. Exhausted
38. Hibernia, to poets
39. Denomination
42. Lariats
45. Preschooler
46. At any time
47. Swimmer's distance
48. Verdi opera
49. Maxim
51. Killed
52. Cut into cubes
53. Knockout punch : slang

DOWN

1. Waltz, for one
2. To begin with : 4 wds.
3. Alec Guinness' title
4. "Make — while the sun shines"
5. Intend
6. Cocky behavior
7. Midday
8. Coagulate
9. Villain's nemesis
14. Defrost
15. Solemn vow
16. New York Bay island
18. Phonograph record
19. Certainly
22. It "broke the camel's back" : 2 wds.
24. San — Obispo, California
26. Ladder rung
28. Origin
30. Pisa's river
32. Melange
33. Departed
35. Suffix meaning "producer"
39. Oceans
40. Wicked
41. Surrender
43. Avid
44. Raced
49. Bustle
50. Hubbub

Solution is on page 382

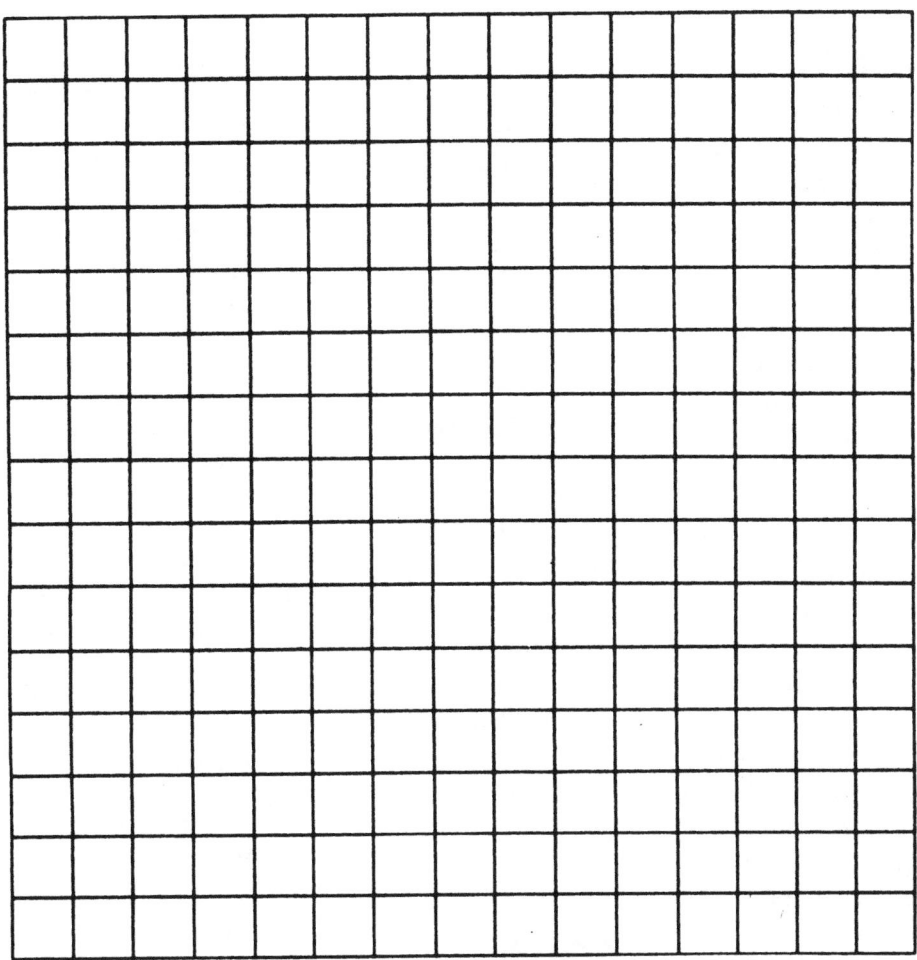

CHALLENGER DIAGRAMLESS

As in the Special Challenger Crossword (21), we have not given you such helps as "2 wds.," "hyph. wd.," and "slang"; but in the spirit of fair play, all foreign words and abbreviations are so indicated. This Diagramless is 21 boxes wide by 21 boxes deep. Starting box is on page 393.

ACROSS

1. Scion
4. Magnetite, e.g.
5. Runs up, as debts
8. Sirius, e.g.
9. Medicinal leaves
14. Amounts: abbr.
18. Colosseum official
21. Means to an end
22. Intrepid one
23. Peninsula on the Black Sea
24. Hunter of myth
26. Organic compound
27. Motive
29. Worn out
31. Actress Reid
32. Small barracuda
33. Avid
35. Japanese statesman
36. Large: prefix
40. Kenton or Smith
43. Aromatic herb
45. At a distance
46. Arab chieftain
48. Lubricates
50. See 45-Across
52. Retaliatory reply
56. Theban poet
60. Sci-fi film classic
62. Blessing

63. Nary a soul
64. Sister of Ares
66. Set-to
68. Verdon, et al.
69. Pshaw!
71. Miller's salesman
75. Gambrel, e.g.
77. Valley
78. Stow cargo
79. Vest
81. Air for Scotto
82. Rich cake
84. Goodies
87. Smirk maliciously
88. Mukluk
89. Bursts of cheers
90. Doesn't exist
91. Serfs
93. Marino, et al
94. Annoy
97. Wing, of a kind
98. Director Elaine

DOWN

1. Not worth a —
2. NHL idol
3. Promontory
5. Appian Way, e.g.
6. Lowest point

7. Beth Henley's Pulitzer-Prize play
8. Pouchlike part
10. School collar
11. And not
12. Something audible
13. Ho greeting
14. 1984 Cambodian drama
15. Legislature forum: French
16. Principal: prefix
17. Single
19. "... one giant — for mankind"
20. Relieves
25. Yuletide beverage
28. Web-footed mammal
30. Koppel
34. *Carnaval* city, for short
36. Damage
37. Milton's "spicy nut-brown" drink
38. Part of C in C: abbr.
39. Origin
41. Friend: French
42. Bite
44. Sass
47. A Reiner
49. Singer Phoebe
51. Poetic "always"
53. Weep aloud

160

54. Likewise
55. Habituate
57. Pronghorn female
58. Dancer Jillian
59. Thing, in law
61. Wire measure
65. "Fa" follower
67. Wrongful acts: law

69. Discloses
70. 1979 Sigourney Weaver sci-fi film
72. "Welcome" symbol
73. Sun-dried brick
74. Pianist Peter and family
76. Gumbo
77. Spanish artist

79. Nijinsky forte
80. Seagoing
83. *Bon* —
85. Hue
86. Snake sound
92. A son of Noah
95. Winglike part
96. Cunning

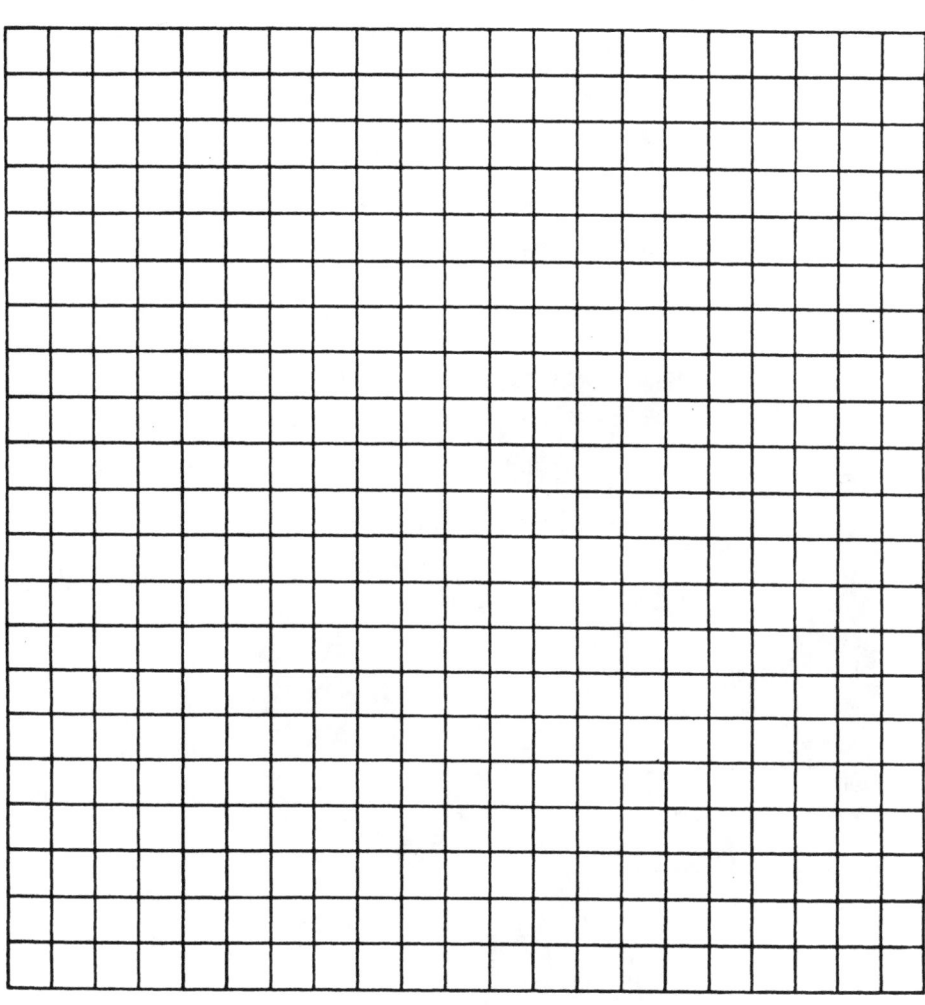

Solution is on page 382

ACROSS

1. Labels
5. Shove
9. Permit
11. As of (then)
12. Filled
14. Summer shoe
15. Conclude
16. Tan
18. Ancient
19. Sprite
21. Actress Farrow
22. Too
23. Affirmative answer
25. Rub out
27. See
29. Magic lamp inhabitant
30. Writing tool
32. Golf score
33. Attempt
35. Make lace
37. Evergreen
38. Foundations
40. Decade
42. Mohawk, for one
44. Term
46. Strict
47. For better or —
48. Sharpen
49. Gardener's enemy

DOWN

1. Story
2. Solo
3. Willingly
4. Turf
5. Brooch
6. Incomplete
7. Burn
8. Kept
10. Moist
11. Speak
13. Hoover or Aswan
14. Trap
17. Hot dogs
20. Not as many
22. Valuable item
24. Transgress
26. Viper
28. Giant
29. Word with "rock" or "vegetable"
31. Mother —
32. Spotted horse
34. Still
36. Brief
37. Salmon and trout
38. Prohibit
39. Mend
41. Require
43. Wrath
45. At the present time

MEDIUM

Solution is on page 382

ACROSS

1. Brief sleep
4. Hearty dish
8. Chatters
12. Conceit
13. Book leaf
14. — Kazan, movie director
15. Marriage celebration
17. Child's exclamation of approval
18. Mooselike deer
19. Mend, as socks
20. Artificial waterway
23. Roy Rogers' horse
26. So be it!
27. Healthy
28. "So" follower
29. However
30. Type of hat
32. Mink product
33. Exists
34. Certainly!
35. Yield
36. Gift for Dad
38. Pisa's landmark
39. Runner's contest
40. Existed
41. Jean Stapleton role
43. Recorded events of the past
47. City in Alaska
48. Do a household chore
49. Payable
50. Bambi, for one
51. Follow, as orders
52. Morning mist

DOWN

1. Recent
2. Grow older
3. Pea's "home"
4. Allow to flow over
5. Vat
6. Hen product
7. You and I
8. Mr. Burns, of comedy
9. Beside the length of
10. Auction offer
11. Speak
16. Martin or Jones
17. Merrily
19. Dull
20. Log house
21. Entertain
22. Snare
23. Trio number
24. Evade; escape
25. More unusual
30. Language spoken in Amsterdam
31. A Great Lake
32. Not many
34. Peggy Fleming, for one
35. Price
37. Felony
38. Flavorful
40. Like a sage
41. Conclude
42. Mother of 50-Across
43. Wheel's center
44. Peculiar
45. Regret
46. Evergreen tree
48. Perform

Solution is on page 382

EASY

ACROSS

1. Baked dessert
4. Bread scrap
9. Astronaut Grissom
12. Plus
13. It "makes waste"
14. Make angry
15. Enjoy a snow sport
16. High card
17. Big
19. Minor job
21. Holy books
22. Steeple
24. Touches
25. Huff and puff
26. Courageous
27. Half a quart: abbr.
29. Omelet item
30. Drench
31. Cow's call
32. Dover's State: abbr.
33. Call on
34. Sight common in Iowa
35. It makes dough rise
36. Small pies
37. Consistency of pudding
39. Hyde —, FDR's home
40. Word of greeting
41. Hoover or Grand Coulee
42. Shade tree
45. Feel poorly
46. Deadly knot
48. Dark bread
49. Dr.'s assistants: abbr.
50. Clothe
51. Stitch

DOWN

1. Daddies
2. Writing fluid
3. Newspaper chief's job
4. Pursue
5. Towel or hat holder
6. Utilize
7. Alp: abbr.
8. Have faith in
9. Lasses
10. Impulse
11. Visualizes
18. Ready, willing, and —
20. Mr. Garfunkel
21. Fairy tale, "Beauty and the —"
22. Drove (a car) too fast
23. Book leaf
24. Apple or pear
26. Cow's nickname
27. Harbor
28. Male turkeys
30. Ring gem
31. Felt-tipped pens
33. Calf meat
34. Distant
35. Hollers
36. Domesticates
37. Scorch
38. Bridle strap
39. Free ticket
41. Female deer
43. Caustic substance
44. Kitten's cry
47. — else!

Solution is on page 382

ACROSS

1. Policeman
4. Not as new
9. Parishioner's seat
12. Publicize
13. Famed U.S. battleship
14. Actress Gabor
15. Farming job
17. Ending for "baro" or "thermo"
19. Very small amount
20. Lofty structures
21. In the thick of
23. Ohio or Missouri
24. Mislay
25. Yearns (for)
26. You and I
28. — dance
29. Lessees' fees
30. Concealed
31. Preposition
32. Time units
33. Instance
34. Cotillions
35. Candid
36. Stocks the pantry
38. Be a nag
40. Odor
41. Outlaws
44. Clever person
45. Gush forth
47. Be mendacious
48. Plea at sea
49. Comforts
50. Nay's opposite

DOWN

1. Mushroom part
2. Squeak cure
3. Word of honor
4. Neglect
5. Country byway
6. Sarcastic remark
7. Alphabet letter
8. Takes away
9. Falk or Marshall
10. At all times
11. "No more —, no more bloodshed" (Menachem Begin)
16. Broad
18. Flock members
20. Colors, as hair
21. Singing voice
22. Landing site of 7/20/69
23. Skating arenas
25. Pares
26. Knowing
27. Utopia
29. Set loose
30. With gaiety
32. Cordial
33. Measure of wood
34. Wellingtons or jodhpurs
36. Adages
37. Threesome
38. Custody
39. Aardvark's diet
41. Jitney
42. Stalemate
43. Irish, for one
46. Keystone State: abbr.

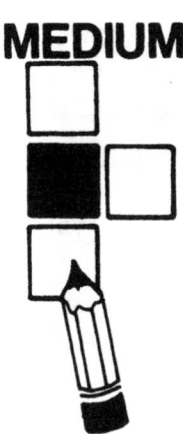

MEDIUM

Solution is on page 382

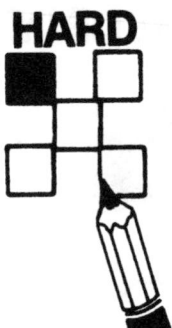

HARD

ACROSS

1. Jolt; shock
4. In a container
9. — Wednesday
12. Altar promise: 2 wds.
13. Animated
14. Hilo garland
15. Plays a Halloween game: 3 wds.
18. Goosefoot
19. Notable time
20. Dance routines
22. 1971 Woody Allen film
26. Red wine
27. Like Chicago, at times
28. French article
29. Cowboy Rogers
30. Raves
31. Symbol of neatness
32. Toward
33. Card combinations
34. Metal sources
35. Provokes a parry
37. Unaccompanied
38. Cubes are made of this
39. Scored a hole-in-one
40. Out of favor: 3 wds. (slang)
46. Iacocca
47. Receiver of gifts
48. Mongrel
49. Musician Brown
50. Visionaries
51. Perfect, on some scales

DOWN

1. Triangular sail
2. Fuss
3. Theft
4. Bistros
5. Very much: 2 wds.
6. Letter opener
7. Saint's first name
8. Hinges (on)
9. Singer Jones
10. Bishop's office
11. That man's
16. Labor Day month: abbr.
17. Supplicate
20. Herring
21. Comb part
22. Restrains
23. Pismires
24. Sigourney Weaver movie
25. Touch, e.g.
27. Disney
30. Sows once more
31. Commodity
33. "How — wood could . . ."
34. Spread
36. Formal customs
37. Suffers
39. Ripening agent
40. Cicero's State: abbr.
41. Maiden name
42. Unknown John
43. Single
44. "A Boy Named —"
45. Sea eagle

Solution is on page 383

ACROSS

1. Untrained
4. Young male
7. Darken the skin
10. Lyric poem
11. Protagonist
12. Go it alone
13. Most impudent
15. Stairs
16. Camera glass
17. Elegant: slang
18. Loses color
20. Milkmaid's need
21. Chicago district (with "the")
22. Unspoken
26. Traveler's stop
27. Push roughly
28. By way of
29. Tiny viewing aperture
31. At an angle
32. Red-ink entry
33. Economy size
34. Show a connection
37. Damage
38. Presses
39. Begin a flight: 2 wds.
42. 16 fluid ounces
43. Like the driven snow
44. Poe's "The Murders in the — Morgue"
45. Visualize
46. Lifetime
47. Final part

DOWN

1. One of the Reiners

2. Big fuss
3. Fully cooked: hyph. wd.
4. Reduced amount
5. Garfunkel
6. Perform
7. Rodgers and Hart's "On Your —"
8. Mont Blanc, Matterhorn, et al.
9. Inquisitive
11. Layers
12. Stable compartment
14. Profound
15. Kind of rule
17. Shape by cutting
18. Toss, as a coin
19. Excellent: 2 wds.

20. Combines, as resources
22. "— Life Is It, Anyway?"
23. Always
24. Birds do it
25. Surfeit
27. Call the —, give orders
30. Factory
31. Reveal
33. Michigan or Ontario
34. Tatters
35. Iroquoian tribe
36. Isolated; by oneself
37. Tortoise opponent
39. Pull hard
40. Amusement
41. Sustained
43. Neighbor of Oh.: abbr.

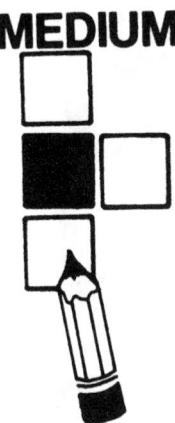

MEDIUM

Solution is on page 383

EASY

ACROSS

1. Harness part
4. Ohio, for one
9. Space; opening
12. Wedding words: 2 wds.
13. Claw
14. Brazilian city, for short
15. Trash
17. Swap
19. Arrests
20. Legal document
21. Wound marks
23. Cultivated spots
26. Gym mats
27. Peels
28. Exclamation of surprise
29. Fuss
30. Carried
31. Bakery item
32. Scale note
33. Window glasses
34. Foundation
35. Abandons
37. More painful
38. Bacon's "chums"
39. Bazaar
40. Metal alloy
42. Party item
45. Pea's "casing"
46. Avoid
48. Pair
49. "—! We Have No Bananas"
50. Goes out with
51. Gel

DOWN

1. Large
2. Ms. Lupino
3. Violent whirlwind
4. Attempts
5. Labels
6. Pub brew
7. In the direction of
8. Went in
9. Rank
10. Help
11. Edgar Allan —
16. Bans
18. Crimson and scarlet
20. Challenges
21. Practices boxing
22. West Point student
23. Fence doors
24. Din
25. Transparent
27. Small lakes
30. Snarled
31. Birds sometimes called "Polly"
33. Book feature
34. Seethe
36. Marsh grasses
37. Bargain events
39. Lose color
40. Secret agent
41. Foot digit
42. Baseball club
43. Be in debt
44. Negative word
47. Dogwood State: abbr.

Solution is on page 383

ACROSS

1. Swiss mountains
5. Gala affair
9. Young rascal
12. Genuine
13. Baking chamber
14. Mediterranean, for one
15. Not inclined to worry
17. Country stop
18. Industrious insect
19. Entire amount
20. Newspaper edition
22. That man's
23. African antelope
24. Settler's home
27. Insect's antennas
31. Doing business
32. We — to please
33. Factual
34. Marriage
36. Freight boat
37. Conclude
38. Chess pieces
39. Saber
42. Stretch the truth
43. Joan of —
46. Track circuit
47. Exactly alike
50. Abel's mother
51. Excellent: 2 wds.
52. Actress Moreno
53. Lair
54. Close by
55. Paradise

DOWN

1. Region
2. Lanky
3. Bygone
4. Foxy
5. Deceives
6. Wicked
7. Decade number
8. Motor
9. Egyptian goddess
10. Bill of fare
11. Window glass
16. Profit
21. Moslem ruler
22. Impede
23. Valuable person
24. Dairy animal
25. King Kong, for one
26. Four-poster
27. Seedy fruit
28. Blunder
29. Carpet
30. Visualize
32. To — fro
35. Geronimo or Cochise
36. Root vegetable
38. Coal digger
39. Snow vehicle
40. Flutter, as a flag
41. Not shut
42. Singer Horne
43. Caustic fluid
44. Proportion
45. Family tribe
48. Bambi's mom
49. Wrath

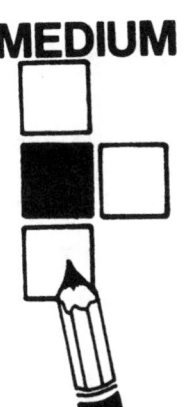

MEDIUM

Solution is on page 383

169

BIBLE CROSSWORD   MEDIUM

by RUSS CARLEY

Bible references in this puzzle are from the King James Version. You'll find it stimulating to solve, and may discover you know more about the Bible than you think you do.

ACROSS

1. I will — down my life for thy sake. *St. John 13:37*
4. The Lord maketh —, and maketh rich. *I Sam. 2:7*
8. Joseph's — of many colours
12. Blessed — the meek. *Matt. 5:5*
13. They . . . were all baptized of him in the —r of Jordan. *Mark 1:5*
14. Simon, (whom he — named Peter), and Andrew. *Luke 6:14*
15. The — of Galilee
16. Melchisedec, king of S— . . . blessed him. *Heb. 7:1*
17. Oh that I had wings — a dove! *Ps. 55:6*
18. We . . . were desired to — with them seven days. *Acts 28:14*
20. He will laugh at the t— of the innocent. *Job 9:23*
22. S—, and ye shall find. *Matt. 7:7*
24. We came . . . unto Coos, . . . and from — unto Patara. *Acts 21:1*
28. Go unto my country, and to my —. *Gen. 24:4*
32. Women — themselves in modest apparel. *I Tim. 2:9*
33. If th— eye offend thee, pluck it out. *Mark 9:47*
34. A thousand years . . . are but as —terday. *Ps. 90:4*
36. Is any thing — hard for the Lord? *Gen. 18:14*
37. Every man at his best — is altogether vanity. *Ps. 39:5*
40. We should serve in — of spirit, and not in . . . oldness. *Rom. 7:6*
43. — is turned into joy before him. *Job 41:22*
45. — Lord is my shepherd. *Ps. 23:1*
46. The cedars of Leb—
48. Saul — David with his armour. *I Sam. 17:38*

52. Whither have ye made a — to day? *I Sam. 27:10*
55. — great stones upon the mouth of the cave. *Josh. 10:18*
57. Adam and —
58. Let us go up at —. *Num. 13:30*
59. The water thereof was —d up. *Rev. 16:12*
60. Thou has b— faithful. *Luke 19:17*
61. What — is this that ye have done? *Gen. 44:15*
62. They shall build the old wa—, they shall raise up the former desolations. *Isa. 61:4*
63. I . . . . will — them as gold is tried. *Zech. 13:9*

DOWN

1. I am the first and the —. *Rev. 1:17*
2. He ascended from Caes— to Jerusalem. *Acts 25:1*
3. He reigned one — in Jerusalem. *II Chr. 22:2*
4. Give ear, O Lord, unto my —. *Ps. 86:6*
5. Thou anointest my head with —. *Ps. 23:5*
6. Let us pass — unto the other side. *Mark 4:35*
7. Whose soever sins ye —, they are remitted unto them. *St. John 20:23*
8. And God — the dry land Earth. *Gen. 1:10*
9. Can the fig tree . . . bear —ve berries? *James 3:12*
10. —, and it shall be given you. *Matt. 7:7*
11. Put it upon . . . the great — of their right foot. *Ex. 29:20*
19. They passed through the — sea as by dry land. *Heb. 11:29*

21. —b . . . took to wife Jezebel.
    I Ki. 16:30, 31
23. He opened not the doors . . .
    therefore they took a —, and
    opened them. *Judg. 3:25*
25. Write it before them in a table,
    and — it in a book. *Isa. 30:8*
26. If thou be the Son of God, come
    down from the —s. *Matt. 27:40*
27. Son of Seth
28. Let him — me with the kisses of
    his mouth. *Song 1:2*
29. Lead us not — temptation. *Matt.
    6:13*
30. Be not far from me; for trouble
    is —. *Ps. 22:11*
31. He shall be cast into the — of
    lions. *Dan. 6:7*
35. At even . . . the sun did —. *Mark
    1:32*
38. With silver, iron, tin, and lead,
    they — in thy fairs. *Ezek. 27:12*
39. These also shall be unclean unto
    you . . . the ferret, and the
    chamel—. *Lev. 11:29, 30*

41. Jonas was three days and three
    nights in the — belly. *Matt.
    12:40*
42. Father of Abner
44. These are the — which I spake
    unto you. *Luke 24:44*
47. They shall come . . . from the
    —h, and from the south. *Luke
    13:29*
49. The bridegroom cometh; go ye
    out to — him. *Matt. 25:6*
50. Trust ye in the Lord for —.
    Isa. 26:4
51. This night, before the cock
    crow, thou shalt — me thrice.
    Matt. 26:34
52. Thy — and thy staff they com-
    fort me. *Ps. 23:4*
53. Speak not evil — of another.
    James 4:11
54. Moses hid his f—; for he was
    afraid. *Ex. 3:6*
56. The same . . . is truth, and is
    no —. *I John 2:27*

Solution is on page 383

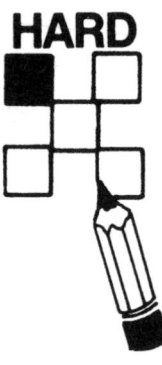

HARD

ACROSS

1. Attorney, Melvin —
6. Confusion
11. Oriental greeting
12. Young cow
14. Melt
15. Sacred song
17. More or less
18. Operated
19. Narrow inlet
20. Woman's nickname
21. Certain degree: abbr.
22. Orally
23. Arizona Indian
24. French chemist
26. Naive
27. Drives slantingly
28. Legal order
29. Salmonlike fish
31. Warship
34. Pitch
35. Claude, of film
36. Mr. Pacino
37. Stopover
38. Proclaim
39. Vichy, e.g.
40. Greek letter
41. Not advanced
42. At that time
43. Ski downhill at full speed
45. Queen Victoria's son
47. Serf
48. Lodges

DOWN

1. Name of an island group north of Cuba
2. Dash
3. TV's "L.A. —"
4. Spanish article
5. Irreverent
6. Kind of beet
7. Detained
8. Intention
9. Derived from
10. East Indian plant
11. Sandal feature
13. Word with "holiday"
16. Peevish
19. Armada
20. Michelangelo work
22. Coral island
23. Smug ones
25. Relentless
26. Pulverize
28. Feature of an antique washer
29. Transports, in a way
30. Bavaria's capital
31. Minor deity
32. Candles
33. African antelope
35. Drive (out)
38. Mediocre: hyph. wd.
39. Cheat
41. He played a Siamese monarch
42. Duet
44. Pronoun
46. Solve

Solution is on page 383

ACROSS

1. Mr. Mineo
4. Articles
9. Take a chair
12. Raw metal
13. Metal bolt
14. Historic age
15. Shop
17. Mobile's State: abbr.
18. Mover's truck
18. Half a pair
21. Oak or elm
23. Edges
27. Takes care of
30. A Great Lake
31. Unwind
33. Jolson or Capp
34. Do sums
35. Gave (out) sparingly
36. Miss Gardner
37. Compass point
38. Peels
39. Cut, as hair
40. Teach
42. Leaves helpless
44. Table supports
46. Male heir
47. Buddy
49. Building wing
51. It follows "roller" or "ice"
55. Part of a wedding vow: 2 wds.
56. Elevate
58. Use the oars
59. Unused
60. Stairs
61. Organ of sight

DOWN

1. Distress signal

2. Mr. Linkletter
3. Mr. Durocher
4. Worth or Dunne
5. It follows "la"
6. A Gabor
7. Thaw
8. Began
9. "Lucky" number
10. A Gershwin
11. Sunbather's goal
16. Went by car
20. Mistake
22. Slippery fish
23. "Beauty and the —," children's tale
24. Command
25. Free (of)
26. Auctions

28. TV's Letterman
29. Smacks
32. Sleeveless garments
35. Hazards
36. Miss Miller
38. Crusted dessert
39. Submerged
41. Permit; let
43. Prickly-stemmed flowers
45. Wooden strip
47. Brooch
48. Fruit drink
50. Fib
52. Exist
53. Plaything
54. Ram's mate
57. Mexican's language: abbr.

EASY

Solution is on page 384

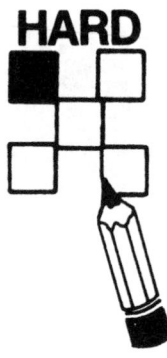

HARD

ACROSS

1. Potato
5. Military district
11. Beatles member
12. Mounted policeman
14. Cookout site
15. Lease
16. Compass point
17. One who: suffix
18. Fragment
20. Young seal
21. Stocky
23. Festive event
24. Sword handle
25. Statistics
26. Obliterate
29. Clergy member
30. Lab bottle
31. Destroy
32. Links cry
33. Caroler, e.g.
37. Before, to poets
38. Certain dimension
39. Conceit
40. Scale tone
41. Sea: Latin
42. Coronet
44. Brighten
46. Lewis' Gantry
47. Mute
48. Avian home

DOWN

1. Squirrel away
2. Feminine name
3. Swiss canton
4. Football maneuver: 2 wds.
5. Thoroughfare
6. Upright
7. Geometric solid
8. Wee one
9. Musical work: abbr.
10. Consequences
11. Grill adjunct
13. Meal
19. Cruise sight
20. Step
22. Pursue
23. Profits
25. Scare
26. Decadent; soft
27. British coins
28. Cabby's customer
29. Flat-bottomed boat
31. Beaver, for one
33. Lorelei
34. Competitive groups
35. Wading bird
36. Loud noise
38. Surfer's quest
41. Unit of length
43. Of: suffix
45. Fifty-one, in old Rome

Solution is on page 384

ACROSS

1. Imitator
5. Prohibit
8. Horseback game
12. Wander
13. Fib
14. Amongst
15. Be introduced to
16. Mobile's State: abbr.
17. Orange skin
18. Long, narrow pieces
20. Packing boxes
22. Turned
24. Tied, as shoes
27. Crosses out
31. Highest card
32. Fishing pole
33. Ms. Gardner
34. River boat; liner
37. Update, as a subscription
39. Matured
41. "Leatherneck"
44. Went out
48. Woe is me!
49. Had lunch
51. Ocean current
52. Lion's tresses
53. Turner or Knight
54. Foretoken
55. Picnic pests
56. Speak
57. Lease

DOWN

1. Upper limbs

2. Rhymster
3. Always
4. Go to bed
5. Explosion
6. Feel sick
7. Responded
8. Formal march
9. Leave out
10. Row, as of people
11. — or evens
19. Pea container
21. Kin: abbr.
23. Worship
24. — Vegas, Nevada
25. Perform on stage
26. Alphabet letter
28. Beige

29. Adam's mate
30. Carpenter's tool
32. Says again
35. Comes up
36. Hour part: abbr.
37. Actor Harrison
38. Newspaper head
40. Poor
41. Papa's mate
42. Actor Alda
43. Rave
45. Clock information
46. Genesis garden
47. Result of a "fender-bender"
50. Oolong or pekoe

EASY

Solution is on page 384

MOVIE-TV CROSSWORD

by MYRTLE BAZEMORE

ACROSS

1. — Selleck, of TV's *Magnum, P.I.*
4. *Never — Anything Small*, 1959 James Cagney/Shirley Jones movie
9. — *Shift*, 1984 Goldie Hawn comedy
14. Actress Lupino
15. Rub out
16. — *Thy Father*, 1971 TV movie
17. *The More the* —, 1943 film
19. *The — Man*, Powell/Loy movie
21. — *and Pa Kettle*
22. — *Day at a Time*, TV comedy
23. *Bus* —, Monroe classic
24. — *Anybody Seen My Gal?*, Piper Laurie/Rock Hudson musical
25. TV show, *The Paper* —
28. — *John Doe*, Gary Cooper film
29. Offers (a price)
30. — *Come the Coeds*, Abbott & Costello comedy
31. *Don't Go — the Water*, Glenn Ford comedy
32. Central part
33. Annoy
34. — *Apache*, John Wayne movie
35. Actress, Bernadette —
38. *There's — Business Like Show Business*, 1954 movie
39. — *the High Country*, 1962 western
40. Ice-cream holder
41. *The Bridge — the River Kwai*, 1957 film
42. *Charlie's* —, one-time TV hit
44. *This — is Mine*, 1943 Charles Laughton movie
45. Actor's hint
46. Actor Majors
47. Francis — Coppola
48. Strong, glossy fiber used for making burlap sacks
49. MacMurray of TV's *My Three Sons*
51. — *Hand Luke*, Paul Newman movie
52. Alma —, school one has attended

53. *Logan's* —, 1976 science-fiction film
54. *A Shot in the* —, 1964 Peter Sellers comedy
55. Actor Chaney, Jr.
56. Actor Pacino
57. Unfurnished; empty
58. Soap opera, — *Hospital*
62. Iron or steel
64. Gave off light
66. Lifetime
67. Wear away
68. Bryant Gumbel's morning show
69. Make lace

DOWN

1. Comedian Conway
2. — *to Billy Joe*, 1976 movie
3. Impair
4. Fishing net
5. *Under the Yum Yum* —, Jack Lemmon comedy
6. *A Flea in Her* —, 1968 French comedy
7. Soap opera, — *the World Turns*
8. *The Scarlet* —, 1926 Lillian Gish film
9. *Don't Give up the* —, Jerry Lewis comedy
10. *How the West Was* —, Gregory Peck/Henry Fonda/James Stewart western
11. *The Lion — Winter*, 1968 O'Toole/Hepburn film
12. Wanderer
13. *Splendor in the* —, Natalie Wood/Warren Beatty movie
18. *Honeysuckle* —, Willie Nelson/Dyan Cannon movie
20. *Some Like It* —, Tony Curtis/Marilyn Monroe comedy
23. Chair
24. *No Place to* —, 1981 TV movie
25. *The — Syndrome*, Jane Fonda/Jack Lemmon film
26. Wading bird
27. Noah's vessel
28. Simple
29. *Love At First* —, 1979 comedy

31. Signals "yes"
32. Repair
34. *The Odessa —*, 1974 Jon Voight movie
35. *On Golden —*, 1981 hit
36. *— 66*, old TV adventure series
37. Scoff (at)
39. *Brady Bunch* father, Robert —
40. Actor/director Reiner
43. Singer Campbell
44. *Don't — Now*, Donald Sutherland thriller
45. Slice
47. *The Emerald —*, 1985 film
48. Actress Fonda

49. Picture holder
50. Sovereign
51. *— Wash*, Richard Pryor comedy
52. *The — Pit*, Tom Hanks comedy
54. Cowgirl Evans
55. Singer Horne
57. *The Good, the —, and the Ugly*, Clint Eastwood western
58. *Oh, —!*, George Burns comedy
59. *The — Patrol*, TV WWII show
60. Moslem commander
61. *Never — Me Go*, 1953 Clark Gable movie
63. Soap opera, *One Life — Live*
65. *Gung —*, Michael Keaton comedy

Solution is on page 384

177

EASY

ACROSS

1. Evergreen tree
4. Long, narrow piece, as of wood
9. "Yo, ho, ho, and a bottle of —"
12. Expert
13. Inclined (to)
14. Mine product
15. Saved
17. Pulls along
19. Neat
20. Curved roofs
21. Narrow openings
23. Toy babies
25. Small horse
26. Judge's mallet
27. St. Louis' State: abbr.
29. Tatter
30. Stories
31. Acknowledge applause
32. Three feet: abbr.
33. More domesticated
34. Throw; cast
35. Roof slates
36. Appointments
37. Stable compartment
39. Linger
40. Squander
41. Looking glasses
44. Likely (to)
45. What an elm offers
47. Short snooze
48. "Busy" insect
49. Grows weary
50. Timid

DOWN

1. Distant
2. Wintry driving hazard
3. Reposing
4. Potatoes
5. Three-spotted card
6. Fishing pole
7. At home
8. Sells from door-to-door
9. Wanders
10. Coax; incite
11. State of disorder
16. Large town
18. Bun's kin
21. Lively; agile
22. Burden; cargo
23. Valleys
24. Above
26. Hopscotch, for one
27. Greater quantity
28. "Wise" birds
30. Highest
31. Song, "— and Bows"
33. Cause to slant
34. Tresses
35. Savor; sample
36. Ventures
37. Mop
38. Narrow, adhesive band
39. Broad
41. Impair; damage
42. Stadium cheer
43. Secret agent
46. Hello!

Solution is on page 384

ACROSS

1. —! Humbug!
4. Compensate
9. Confederate soldier, for short
12. Self
13. Part of Hispaniola
14. Lyric poem
15. Sightseer
17. Cartoon character Fudd
19. Dispatched
20. Customer
21. Outdoor area
23. Cowboy competition
24. Second word of a fairy tale opener
25. Spouses
26. Male title: abbr.
28. "— North Frederick," movie oldie
29. Put in secret writing
30. Actress Farrow
31. Football score: abbr.
32. Road worker
33. Penny
34. Uses a peeler
35. Packing case
36. Scandinavian country
38. Slim
39. Poke fun at
40. Bedouin
43. Paddle
44. More unusual
46. Enlisted man: abbr.
47. Force open
48. Snowy rain
49. Obtain

DOWN

1. Wager
2. Past
3. Texas city
4. African animal, for short
5. Sunrise direction
6. Ground hole
7. Attending
8. Conceded
9. Young lover
10. First garden
11. Convy or Lahr
16. Restrain
18. Prevarications
20. Blanket
21. Golf stroke
22. Mimicked
23. Goes by horse
25. Made on a loom
26. Coin (money)
27. Fixed ratio
29. Occupations
30. Purpose
32. Writing tablets
33. Baby's bed
34. Arctic explorer
35. Navigation map
36. Standstill
37. Put on
38. Larch, for one
40. Exist
41. High card
42. — my cup of tea, unsuitable
45. Actor Pacino

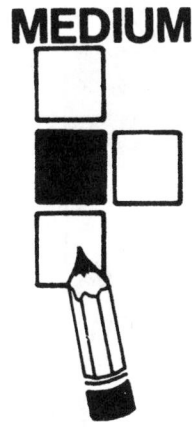

MEDIUM

Solution is on page 384

EASY

ACROSS

1. Friendly talk
5. Small songbird
9. Competitor
11. Capital of Egypt
12. Salem's State
14. Heavy load
15. Writing tool
16. Arise: 2 wds.
18. Frozen water
19. Source of light and heat
21. Moving truck
22. Picnic pest
23. Avid
25. Hen product
26. Spoil the beauty of
27. Chess piece
28. Table support
29. Police-car's signal
31. Boy
32. Variety of rummy
33. Perched
35. Passing craze
36. Extra payment over one's salary
38. Five pairs
40. Truly!
42. Safe
44. Play setting
45. Less well
46. Group of cattle
47. Unwanted plant

DOWN

1. Farmer's yield
2. Employs
3. Street
4. Label
5. Armed conflict
6. Going by bus or car
7. Upright
8. Not any
10. Ship's journal
11. Saucer's "partner"
13. At no time
14. Small roll
17. Paving substance
20. Gave a title to
22. Miss Moorehead
24. Practical joke
25. Corn spike
27. Less
28. Housepainter's aid
29. Transgression
30. Mother —; the world of plants and animals
31. Spear
32. Supreme Being
34. Concise
35. Use a hook and line
36. Honey maker
37. What tailors do
39. Require
41. Conclude
43. Dairy-farm animal

Solution is on page 385

ACROSS

1. Nonsense, to Brits
5. Man's name
8. Champion
12. Vicinity
13. — *Kapital*, Marx work
14. Copied
15. Advance showings
17. Well-known Hollywood street
18. *Senora* Peron
19. Votes in
21. Analyze
24. Sketched
25. Chinese dog
26. Sensible
30. Commotion: hyph. wd.
31. Biblical woman
32. Traveled on horseback
33. Taken aback
35. Pass too slowly
36. Sturdy cart
37. Absolute rulers
38. Nincompoop
41. In the dumps
42. Needle case
43. Press runs
48. Outlet; passage
49. Bolivian export
50. Singing group
51. Oriental nursemaid
52. Choose
53. Beatles movie

DOWN

1. Strike lightly
2. Hockey great
3. Call on
4. Engage (someone) in conversation: 4 wds.
5. Brainstorm
6. Unrefined
7. Stated positively
8. Confront (someone) verbally: 3 wds.
9. *Beowulf* or *El Cid*
10. Part of the overhead
11. Pindaric works
16. Wall creeper
20. Hilo garland
21. New Testament book
22. Filmed
23. Fountain order
24. Frontiersman Crockett
26. Identify with: 2 wds.
27. Ibsen heroine
28. Sixth Jewish month
29. Table parts
34. Three: prefix
37. Young child
38. Leningrad's river
39. News story
40. Game and food fish
41. Bits of thread
44. Short swim
45. Bauxite or galena
46. Nothing whatever
47. Drench

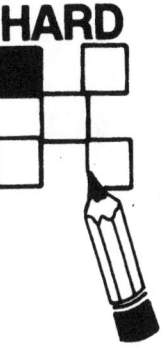

HARD

Solution is on page 385

EASY

ACROSS

1. Waldorf or Caesar
6. That woman
9. Energy
12. Ewes' mates
16. Excuse
17. Rudely brief
19. Wept
21. Wicked
22. Fun contests
23. Region
24. Hasten
25. "Miami —"
26. 6th sense: abbr.
27. Young horse
29. Exchange
31. Required
33. Story
34. Look at fixedly
35. Use the phone
36. Steeple
38. Divide
39. Manager
40. Witnessed
43. Mild and soothing
44. Move aside suddenly
45. Sample (the food)
46. Falsehood
47. Simple
48. Coagulates, as blood
49. Birthday celebration

50. Travel by bus
51. High explosive: abbr.
52. Divide equally
53. Playgrounds
54. Cut into cubes
55. Wood-eating insect
57. Carnivals
58. Store events
59. Roof edge
60. Humorous
61. Quote
62. Stare angrily at
64. West Point student
65. Liberty
68. Religious pamphlet
69. Melodies
70. Snails
71. Prohibit
73. Reckless; hasty
74. Theater platform
75. Digging tool
76. Allot; portion (out)
77. Likely (to)
78. Window material
79. Matching furniture
80. Melted together
81. Certainly!
82. Lease
83. Placards
84. Fence doors
85. Locate
86. Door joint
87. Wile; trick
88. Refresh the memory
91. Racetrack animal
92. Desire
93. Faint, as light
96. Aroma
97. Run off to wed
99. Shoo!
101. Overjoy
103. Monster
104. Thorny flowers
105. Adjust the pitch of
106. Between eights and tens
107. Nourish
108. Marry
109. Sleeping place
110. Plant parts

DOWN

1. Stuffing herb
2. Cry of woe

3. Walk lamely
4. Actor Vigoda
5. Throw away
6. Weighing device
7. Injure
8. Before: poetic
9. Overly modest person
10. Ireland
11. For each
12. Make merry
13. Eager
14. Tiny rodents
15. Snow toy
18. Tells on
19. Map
20. Joan Collins' TV show
28. Bullfight cheer: Spanish
30. Sudden attack
32. Otherwise
33. Wee
34. Ill will; malice
35. Expenses
36. Slope
37. Sticky stuff
38. Beach
39. Dog sounds
40. Carve, as a roast
41. Assistants
42. Unwanted plant
43. Wager
44. Blackboard
45. Linger
48. Onionlike seasoning
49. Artist's need
50. Angered
52. Intelligent
53. Window squares
54. Social appointments
56. Arrive at
57. Hot — sundae
58. Long and persistent attack
60. Snake's teeth
61. Unrefined; vulgar
62. Wine fruit
63. Endures
64. Seaside
65. Apartments
66. Fat
67. Husbands and wives
68. Flat serving platter

69. Become erect
70. Backbone
72. Bright color
74. Slim
75. Recommend
76. Speechless
78. Broad smile
79. Transgressions
80. Secures; binds

83. Horses' fathers
84. Rifle
85. Discharged, as a pistol
86. Anticipated
87. Estimated
88. Housetop
89. Border
90. Opposite of less

91. Stockings
92. Diminish in size, as the moon
93. Copenhagen native
94. Article
95. Untidy condition
98. Deep, as in pitch
100. Young bear
102. Ignited

Solution is on page 385

MEDIUM

ACROSS

1. Scorch
5. Mister: Spanish
10. Extinct birds
15. Barrymore, of "E.T."
19. Ear part
20. Run away to wed
21. Decay
22. Ireland
23. Simians
24. Identifies
25. Sheathed
26. Agitate
27. Fragile
29. Stale
31. For each
33. Social engagement
34. Member of the wedding
35. Headliner
36. Area, as of influence
39. Leontyne or Vincent
40. Trembled
44. Publish
45. Location

46. Animate
47. Sooner than: poetic
48. Mom's sister
49. Lee's opponent
50. Pickling solution
51. London apartment
52. Trinitrotoluene: abbr.
53. Fern leaf
54. Group of lions
55. Taunt
56. Meetings
58. Ordinary writing
59. Perry Mason, e.g.
60. Otherwise
61. Quench
62. Manage despite problems
63. Barrel sides
66. One of 50
67. Amused
71. Zoo compartments
72. Ill will
73. Contract amendment
74. Armed conflict
75. Dentist's request
76. Grin
77. Added liquor
78. Dreadful
79. Small enclosure
80. Make amends
81. Contributor
82. Helsinki natives
83. Calculated guess
85. Companions
86. Affectionate touch
87. Center
88. Softens
89. Peel
90. Refuse to yield
93. Essential
94. Perceived
98. Smart—, whippersnapper
99. Unbound
101. Type type
103. Capture
104. — 'er up
105. Stage direction
106. Cut off
107. Portent
108. Yarn
109. Fortunetellers
110. Ranks of seats
111. Take a break

DOWN

1. Attired
2. Faith and Charity companion
3. Eve's second son
4. Hospital staffer
5. Upper House
6. Raise the spirits
7. Alaskan city
8. Unclose: poetic
9. Limit
10. Opt
11. Hold forth
12. Medicine measure
13. Lyric poem
14. Tranquilizer
15. Certain streetcar
16. Religious ceremony
17. Newsman Sevareid
18. "The Way We —"
28. Two-wheeled wagon
30. Asian staple
32. Surface (a road)
34. Identifying mark
35. Gloss
36. Gaiters
37. Dried fruit
38. Helpful clues
39. Schemes
40. Try to avoid a tag
41. Type of race
42. Expunge
43. Discourage
45. Disposed (with "to")
46. Originate
49. Income before deductions
50. Surpassed, as a record
51. Not so many
53. Dossiers
54. Gossip
55. Narrow gradually
57. Hills of Rome or Deadly Sins
58. Overlay with metal
59. Felt strong affection
61. Fence step
62. Apple juice
63. Extent
64. Uses a VCR
65. Ten-percenter

66. Part of a book
67. Chops into cubes
68. Cord
69. Deserves
70. Frock
72. Struck hard
73. Superlative reviews
76. Alarms
77. Least large
78. Conductor

80. Andy's partner
81. Festive
82. Paying passenger
84. Frozen hanger
85. Rhythmic patterns
86. Feeds a party
88. Pinchpenny
89. — the Great of Russia
90. Floating platform

91. Alias Charles Lamb
92. Trade for money
93. Ballot
94. Jackknife, for one
95. Docile
96. Supplements (with "out")
97. Depression
100. Single
102. Hawaiian garland

Solution is on page 385

HARD

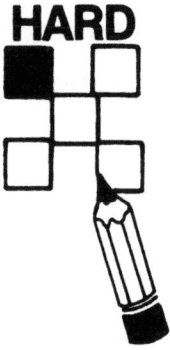

ACROSS

1. Brief looks
6. Spirited horse
11. Menu item
15. Proper
19. Eagle's home
20. Fashion accessory
21. Italian river
22. Knowledge
23. Leading character
25. Reclined
26. Lily plant
27. Assistant
28. Devastate
29. Land
31. Penny
32. Very small
33. Harrow blade
34. Precious metal
35. Abound
37. Golf cup
38. Bucket
39. Tie
43. Write awkwardly
46. Trade center
47. Plant insect
48. Deer
49. Circus performer
50. Tulip, e.g.
51. Wall painting
52. At this place
53. Chess piece
54. Posture
55. Doctrine
56. Square mesh lace
57. Social insect
58. Chore
59. Montana city
60. Drinking cup
61. Annoys
63. Memos
64. Style
68. Hardwood
69. Singing voice
70. Girl
71. Regret
72. Shoulder wrap
75. Arbor
76. Overlook
77. Deck officer
78. Gain by work
79. Slopes
80. Price
81. Appraised
82. Unit of work
83. Ballads
84. Set of actors
85. Metric measures
86. Strips of rind
88. Roll of cloth
89. Hodgepodge
90. Nearest to
91. Edible grain
92. System of signals
93. Public transport
96. Allows
98. Automatons
101. Throw
102. Combat vehicle
103. Rainbow
104. Encourage
105. Skillful perform-
     ance: 3 wds.
108. Tipple location
109. Essence
110. Bird of prey
111. Leg joint
112. Legume
113. Camp shelter
114. Frock
115. Readjust, in a way

DOWN

1. Custard apple
2. Weird
3. Eat away
4. Soaring device
5. Body of water
6. Married person
7. Grecian garment
8. Ireland
9. Alphabet letter
10. Motown
11. Dieter's fare
12. Of the mouth
13. One
14. Hair style
15. Put
16. Person imitated:
    2 wds.
17. Strong metal
18. Encounter
24. Cookout device
30. Building wing
33. Dejected
34. Clothing
36. Terminate
37. Bird of prey
38. Bounded area
39. Binge
40. The one there
41. Front
42. Length measures
43. Jettison
44. Copy
45. Ancestors
46. Perfume ingredient
47. Family members
50. Foreman
51. 39.37 inches
52. Lofty
54. Picnic spot
55. Certain teacher
56. Commotion
58. River duck
59. Radius and ulna
60. Bulk
62. City
63. Salamanders
64. Rapid
65. Incensed
66. External
67. Requirements
69. Grasping device
70. Register
72. Ooze
73. Rabbit's kin
74. Mendoza's land
75. Thrill: slang

76. Greatest amount
77. School subject, for short
79. Legal agreement
80. Short visit
81. Ascent
83. Cardinal number
84. Glided downhill
85. Serving utensil
87. Decrease
88. Wager
89. Crowds
91. Musical work
92. Ringlets
93. Sailing vessels
94. Family member
95. Trapshooting
96. Tree part
97. Great Lake
99. Hautboy
100. Swiss capital
101. Very large
102. Musical sound
106. Rowing need
107. Distant

Solution is on page 385

SPECIAL CHALLENGER CROSSWORD

by LOUIS SABIN

Here is a real toughie for you. We have omitted giving you such helps as "2 wds.," "hyph. wd.," and "slang"; but in the spirit of fair play, all abbreviations and foreign words are so indicated.

ACROSS

1. General meaning; drift
6. Greek letters
11. "Hit the road!"
16. Fashion
17. Bouquet
18. Savile Row workers
21. Passenger carrier
23. Place of pastoral peace
24. Cinnabar or sphalerite
25. Broke
26. English metaphysical poet
28. Greek dawn goddess
29. Primitive plant
31. Mended
32. Golf goof
33. Branch of learning
34. Machinations
36. German article
37. Dorset yachting center
38. Rajah's wife
39. State council
41. Exemption from compulsion
43. Tobacco processors
44. Vincent Lopez's radio theme song
46. Cozy spots
47. Punctuation mark
48. Matador's garb
52. Retaliates for
55. Register
56. Voracious eel
57. Sharpened
58. Gem cutter's disk
59. Celebrity
60. Old Nick

61. Spells
62. Harass
63. Jacques Tati film classic, "— Oncle"
64. Somewhat dated letter opener
65. Short-legged dog of Wales
66. Pianist-bandleader
67. Quickens
69. Taciturn
71. Eisenhower's vice-president
72. Capt. Queeg's ship
73. Orient
74. Return to the dorm
76. Covers, in a way
78. Worried about
82. French clerics
83. Small openings
84. Actor Reiner
86. Winner of the '83 Indy 500
87. Napoleon and Robert Fulton, to name two
88. Jouster's gear
89. Agricultural machine
91. Strip of wood
92. Southern constellation
93. Phonetic series
94. Kids' kin
96. American humorist
97. Emulates Solti or Muti
99. Depot boss
102. Distresses
103. Order out
104. Get an impression
105. Divagate
106. Argot
107. Scornful expression

DOWN

1. Tests for fit
2. Slippery type
3. Ointment of the ancients
4. Siouan Indians
5. Scraped (out)
6. Old military machine
7. Went astray
8. Insectivorous amphibian
9. French friend
10. Playing fields
11. Position
12. "Laugh-In" made her a star
13. Staple food
14. Wing
15. American speech base
16. Songstress King
19. Disorderly person
20. "Mouths off"
21. Easy victories
22. Fasten with a peg
27. Unctuous
30. 19th-century feminist leader
32. Classifies
33. Brother of Moses
35. Dunce's perch
37. Bothersome
38. Guided
40. Prankish sprite
42. Irish dramatist
43. Small inlets
45. Town in Spanish mercury-mining region
47. French coin
48. Historic Alabama town
49. Coalition

50. They are used by 18-Across
51. Small quantities
52. Stendhal novel, "Le — et le Noir"
53. She "Was a Lady"
54. Celerity
57. Shrewd negotiations
60. Suppressed
61. American frontiersman
62. Wickerwork materials

64. Lengthy garments
65. Cheats
66. Highway users
68. Digs for 24-Across
69. One who is concerned
70. "Nerd"
72. Revels
74. Dinner courses
75. Spain and Portugal
76. ¿— no? Why not?
77. Former Italian coin
79. One who tells
80. Escapee

81. Mail-room device
83. Finicky
85. Individuals
88. Sicilian volcano
89. Drive home a run
90. Supply new personnel for
93. Maple genus
94. Input
95. Gratify utterly
98. TV schedule abbreviation
100. Hindu cymbals
101. Haggard novel

Solution is on page 385

189

DIAGRAMLESS

EASY

This Diagramless is 15 boxes wide by 15 boxes deep.

ACROSS

1. Buddy
4. Spider's network
7. Window sections
9. Confined (in)
11. Shorten
13. Shopper's good buy
15. Picasso's field
16. Neptune, Mars, etc.
18. Golfer's gadget
19. Fender mishap
21. Cake layers
22. Baseball glove
23. Harvest a crop
25. Fish eggs
26. Sports enthusiasts
27. Angers; irritates
29. "Love Is a Many Splendored —"
31. Put down (carpeting)
32. Country lodge
33. Ballots
35. Sharply inclined, as a hill
37. Show concern (for)
38. Spinning toy
40. Mild oath
42. Gluttons
43. Twosomes
45. Men's social
47. Make a mistake
48. "Hit the —," lose one's temper
50. Hasten
51. Under the —, somewhat sick
53. Chivalrous; knightly
55. Scoff (at)
56. Aim (a finger) at
57. High explosive: abbr.
58. Marry

DOWN

1. Sears, to Roebuck
2. Picnic pest
3. Jump, frog-style
4. "Star —"
5. Urge (on)
6. Throbbing
7. Less adulterated, as air
8. Claylike sediment
9. Mousers
10. Counts calories
11. Scoundrel
12. Dens
13. Tam's kin
14. Butterfly snare
17. New: comb. form
20. Suitmakers
22. Polite behavior
24. Dish
26. Gave a parking penalty to
28. Spud bud
30. Wallop
33. Tramp; hobo
34. Porch step
35. Bit of parsley
36. In draw poker, cards dealt to a player which are playable as is: 2 wds.
37. Apple centers
39. Lubricate
41. Sully; stain
42. Chop down
43. Squint (at)
44. Easy task: slang
46. Obtain
48. Newsman Huntley
49. Glisten
52. "Sawbuck"
54. Falsehood

Solution is on page 386

DIAGRAMLESS

EXPERT

This Diagramless is 17 boxes wide by 17 boxes deep. Starting box is on page 393.

ACROSS

1. Icy fruit-flavored confection
6. Skewbald
7. College bigwig
11. Person in a dominant position: 2 wds. (slang)
12. Trek beasts
14. High moccasin
15. Nontaxable item: abbr.
16. Relinquish (an office, e.g.) under compulsion: 3 wds.
20. Hideaway
21. Hebrew prophet
22. Action; performance
23. Coffin stand
24. Freight unit
25. Celtic sea god
28. Alphabet letters
29. Hurons' land, c. 1600: abbr.
30. Ambler or Clapton
32. One's cousins, e.g.: abbr.
34. Full of ardent anticipation
36. Active one
38. Naval rank: abbr.
41. Sound from Sandy
42. Lilliputian
43. Card game

44. Turner or Louise
45. Haughty
47. Prongs
48. Attention-getting sound
51. Provide a connection: 3 wds.
53. Ike's WWII domain: abbr.
54. Stroke for Pat Cash
55. Stay near, protectively
56. French Riviera city
58. Without: French
59. Means for the performance of some action
60. Epergne

DOWN

1. Half-alien in a science-fiction series
2. Embouchure
3. Brought to ruin
4. Reserve
5. Kind of earth-walled house
7. Senegal capital
8. Approximations: abbr.
9. Pallor

10. Must: 2 wds.
11. Fight; quarrel
13. Golf club
14. Review unfavorably
16. "Oberon" composer
17. Adjusted
18. Remains inconspicuous: 2 wds.
19. Thread shreds
26. Time period
27. Tackle
31. Eye part
33. Get it?
35. Understand
37. Clear, sharp proofs (as of type), for short
38. Dolt
39. Word with "sour"
40. Calgary events
44. Stadium features
46. Tease: slang
47. Therefore
48. New Mexico-Texas river
49. Kickoff
50. South Pacific Polynesian kingdom
51. Coffee mixture
52. Resource-development agency formed in 1933: abbr.
57. Ms. Fabray to friends

Solution is on page 386

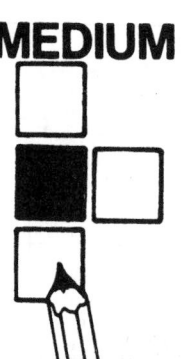

MEDIUM

ACROSS

1. Cork's sound
4. Postal purchase
9. Small enclosure
12. Pitcher handle
13. Of the Pope
14. Affirmative vote
15. Pledge
17. Disturb emotionally
19. Calligraphy need
20. Wallet items
21. Commonplace talk
24. Certain lawbreakers
27. Trims, as a tree
28. Stings
29. Theologist's study: abbr.
30. Devour
31. Apple product
32. Payable
33. While
34. Word with "bear"
35. Computer input
36. POW camps
38. Highly valued person
39. Ponder
40. Legume
41. Faith
43. Passage across
47. Used to be
48. Once more
50. Expert
51. Be in the red
52. Yearns
53. Obtain

DOWN

1. Energy
2. Rower
3. In favor of
4. Backbone
5. Chore
6. Mimic
7. Family member
8. Reckless type
9. Outmoded
10. Observe
11. Tennis need
16. Overlook
18. Wooden pins
20. Prefix with "space"
21. Appeals
22. Use the oven
23. Make a choice
24. He had the "golden touch"
25. Highway
26. Pilfer
28. Nonsense: slang
31. Near the shore
32. Crow's "cousin"
34. In addition to
35. College official
37. Entertain
38. Casual wear
40. Very proper sort
41. A pair
42. Crude
43. Shade of brown
44. Droop
45. Do a baker's task
46. Asian festival
49. Depart

Solution is on page 386

ACROSS

1. Overly plump
4. Capital of France
9. Health resort
12. Possess
13. Get out of bed
14. Salary
15. Became a pensioner
17. Racket
19. English brew
20. Embrace; hug
21. Helped with dishes
24. Observed; noticed
25. Eve's mate
26. Office communications
27. Apiece: abbr.
29. Funnyman Skelton
30. Nile or Danube
31. Distant
32. Pa's mate
33. Face wrinkles
34. Actors in a play
35. Stationery
36. Loses color
37. More nasty
39. Evergreen tree
40. Foreigner
41. Cardboard boxes
45. On the sick list
46. Fill with joy
48. Actress Remick
49. — Vegas, Nev.
50. Old-fashioned
51. Ram's mate

DOWN

1. In favor of
2. Great wonder
3. Powerful explosive
4. Peeled
5. Vicinity
6. Free (of)
7. Exists
8. Ted Kennedy, for one
9. Watched secretly
10. Free ticket
11. "Yes" votes
16. News bit
18. Raw metals
20. — back, returns
21. Toasty
22. Thought
23. Flat cushion
24. At no time
26. Coal digger
27. Lessen (a pain)
28. — and crafts
30. Became mature, as fruit
31. Fashion craze
33. Division of traffic
34. Shopping wagon
35. Buckets
36. Shot (a gun)
37. Post (a letter)
38. Singer Fitzgerald
39. Destiny
41. Mouser
42. Spanish "rah"
43. Modern
44. Look at
47. Musical tone

EASY

Solution is on page 386

ACROSS

1. Strike lightly
4. Health clubs
8. Apprehends
12. Drink-cooler
13. Harbor
14. Woodwind instrument
15. Be mistaken
16. Word used in division
17. Only
18. Order
20. Volcano mouth
22. Before, to poets
23. Slide, as on ice
24. First person
26. Exchange
27. Merry
30. Cooking vessels
31. Concealed
32. Turn toward
33. Golf peg
34. Contend (with)
35. Mine finds
36. Challenge
37. Child's "pie" ingredient
38. Powerful
41. Touch lovingly
44. Prayer ending
45. Always
47. Brief sleep
48. Confined (with "up")
49. Baseball team
50. Conceit
51. Picnic pests
52. Adjusts, as a clock
53. Rodent

DOWN

1. Evened, as a score
2. Land measure
3. Penetrate and spread through
4. Backbone
5. Small body of water
6. Creative work
7. Military enclosure
8. Wanderer
9. Assist in wrongdoing
10. Dull person
11. Prophet
19. Upper limbs
21. Tear
23. Steal: slang
24. Likely
25. Female deer
26. Makes a hem
27. Lawn tender
28. Expert
29. Favorable response
32. Quartet number
34. Is able to
36. Fender flaws
37. Female horses
38. Mama's spouse
39. Prophetic sign
40. Canvas shelter
41. Penny
42. Heroic tale
43. Stain
46. Compete (for)

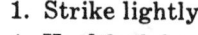

MEDIUM

Solution is on page 386

ACROSS

1. Separate with a sieve
5. Wealthy persons: British (slang)
9. Relative by marriage: hyph. wd.
11. Restricts
13. Brilliant reflection
14. Representative person or thing
16. "Height" of fashion
17. Make fit
19. Fish eggs
20. Frighten greatly
22. Early stringed instrument
23. Unctuous
24. Borsch ingredients
25. Petite
27. Rough
28. Examine carefully
29. Trading center
30. Go by
31. Morally debased
34. Circle part
35. Piebald horse
36. Tear
38. Free (a person) from pain
40. Intact
42. Fraud; lie
43. Solemn; sedate
44. Small valley
45. Compass point

DOWN

1. Sound of longing
2. Small bay
3. Sweetheart
4. Paving material
5. Sharply cold
6. Leave out
7. Bridle part
8. Tales
10. In a tired manner
11. Foliaceous
12. Insincerely suave
15. Snakelike fish
18. Pickle flavoring
21. Highways
22. Curios, antiques, etc.: var. sp.
24. Pushcarts
25. Gazed fixedly
26. Took control by force (with in)
27. Male deer
28. Practice boxing
29. French painter, Claude —
31. Formally polite
32. Search; investigation
33. Mah-jongg pieces
35. Fruit rind
37. Chic; jaunty
39. Frost, as a cake
41. By what means?

HARD

Solution is on page 386

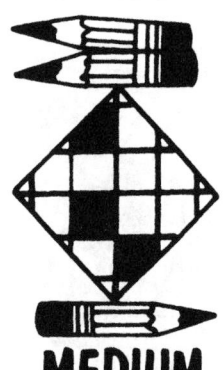

MEDIUM

ACROSS

1. Lose color
5. Equipment, as for a job
9. Big fuss
12. Candid; frank
13. Formerly
14. Crash (into)
15. Musical sign
16. Sufficient
18. Like a pinto pony
20. Citified
21. Begin
23. Tories' opponents
25. Great Lake
26. Coast
27. Depart
29. Lobe location
30. Grin
31. Possessed
32. — goodness!
33. Word with "broke" or "mason"
34. Pulley belt
35. Auditorium feature
36. Melodies
37. Super
39. Eatables
40. Means of communication
43. Kind of amphibian
46. — a girl!
47. Row of seats
48. Enormous
49. Spelling contest
50. Paradise
51. One-dish meal

DOWN

1. In favor of
2. Mimic
3. Lose hope
4. Whole
5. Prod into action
6. Conclude
7. Perfect serve
8. Need
9. Nomadic people
10. Information
11. Portent
17. Plead with
19. "— tu, Brute!": Latin (Shakespeare)
21. Appear
22. Busboy's need
23. Complain peevishly
24. Golfer's target
26. Air pollution
27. Work crew
28. At —, quarreling
30. Law
31. Publicity leaflet
33. Male deer
34. Fair stalls
35. Feel
36. Therefore
37. Spoken smoothly and easily
38. Have status
39. Boston —, house plant
41. Assist
42. Aitch preceder
44. Mature
45. Lawn moisture

Solution is on page 387

ACROSS

1. Sack
4. Texas shrine
9. Single item
12. Playing card
13. Contributor
14. Puppy's foot
15. Make an effort
17. Curtain
19. Fib
20. Trader
21. Confident expectation
24. French capital
25. Thorny flower
26. Lace trimming
27. In this way
29. Frozen water
30. Tinker Bell, for one
31. Spider's handiwork
32. All right
33. Elaborate
34. Narrow road
35. Flat-bottomed boat
36. Mommy's spouse
37. Rages
39. Uncooked
40. Blender setting
41. Heating chamber
45. Presidential nickname
46. Waken
48. Floor covering
49. Actor Beatty
50. Fragment
51. Alcott heroine

DOWN

1. Bleat
2. Perform
3. Receive
4. Let in
5. Horse's gait
6. Picnic pest
7. St. Louis' State: abbr.
8. Neat in arrangement
9. Milky gems
10. Neck part
11. Pitcher
16. Otherwise
18. Wood bar
20. Milk processing place
21. Group of three
22. Large stone
23. Employ
24. Cost
26. Snake's teeth
27. Dispatch
28. Heed (instructions)
30. Crop reapers
31. Lump
33. Transportation fee
34. Grass locale
35. Uninterested
36. Challenged
37. Bridge part
38. Toothpaste container
39. Trick
41. Mink or sable
42. Upper limb
43. Billiards stick
44. Hen product
47. Cry of surprise

Solution is on page 387

ACROSS

1. Wagers
5. — the question, proposes marriage
9. Flowback
12. Region
13. Notion
14. Female deer
15. Bound
16. Great number
17. Female sheep
18. Summon: 2 wds.
20. Rational
22. Allow
23. Stitch
24. —, re, mi
26. Expected wishfully
29. "Mary — a little lamb"
30. Pull behind
31. December 24 or 31
32. Fall behind
33. Keep away from
34. Table support
35. Strike
36. Borsch ingredients
37. Physician: abbr.
38. Took a chair
39. Skillet
40. Money for waiters
42. Oared
46. Butter serving
47. Sailors
49. Positive
50. Presidential nickname
51. Redact
52. Persia, today
53. Precious stone
54. Alaskan city
55. Bird's home

DOWN

1. Baseball clubs
2. Canal of song
3. Prom attendee
4. Seats for horsemen
5. Aviator
6. Fragrance
7. Favorite
8. Talked back to
9. Paradise
10. Retired formally: 2 wds.
11. Hive dweller
19. Nourished
21. Word of disgust
23. Droop
25. Possesses
26. Clutched
27. Catch up with and go beyond
28. Wooden nail
29. Head covering
30. Definite article
32. Illuminated
33. Dispatches to a central point: 2 wds.
35. Hurry
36. Inadequate
38. Madrid's country: abbr.
39. Adhesive
41. Account entry
42. Demure
43. Entice
44. Historic periods
45. Fender mishap
46. Sty dweller
48. Fuss

MEDIUM

Solution is on page 387

200

ACROSS

1. Lady
6. Stir up (a fire)
11. Excuse
12. Pressing
14. Even
15. — a, not any
16. You and I
18. Before: poetic
19. Girl of WWI song
21. Transgress
22. Summer theater: hyph. wd.
24. Crave
25. Noble gas
26. Burn slightly
27. Not on the right note: hyph. wd.
30. "Cherry —," rescue crane
31. — -be, intended
32. Pitcher's "no-no"
33. Facial feature
34. Secondary position: 2 wds.
38. Overhead trains
39. Stitch again
40. Payable
41. Concerning
42. Dunce
43. Baking chambers
45. Twofold
47. Leases
48. American Beauties
49. Untidy

DOWN

1. Men
2. Watchful
3. Greg Louganis, for one
4. Presidential nickname
5. Podded plant
6. Reddish-brown
7. Characteristic
8. Monster
9. Anthem writer
10. Printer's measure
13. Darting pain
17. Go in
20. Sailor's call
21. Submerged
23. Joint
24. Candle parts
26. Useful caterpillar
27. Possessor
28. Duped
29. Fret, as a baby
30. Tempo
32. Sews loosely
34. Popular girl
35. Anthony and Barbara
36. *Tias*
37. Girl's nickname
39. Steals from
42. Batman and Robin, for example
44. Neckline style
46. Noun-forming suffix

HARD

Solution is on page 387

BIBLE CROSSWORD MEDIUM

by RUSS CARLEY

Bible references in this puzzle are from the King James Version. You'll find it stimulating to solve, and may discover you know more Bible than you think you do.

ACROSS

1. The Lord called Samuel: and he answered, — am I. *I Sam. 3:4*
5. Thou shalt be dumb, and not — to speak. *Luke 1:20*
9. They are — with the showers of the mountains. *Job 24:8*
12. He shall rule them with a rod of —. *Rev. 2:27*
13. The land is, . . . fat or —. *Num. 13:20*
14. Adam and —
15. The rich man also —, and was buried. *Luke 16:22*
16. They — unto them such things as they required. *Ex. 12:36*
17. —der . . . unto Caesar the things which are Caesar's. *Matt. 22:21*
18. They . . . could — both the right hand and the left. *I Chr. 12:2*
20. The nations shall be . . . a dry land, and a —. *Jer. 50:12*
22. They —d like the colour of burnished brass. *Ezek. 1:7*
26. Thy —d and thy staff they comfort me. *Ps. 23:4*
27. He will — the one, and love the other. *Matt. 6:24*
28. Lord, I believe; help thou mine —. *Mark 9:24*
33. How long will it be — thou be quiet? *Jer. 47:6*
34. He . . . healed all that were —ck. *Matt. 8:16*
35. Le— us not into temptation. *Matt. 6:13*
36. It is high time to awake out of —ep. *Rom. 13:11*
37. They were thy —s; they traded in thy market. *Ezek. 27:17*
40. Be in rest and at —. *Jer. 46:27*
41. The Lord is —ghteous in all his ways. *Ps. 145:17*
42. Son of Kenaz
44. The — that killeth any person . . . may flee thither. *Josh. 20:3*
48. My lord . . . shall begin . . . to — and drink *Luke 12:45*
49. Son of Noah
50. The city was pure gold, like unto c— glass. *Rev. 21:18*
52. He went — the house of God. *Luke 6:4*
56. Two are better than —. *Eccl. 4:9*
57. None is so fierce that — stir him up. *Job 41:10*
58. Lord, make me to know mine end . . . that I may know how f— I am. *Ps. 39:4*
59. The — Commandments
60. Have they not —? have they not divided the prey? *Judg. 5:30*
61. Leah was tender —; but Rachel was beautiful. *Gen 29:17*

DOWN

1. There is nothing —, which shall not be manifested. *Mark 4:22*
2. —, the family of the Erites
3. Be thou like a — or a young hart. *Song 2:17*
4. They shall perish, but thou shalt —. *Ps. 102:26*
5. The four and twenty elders . . . worshipped God that sat on the throne, saying, Amen; —. *Rev. 19:4*
6. He casteth out devils through —lzebub the chief of the devils. *Luke 11:15*
7. The voice of the turtle is heard in our —. *Song 2:12*

202

8. He — into the house of God. *Matt. 12:4*
9. They — brought to Babylon. *Matt. 1:12*
10. His righteousness remaineth for —. *II Cor. 9:9*
11. Lot . . . pitched his — toward Sodom. *Gen. 13:12*
19. A— of me whatsoever thou wilt. *Mark 6:22*
21. The Song of —omon
22. Brother of 49-Across
23. Children, obey your —nts. *Eph. 6:1*
24. Give . . . these little ones a cup of cold w—. *Matt. 10:42*
25. On earth peace, good will toward m—. *Luke 2:14*
29. The people . . . — the wall, to throw it down. *II Sam. 20:15*
30. The prophet —ah . . . prayed. *II Chr. 32:20*
31. I will only, without doing anything —, go. *Num. 20:19*
32. He shall not — quietness in his belly. *Job 20:20*

34. They . . . shall . . . burn the weapons, both the — and the bucklers. *Ezek. 39:9*
38. Ye shall — for sorrow of heart. *Isa. 65:14*
39. — man can serve two masters. *Matt. 6:24*
40. Be perfect and —, wanting nothing. *James 1:4*
43. The kingdom of heaven is at —nd. *Matt. 3:2*
44. He — an arrow. *I Sam. 20:36*
45. Go out quickly into the streets and —s of the city. *Luke 14:21*
46. Let all the people say, —. Praise ye the Lord. *Ps. 106:48*
47. They neither sow nor —. *Luke 12:24*
51. Blessed — the pure in heart. *Matt. 5:8*
53. Let your yea be yea; and your —, nay. *James 5:12*
54. Bind them . . . and — them about thy neck. *Prov. 6:21*
55. I am an — man, and my wife well stricken in years. *Luke 1:18*

Solution is on page 387

203

MOVIE-TV CROSSWORD

by MYRTLE BAZEMORE

ACROSS

1. Chili maker on TV's *Alice*
4. *— Door*, Katharine Hepburn movie
9. Amid
14. Actress Gardner
15. *— Thy Father*, 1971 TV movie
16. Thin cookie
17. Actor, Robert —
19. *The — To Singapore*, Hope/Crosby movie
21. Old Dominion State: abbr.
22. *Bells — Ringing*, Judy Holliday movie
23. *— in the Dark*, Ginger Rogers and Ray Milland movie
24. Cozy room
25. *The Cat from Outer —*, Sandy Duncan movie
28. *The Hired —*, Peter Fonda movie
29. Actor Reynolds
30. Game show, *What's My —?*
31. Movie starring Steve McQueen, *The — Pebbles*
32. Connection
33. Actress Claire
34. Actress Minnelli
35. Primetime soap opera
38. Actress Olivia — Havilland
39. *— the High Country*, 1962 Joel McCrea/Randolph Scott movie
40. *The — of the Roman Empire*
41. *— Big*, Jane Wyman movie
42. *— from Alcatraz*, Clint Eastwood film
44. *I Love Lucy* star
45. TV's *One Day At a Time* mom
46. *— Girl Friday*, Cary Grant/Rosalind Russell movie
47. Golfer's shout
48. Legal claim
49. *Charlie — at the Opera*
51. TV's *The Man — U.N.C.L.E.*
52. Wed
53. *Cat on a — Tin Roof*, Elizabeth Taylor/Paul Newman movie
54. *— Me in St. Louis*, Judy Garland film
55. Actor Dailey

56. *— Happened One Night*, Gable/Colbert movie
57. *Boys —*, Spencer Tracy movie
58. Tony — of 20-Down
62. Of punishment
64. Lively TV performer
66. Charlotte —, TV's Mrs. Garrett
67. Skier's delight
68. "Four-bagger"
69. *— Minute Warning*, Charlton Heston movie

DOWN

1. Spoil
2. Actress Arden
3. Youth
4. Singer, Dinah —
5. Ripped
6. *Kate — Allie*, TV comedy
7. *— West*, Marx Brothers film
8. *The — Boy*, Jerry Lewis movie
9. *Since You Went —*, Claudette Colbert movie
10. *Diary of a — Housewife*, 1970 movie
11. *— Mice and Men*, Lon Chaney, Jr. movie
12. *— Say Goodbye*, Rock Hudson film
13. TV's *Lou —*
18. *— the Nation*
20. TV's *The — Couple*
23. Actress Turner
24. 1971 Dennis Weaver TV movie
25. Playground sight
26. Evergreen trees
27. Collection of sayings
28. Vapor of fog
29. Comedian Cosby
31. *The Other — of the Mountain*, 1975 movie
32. *Walking —*, 1973 movie
34. Hot — Houlihan, *M*A*S*H* role
35. Cowgirl Evans
36. Ed — of 13-Down
37. *The — and Cher Show*

39. *Singin' in the* —, Debbie Reynolds movie
40. *The Egg and I* setting
43. Informal talk
44. Cowboy's footwear
45. On the —, broadcasting
47. Gene Hackman movie, *The — Connection*
48. *This — Is Mine*, Charles Laughton movie
49. Estrada's TV show
50. James Brolin's series
51. *Never So* —, Sinatra movie

52. Estate
54. Burrowing animal
55. Venture upon
57. — *Roots*, Van Heflin film
58. Los Angeles footballer
59. Actor Carney
60. *I Am the* —, Edward G. Robinson movie
61. Bowery Boy Gorcey
63. — *Man of Her Own*, Gable/ Lombard movie
65. *Gung* —*!*, 1943 movie

Solution is on page 387

ACROSS

1. Beach tents
8. "Aida," for one
13. Play the "ham"
14. Sturdy material
15. California city
16. Rub out
17. Certain electrical flow: abbr.
18. Whets
20. Decade number
21. Dorothy's State: abbr.
24. — up, accelerate
25. River curve
26. Decree
28. Prophet
30. Helicopter parts
32. Snoozes
36. Layer
38. Madame Curie
39. Track circuits
42. The: Spanish
44. Harpo —
45. Doctor's organization: abbr.
46. Identical duplicate
48. By
49. Great vigor
51. Change regions, as birds
54. Senator Kefauver
55. Shoulder ornament
56. Prepare
57. Ripe tomato quality

DOWN

1. Joint signer
2. Alligator pear
3. Fourposter
4. Exist
5. Poet, Ogden —
6. Stage player
7. Removes peach pits
8. Lyric poems
9. For each
10. Maternal relation
11. Up and about
12. Correct
19. Nights before
22. Young insect
23. Edinburgh natives
25. Minnowlike fish
27. Three: prefix
29. Shade tree
31. Vend
33. Historic period
34. Freebooters
35. Groups of six
37. Boarder
39. Aged beer
40. Entertain
41. *Trattoria* dish
43. Wading bird
46. Homey
47. Mild oath
50. Actor Knight
52. Operate
53. Pub order

Solution is on page 388

ACROSS

1. Received
4. Backbone
9. Compass point
12. Fruit drink
13. Pavarotti's voice
14. Crusted dessert
15. Winter, summer, etc.
17. No longer together
19. Overhead trains
20. Consumer
21. Gleem
24. Tennis shoe
27. Harbor
28. Lions' dens
29. USA's smallest: abbr.
30. Dined
31. Tracks down
32. — and reel
33. Concerning
34. Peels
35. Conceal
36. Baby who naps a lot
38. Aspects
39. Licks up
40. Allow
41. Coastline
43. Sneaky persons
47. Apple seed
48. Of the fleet
50. Singer, Peggy —
51. Mimic
52. Breaks (off) suddenly
53. Cut the grass

DOWN

1. Car fuel

2. Lyric poem
3. Pekoe, for one
4. Shoulder wrap
5. Ballpoint items
6. — and outs
7. Negative vote
8. Chalkboard needs
9. Glowing bit of fire
10. Knight's title
11. Sopping
16. Dispatched
18. Pod vegetables
20. Divisions of troops
21. WAVE's sisters
22. Traveler's stop
23. Make angry
24. More rational
25. Wear away slowly

26. Motor trips
28. Entices
31. Occurs
32. Free (of)
34. Alligator —, avocado
35. Smacks
37. Wed in secret
38. Glues shut
40. Jump, frog style
41. Health resort
42. Word repeated before "hurray!"
43. Charleston's State: abbr.
44. Shade tree
45. Durocher of baseball
46. Stitch
49. One

EASY

Solution is on page 388

SHANEANIGANS   HARD

by TED SHANE

You'll find zany definitions in this crossword by Ted Shane, so please look out for traps. For example, the definition for 6-Down is "Dogie circuses" and the answer is RODEOS. The clues are sly, so be careful.

Solution is on page 388.

ACROSS

1. Ah! the memory of sliding down a banister!
7. Wheel that is already oiled
13. Plant that says, "I yam what I yam."
14. This is what you get in a drug store
15. Every day is Sun-day to this Egyptian god
16. 14 lbs. of ambulating joy, has his ups and downs, is highly prized by parents
18. Where to stay during Miami hurricanes
19. Never say the backyard of a ship, say this
21. Absolutely positively has to have
22. Put this in backwards to come out on top
23. 'Tain't fur
25. A word to test your metal
26. What to do with Aunt Millie's hand-made birthday gift monstrosities
27. Woes by any other name
29. What it did for the Weathermen's picnic
31. Go for a sidetrip on the Road of Truth
32. His Latin name is *Rattus Rattus* Forget all that and the cattus
33. Girls who are dyeing to meet Mr. Right and often blush to the dark roots of their hair
36. . . . *to be continued in our next* . . .
39. What Mrs. Snootysnooz puts on for public occasions
40. Big hole in a coat
42. Likewise ditto
43. Short streets
44. Indoor aviators

46. Cooperative Union of Vegetarians (they have no meat-ing place)
47. With N this is explosive
48. Technicolored sparrows
50. The end of the racecourse
51. The all-over-America typical football team
53. How did the tightrope walker educate her daughter? She —
55. Baker's bailiwick
56. You won't get this one without strain

DOWN

1. March-to-June: past tense
2. Lazy baker
3. Tag a fellow and he's this
4. What you'd find in a velfry
5. noitnetta yaP
6. Dogie circuses
7. What it is in Argentina when it's hot here
8. My, but they're ashamed of their descendants!
9. Father: 1890 etiquette
10. Thanks, old chap!
11. At ease, in a $5-word way
12. What everything is for the apartment seeker
17. Common German article
20. Stitch-in-time guys
22. Chief who had the car and city named for him
24. What the careless driver fell asleep at in the 1880's

26. People who tell you they can live on their incomes in these inflationary times
28. What the contented male is well
30. If he is and she is, too, they —
33. Re-juices a roast
34. Kind of Brown Jug
35. What the old salt called his daughter Sal
36. Fishes that melt in your mouth

37. Causes a crinkle in malar regions
38. These always get the first prise
41. Playground in South America
44. Fuss fuss fuss fuss fuss
45. EXTRA! MAN IN BUS OFFERS ONE TO WOMAN! WOMAN FAINTS!
48. Eggibus romanus
49. Another kind of prise
52. This is almost the end
54. This is The End: abbr.

ACROSS

1. Gloomy; not cheerful
6. Friars
11. Citrus fruit
12. Happenings
14. Work on the lawn
15. Fixed portion
16. Oil-drilling devices
17. Word with "file" or "polish"
19. Vocalist's syllable
20. Compass point
21. Strike forcefully: slang
22. Commotion
23. Vanish
24. Strong metal
25. Glaring
27. Bubbles
28. Baronets' wives
29. Narrow valley
30. Eye part
31. Endure
32. Economists' barometer: abbr.
35. Total: abbr.
36. "Who's — sleeping in my bed?"
37. Buckeye State
38. More tidy
40. Japanese garment
42. Vincent van Gogh, for one
43. Classroom item
44. Religious groups
45. Bakery products

DOWN

1. Very intelligent type
2. At —, free
3. Concludes
4. Mature
5. Ted, of the Senate
6. Deserve
7. Like an egg
8. Tennis need
9. Made, as a sweater
10. Tales
11. Cruel man
13. Growl fiercely
18. Pub order
21. Excludes
22. Mr. Laurel
23. Charges
24. Prophet
25. They till the soil
26. Copy
27. Covering
28. Miss Ross
29. Command to a horse
31. Convy and Parks
32. Phantom
33. Dressed to the —, decked out
34. Below average
36. Most suitable
37. Mr. Sharif
39. Twitch
41. A Gershwin

MEDIUM

Solution is on page 388

ACROSS

1. Paving material
4. Roles
9. Be nosy
12. Actress MacGraw
13. Idolize
14. Caviar base
15. At no time
17. Voting tickets
19. Hearing organs
21. Scheme
22. Cardboard containers
25. Stalks
28. Actor Pacino
29. Insect's bite
31. Glasgow native
32. Tear
34. Hockey or baseball
36. Foot digit
37. Semester or quarter
39. Group of bees
41. Compass reading
42. See 9-Across
44. Smudged
46. Pasture sounds
48. Rational
49. Sparkle, as a star
52. Male choir voice
55. Existed
56. Large bird
58. Attempt
59. Small bill
60. Rose from a chair
61. View

DOWN

1. Light-brown
2. Tavern order
3. Nile or Amazon —
4. Colorful tropical birds
5. Commercial
6. Actor Lowe
7. Snare
8. Vends
9. Shield from harm
10. Decay
11. Affirmative word
16. Has lunch
18. Building sites
20. Cuts with scissors
22. Horse-drawn vehicles
23. E.T., for one
24. Winter weather events
26. Bullwinkle, for one
27. Knight's horse
30. Metric weight units
33. Vow
35. Picked up the tab
38. Earth's satellite
40. Lion's neck hair
43. Prods
45. Leases
47. Thin strip
49. Couple
50. Pale
51. The self
53. Metal source
54. Deli bread
57. — and behold!

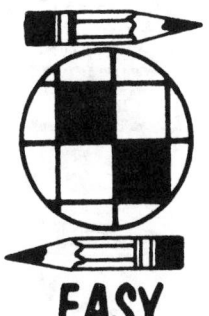

EASY

Solution is on page 388

ACROSS

1. Car fuel
4. Pierces with a dagger
9. Play a role
12. Music or poetry, for example
13. Traveler's "home"
14. Female deer
15. Small, round vegetable
16. Single
17. Wear away
19. Allows
21. Traps
22. Chimes
24. Sign of achievement
25. Mine deposits
26. North and South —, earth's axes
27. Raleigh's State: abbr.
29. Help
30. More rational
31. Zodiac sign
32. Compass point
33. Stories
34. Greenish-yellow fruit
35. Surfaces, as on a cube
36. Adhesive
37. High-spirited horses
39. Lubricates
40. Clean a slate
41. First woman
42. Aged
45. Ignited
46. At no time
48. Neither's "partner"
49. — Angeles
50. Heavenly bodies
51. Pigpen

DOWN

1. Vacant place
2. Common verb
3. Stopped by malfunction
4. Vaccinations
5. 2,000-lb. units
6. Dined
7. "Let It —," Beatles tune
8. Slim
9. Love greatly
10. Secret language
11. Golf pegs
18. Cloths for cleaning
20. Overhead railways
21. Shopping specials
22. Fur scarfs
23. Great Lake
24. What Fido buries
26. Turns ashen
27. Tidy
28. Apple center
30. Makes unhappy
31. Courses of instruction
33. Evens, as a score
34. Buddy
35. Chairs, for example
36. Docks
37. Exchange for money
38. Threesome
39. Finished
41. Miss Gabor
43. Abraham's nephew
44. Arid
47. 1982 Spielberg film, for short

EASY

Solution is on page 388

ACROSS

1. Professional penman
7. Boutiques
12. Victory wreath
13. Maker of garments
15. Existing naturally
16. Refer indirectly
17. Direct (a ship)
18. Bride's garb
20. Singer Davis
21. Lock opener
22. Caution
23. Record electronically
24. Goodbye: British
25. Nigerian seaport
26. Hit
29. Arm muscle
30. Unpolished
31. He played Batman
32. Ready
33. Type
34. Prefix meaning "wrong"
37. Fitting
38. Greek portico
39. Art —, 1920's and 30's style
40. Luxurious: slang
42. Zodiac sign
44. Continuing story
45. Stir up
46. Twilled fabric
47. Hunting dog

DOWN

1. Slippery
2. Narrow boat
3. Flowing too freely
4. Asian country
5. Casino transaction
6. Raise
7. Spot
8. Vestibule
9. Lubricate
10. Bird's feathers
11. Soft drink: 2 wds.
14. Rest period
19. Notable time period
22. Ship's trail
23. Diplomatic asset
24. Ocean rhythm
25. Shopper's need
26. Orts
27. Certain base hits
28. Breach
29. Scolds
31. Pay court to
33. Fashion
34. Deserve
35. Sharp, as a pain
36. Defeated one
38. Carpet type
39. Conduit; outlet
41. Poitier movie, "To —, with Love"
43. Chopping tool

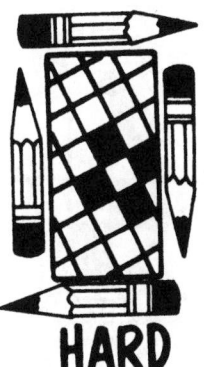

HARD

Solution is on page 389

ACROSS

1. Procedure
4. Jet
9. Flock member
12. Bard's "before"
13. Print-shop stock
14. Fun-loving
15. Of teeth
17. What some earrings do
19. Bauxite, etc.
21. Office furniture
22. Neglects
25. Keats' output
27. Domicile
28. Milk bottles' successors
32. Sign of freshness
33. Goal
34. Luau souvenir
35. Shock
38. Clip (wool)
40. A Berlin
41. Cite
42. "Lift"
45. Word with "Honor" or "Highness"
47. Secreted
49. Languished
53. Number from "A Chorus Line"
54. No way!
56. Before now
57. Prison: slang
58. Rock-and-roll dance
59. Caldron

DOWN

1. Week member: abbr.
2. Have being
3. Hankering
4. Not crowded
5. Ashen
6. Raise (the ante)
7. Florid
8. Merchant
9. Soufflé base
10. One way to get on base
11. Orbs, to a poet
16. Blabbed
18. Vireo's retreat
20. "High —," 1956 film
22. Fleeting fashions
23. Aid in crime
24. Minnesota's neighbor
26. Aswan, for one
29. A shortening
30. Shipshape
31. Paddock papa
33. Pacino and Jolson
36. Perused
37. Knack
38. Whipper-snapper
39. Pitch, in baseball talk
42. Boutique
43. Fork prong
44. Utopia
46. Is beholden to
48. Original
50. Spigot
51. Self-esteem
52. Stipple
55. Six, in old Rome

MEDIUM

Solution is on page 389

ACROSS

1. Busy insect
4. Permit
9. Body of water
12. Paddle
13. Keyboard instrument
14. Fryer
15. Seized firmly
17. Bird's perch
19. Exchanged for money
20. Dress parts
21. Seasoning
23. Erected
24. Long and slender
25. Cent
26. Ma's mate
28. Hen product
29. Loud, metallic sound
30. Ungentle-manly person
31. Dover's State: abbr.
32. Suspicious, as a character
33. Dull sound
34. Scottish families
35. Seethes; churns
36. Chef's garments
38. Fuel for a locomotive
39. Muscular strength
40. Birthday-cake items
43. Great number
44. Marry secretly
46. Actress Gabor
47. Compass reading
48. Alleys
49. Garden moisture

DOWN

1. Small marsh
2. Hearing organ
3. Deleting, as pencil marks
4. Red fruit
5. Fibbed
6. Youth
7. Switch setting
8. Toiling
9. Baseball or soccer
10. "— of Eden," Steinbeck novel
11. Picnic visitors
16. Foot garment
18. Greasy
20. Bright and cheerful
21. Snow vehicle
22. Book part
23. String of —, necklace
25. Schemes
26. Patriot Revere
27. Totals (up)
29. Television-set selection
30. Made cool
32. Road sign
33. Amphibian
34. Shipping box
35. Dog's treats
36. Skilled
37. Paid athletes, for short
38. Superman's garment
40. Against
41. First woman
42. Viewed
45. New Orleans' State: abbr.

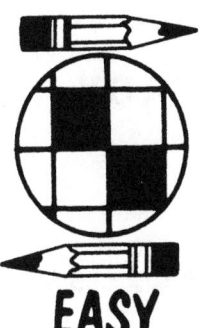

EASY

Solution is on page 389

JUMBO CROSSWORD

EASY

ACROSS

1. Apple's center
5. Among
9. Stretch across
13. Milky gem
14. VIP's car, usually
15. — Polo, traveler
16. Clergyman: abbr.
17. Sink
18. "On the ball"
19. Boxing-match sites
21. Domesticate
23. Look at
24. Country roads
25. Destiny
26. Mrs. Truman
27. Formal argument
29. Be victorious
30. Sedan, for one
33. Coal deposit
34. Snowy season
37. Keys, at times
39. Place for a glove
40. Richmond's State: abbr.
41. Rely (on)
42. Finished
43. Favorite
44. Have a snack
45. Penny
46. Botch (up)
47. Hit, as a fly
49. Wharf
50. Enemy
51. Feed-bag morsel
52. — shirt, pullover
53. More drab
56. Public notice
57. Plane's takeoff
59. Accomplish

60. Say aloud, as a poem
62. Sofa supports
63. Vigor; energy
64. Smallest bill
65. Upon
66. Lion's hair
67. Do an office task
69. Song for two
70. Punch: slang
71. Plus
72. Dictionary entry
73. Wooded area
76. Certain tag-player
77. Peru's capital
78. Fed, as the lawn
79. Find
81. Use soap and water
82. Avenues: abbr.
83. Volcanic lava
84. Jimmy or Nell
86. Excludes
88. School semester
89. Actors' parts
93. Not at home
94. Lounge about
95. Be careful (of)
96. Idolize
98. Rescued
100. Light brown
101. Disturbs the peace
102. A Great Lake
103. Fewer
104. Male heirs
105. Like the ocean
106. Birch or oak

DOWN

1. It forms reefs
2. "Carmen" or "Aida"
3. Large crow
4. — Paso, Texas
5. Woe is me!
6. Wrong: prefix
7. Mimic
8. Give
9. Mr. Mineo
10. Gift
11. Land measures
12. Memos
15. Miss West
17. Boiler-room, often
20. A Beatty
22. Part of us
25. Devotees

26. Tie together
28. Canary, for one
29. Chablis or rosé
30. Haddock's "cousin"
31. See 7-Down
32. Echo
34. Desire
35. Pre-holiday times
36. Rodents
38. Tidy
39. Goose's cry
42. Adorned
43. Rind
45. Soft drink
46. Burrowing creature
47. Fly high
48. Walk through water
49. "Dummy": slang
50. Mink and ermine
52. Baseball's Rose
53. Place for rubbish
54. Paradise
55. Lariat
57. Eat in style
58. Jog
61. Very chilly
63. Scholarly essays
65. Nimbus
66. Greater in number
67. Be unsuccessful
68. Concerned with
69. The Capitol has one
70. Pestered
72. In support of
73. Speedy
74. Harden, as cement
75. Football plays: abbr.
77. Girl
78. Toasty
80. Comic strip
81. Armed conflict
84. Stopped
85. Propel, as a boat
86. Wild hogs
87. Of sound: prefix
88. Fro's "partner"
90. After some time
91. Rub out
92. Hearing or sight
94. Mr. Brown, of music
95. Car-horn's sound
97. Privileges: abbr.
99. Compete (for)
103. Naval officer: abbr.

Solution is on page 389

HARD

ACROSS

1. Miss Davis
6. Western-saga novelist, Zane —
10. Fodder housing
14. Light amplifier
19. Constellation
20. At any —, anyway
21. Boast
22. Marry secretly
23. North Dakota city
24. Shakespeare's river
25. Wander about
26. Used an adhesive
27. Famous composer
29. Number
30. Like some theaters
31. More confident
32. W.C. Fields' nemesis: 2 wds.
34. Big Apple avenue
37. Remedy
38. Garden
39. Inlet
42. Concur
43. Word with "Coast" or "tower"
45. Cornelia — Skinner
46. Poet
47. Partiality
48. Petite
49. Blockhead: slang
50. Gave up, as by treaty
51. Tree
52. Rock Hudson-Elizabeth Taylor film classic
53. Baseballer Rose
54. Esoteric
55. Scraps
57. Distance runner
58. Fitted out
59. "The Razor's —"
60. Distinction
61. Boat bottom
62. Plantlike animal
65. Lebanon port
66. Vaned water pump
70. Throngs
71. Kiln, for one
72. Discoveries
73. River: Spanish
74. Mete out
75. Coal, gas, or wood
76. Line dance
77. Rosalind Russell vehicle
78. Fashion designer
79. Lichen
80. Fetches balls
81. Heads
82. Long period of time
83. Lady: Spanish
84. Signet
85. Gleason's TV pal and family
87. Abrasive material
89. Became ashen
90. Contracted, as from heat
93. Fastener
94. — State, nickname of Kansas
98. "How — you!," exclamation of disappointment
99. Bottle stopper
100. Depend (on)
101. Texas shrine
102. Relish-tray item
103. Before: prefix
104. As well
105. Becomes weary
106. Choir voice
107. Pod "residents"
108. Valley
109. Follow

DOWN

1. Failure: slang
2. Sandusky's lake
3. Prong
4. Feet: slang
5. Thrill; make eager
6. Idol: 2 wds.
7. Wild talker
8. Certain jacket
9. Hankering
10. Pharaoh's writer
11. Humorous sarcasm
12. Billet-doux: 2 wds.
13. Be in debt
14. Caesar's army
15. Passageway
16. Vinegary
17. Sword
18. Comedian Foxx
28. Gold: Spanish
29. None
30. Very: French
32. Singer Ives
33. Blue-pencil
34. Woman's name
35. Spry
36. Serious play
37. Revolver inventor
39. Detection device
40. Miss Dunne
41. Stated further
44. Closed trucks
45. External
46. Make quiet
48. Scorches
49. Casaba
50. Beliefs
52. Early Sally Field role
53. Nut pine
54. Meeting list
56. Hawker
57. Paragon
60. Allergic disorder
61. California National Park: 2 wds.
62. Bounty of 51-Across
63. Salk's conquest
64. Synthetic fiber
65. The March King's instrument

66. Annex
67. Incensed
68. English sailor: slang
69. Loamy deposit
72. Young horse
75. Doting
76. Carbonize
77. Stringed instrument

79. Religious man
80. Search for
81. Bishop, e.g.
83. Temper
84. Wheel parts
86. Presidential-candidate Landon
87. Artillery volley
88. Main artery
89. Beat

90. Highlander
91. Orifice
92. Downfall
94. What 56-Down and others do
95. Armed conflicts
96. Ostrichlike bird
97. American Beauty, for example
99. Beret
100. Newspaper: slang

Solution is on page 389

SPECIAL CHALLENGER CROSSWORD

"THINK TWICE"   **by JOHN GREENMAN**

Here is a real toughie for you. We have omitted giving you such helps as "2 wds.," "hyph. wd.," and "slang"; but in the spirit of fair play, all abbreviations and foreign words are so indicated.

ACROSS

1. Argued in court
5. Wild plum
9. Old Greek coins
14. Acknowledge
19. Neighbor of Sparks
20. TV wagonmaster, — Bond
21. French composer
22. Cacophony
23. Indic language
24. Within: prefix
25. Barge (in)
26. "Suckers"
27. "Egghead"
30. Bull fiddle
32. Grommets
33. "Lucky Jim" author
35. Indisposed
36. Road-sign letter
37. Positive attribute
39. Bearing
44. Flat fish
47. Bawled
48. Victory: German
49. Billiards game
50. Indian unit of weight
51. Twenty-dollar gold piece
53. Lounge
54. "Ponch" on "CHiPs"
55. Weasels: abbr.
56. Deservedly
57. Sticks, of a sort
58. Illicit fee
60. "Common Sense" man
62. Dally
63. Compass point
64. Cinema twofer
68. Initials seen on Virgin Gorda
71. Excavated
72. Carries on
73. Hawked
75. "Thou liest in Abraham's — ..."
78. TLC dispenser
79. Prophetic sign
81. Seine tributary
82. Words to Brutus: Latin
83. Mole, per Le Carré
86. Colorado Indians
87. Jewish holiday eve
88. Mild oath
89. Stuck in mud
90. 20th-century French composer
91. Actress Gena
93. "Canned"
94. Any whatever
95. *Automne* preceder
96. Parched
97. So-called
101. Social foursome
106. Quickstep
109. Uncertain
110. Ellipsoids
112. Others: Latin
113. Egyptian deity
114. Herringlike fish
115. "No" or "yes" emphasis
116. Patella reflex site
117. "— all sing like ..."
118. Actor Buchholz
119. Turn inside out
120. Backtalk
121. Swiss painter

DOWN

1. Nice Nelly
2. Composer Anderson
3. Provide (with)
4. Delayed reaction
5. Confectionery
6. Comes in at JFK
7. Priest's calendar
8. Esau's land
9. Carbohydrate: suffix
10. Highwayman
11. Klemperer namesakes
12. Place; stead
13. Slav
14. Seraphim
15. Diamond feat
16. Thousands: Italian
17. The Hebrides, e.g.: abbr.
18. Polanski film
28. Injured: French
29. Atelier tripod
31. Belgian city
34. Cyrus the Great, e.g.
37. Cuckoopint plant
38. Blood relatives
39. Pooh's pal
40. Count (on)
41. End of mariner's third watch
42. A Porter
43. Building wings
44. Violin virtuoso
45. Sacred text of Islam
46. Similar
47. Ionian Island
48. Spa feature, usually
51. Setting for car heater
52. Sedgwick and Adams
57. Sorority member, e.g.
59. Teak substitute, sometimes
60. Punitory
61. Rearward

62. Counter-reformation site
65. German physicist and family
66. Ewes' young
67. Topple
68. A potherb
69. West German river
70. That is: Latin
71. Big four-posters
74. Gibberish
75. Taproom draft
76. Another: Spanish

77. Ragout
78. State of mind
79. Grimm character
80. Old-time reward
83. Gift recipient
84. Arabian potentate
85. Bruited (about)
90. "*Winnie- — -Pu*"
92. Finally
93. Insect antenna
94. Cohorts
96. Long, hard look
97. "— Irish Rose"

98. Hebrew letter
99. Play a role
100. Compact
101. Rush
102. Nero's accomplice in crime
103. Military manpower: abbr.
104. Give medicine to
105. Tel —
107. Robles
108. Forearm bone
111. Lay a table, e.g.

Solution is on page 390

221

DIAGRAMLESS   MEDIUM

This Diagramless is 15 boxes wide by 15 boxes deep.

ACROSS

1. Track circuit
4. Sleeveless garment
5. Possesses
8. H_2O
9. Missing
10. Peeled
11. Dangerous
12. Lid
13. Pennies
14. Utilize
15. Stories
16. Takes a break
19. Moslem sacred book
20. Native environment
22. Dieter's meal
23. Trials
27. Penalized monetarily
28. Also
29. Chain parts
30. Rancher's mark
32. Suspends
33. Signal light
34. Assistant
35. Speak in public
36. Mr.'s mate: abbr.
37. Walk in water
38. Needle hole

DOWN

1. At a future date
2. Mimicked
3. For each
4. Feel concern
5. Party givers
6. Inquires
7. Pigpen
8. Signals with the hand
9. Flaxen cloth
10. Work as a model
11. Narrate
12. Mongrel
13. Gem weight
15. Small child
17. Expresses gratitude
18. Comic, Soupy —
19. Young goat
21. Faulty
22. Burn slightly
24. Look steadily
25. Quality of sound
26. Turf
27. Locates
29. Den
30. Ice skate part
31. Proportion
32. Sandwich meat
33. Noisy quarrel
35. Be in debt to

Solution is on page 390

1 2 3

DIAGRAMLESS

MEDIUM

This Diagramless is 15 boxes wide by 15 boxes deep.
Starting box is on page 393.

ACROSS

1. Cease
5. Implore
8. Molten rock
9. Draft animals
11. So be it!
12. Ceremonial acts
14. Tepees
16. Favorite
17. Established
19. Hoards
21. Snare
23. Cover
24. By way of
25. Word with "bath" or "iron"
27. Half a quart
28. Foot digit
29. Youth
31. Behave
32. Unfeeling
33. Concise
35. Plus
36. "Whether you like it or —"
37. Keep a — on, restrain
39. Precipitous
41. Understand
42. Possessive pronoun
43. Cupolas
47. Indy-500 contestant
49. Uncommon
50. Ripped
51. A Great Lake
52. Was victorious
53. Transmit

DOWN

1. Wooden strip
2. Docile
3. Baker's need
4. Trousers
5. Tiresome ones
6. Actor's departure
7. Obtain
10. Cozy place
13. Public employment
15. Like peanuts and pretzels, usually
16. Bicycle feature
18. Contaminate
20. Compete
22. — on the back, compliment
25. Enlistee
26. Gymnast's item
27. Used an adhesive
28. Musical sounds
30. Fender mishaps
32. Elevator cage
34. Caviar
38. Tidy
39. Warning device
40. Skin openings
42. Protagonist
44. Grown-up filly
45. Ireland, poetically
46. Do a gardening task
48. Farm animal

Solution is on page 390

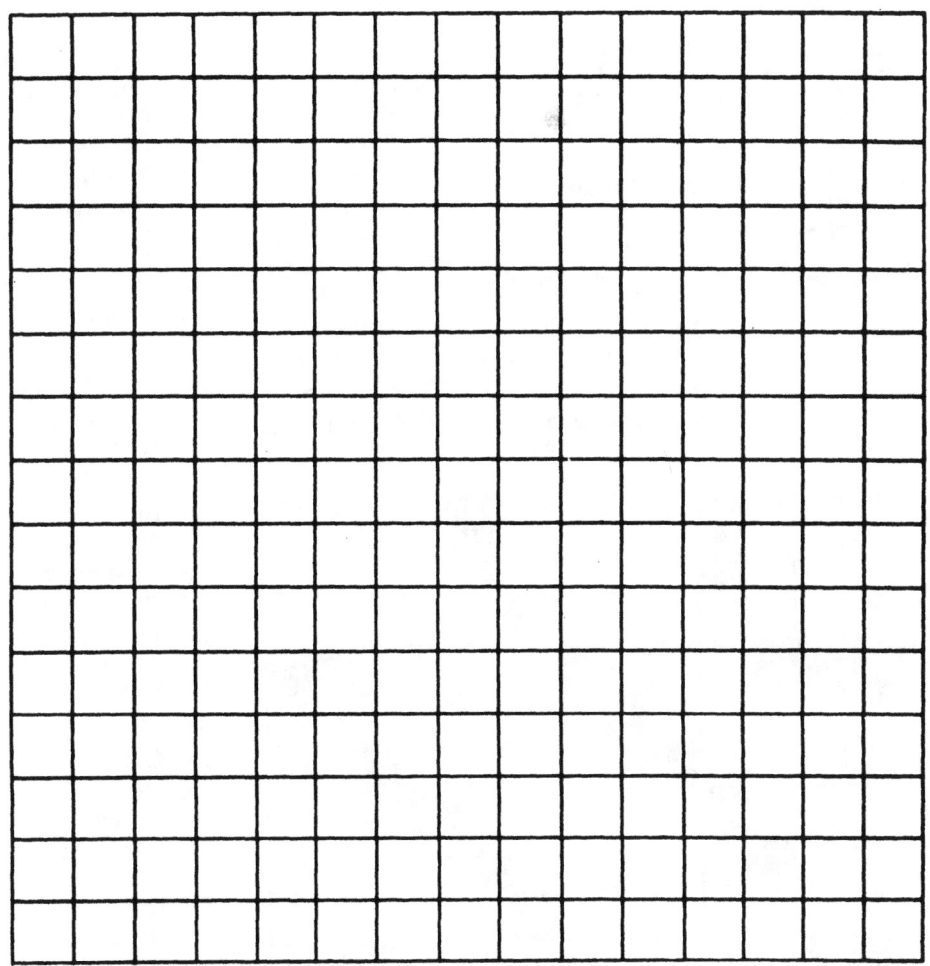

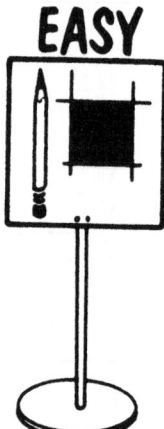

EASY

ACROSS

1. Shea Stadium player
4. Abel's brother
8. Pack too full
12. Actress Gardner
13. Aware of: slang
14. "Jeanie with the Light Brown —"
15. Mom and Dad
17. Couples
18. "Victory" letter
19. "Sawbucks"
20. Social engagements
23. Make believe
26. Biblical garden
27. Supper, etc.
28. Hawkeye State: abbr.
29. Edgar Allan —
30. Canary treats
31. That girl
32. Either . . . —
33. Prolonged look
34. Confront
35. Holders for pekoe, etc.
37. Zoo compartments
38. Buddies
39. Young boy
40. Avoid
42. Nabs and puts into jail
46. Uncommon
47. Piggy-bank opening
48. Crusted dessert
49. Picnic pests
50. Farm crop
51. Opposite of "nay'

DOWN

1. Road guide
2. Actress Gabor
3. Paving stuff
4. Ice-cream holders
5. Poker stake
6. That thing's
7. Negative vote
8. Sings, as a rabbi
9. Salary boost
10. Ventilate
11. Married woman's title: abbr.
16. Level; flat
17. Pares
19. Swap
20. Bus station
21. Worship
22. Golf peg
23. Squints (at)
24. Sister's daughter
25. Challenges
27. Pork, veal, etc.
30. Fur shoulder wrap
31. Witch
33. Shovels' kin
34. Lose color
36. No longer together
37. Supermarket vehicles
39. Jog
40. Historical age
41. Actor Johnson
42. Mobile's State: abbr.
43. Secret agent
44. Gift for Dad
45. Ocean
47. Thus

Solution is on page 390

226

ACROSS

1. Passing fancy
4. Festive
8. Planter's need
12. Frost, as a cake
13. Desertlike
14. Frolic
15. Akin (to)
17. Grind into shreds
18. Notion
19. Stubborn courage; pluck
20. Covers with asphalt
22. Volcanic pits
25. Has a debt
26. Racket
27. Exclamation of pleasure
28. Armed conflict
29. Mends, as socks
30. Falsehood
31. Oral pause
32. "Thin" coins
33. Manufactured
34. Get back
36. Foremost
37. Lyric poems
38. Warble
39. Explosive sounds
41. Competitive event
44. Border
45. First-rate: 2 wds.
46. Visualize
47. Well-behaved
48. Throw
49. Light brown

DOWN

1. Evergreen tree
2. High card
3. Bring
4. Fence openings
5. Region
6. Pot's cover
7. TV commercial
8. Elf
9. Make happy
10. Have lunch
11. Coloring agent
16. Fruit drinks
17. Lawn covering
19. Broad smiles
20. Might; force
21. Informed (of)
22. Kitchen device
23. Hostile attacks
24. Percale item
26. Tom, Dick and Harry
29. Plunges into water
30. Biggest
32. Avoided
33. Candy flavor
35. African river
36. Speeding penalties
38. Male heirs
39. Plead
40. Big fuss
41. Dove's call
42. Ocean
43. Decade number
45. Attending

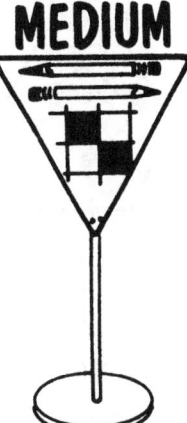

MEDIUM

Solution is on page 390

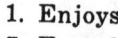

HARD

ACROSS

1. Enjoys
7. Erstwhile European leader
13. Utilize
14. Tempt
15. News organization: abbr.
16. Obscures
18. Exclamation
19. Wheel nut
21. Moon goddess
22. Ad —: Latin
23. Ms. Fitzgerald
25. Seaman's response
26. Milton, for one
27. Muffle
29. Compulsion
31. Sea: French
32. But: Latin
33. Skiing areas
36. Stupifies
39. Describe flatteringly
40. Pub drink
42. Actress, Loretta'—
43. Wilder's "— Town"
44. Drudge
46. Compass direction: abbr.
47. Four, to Cato
48. Evokes
50. From: French
51. Greek isle resident
53. Glossy, opaque substance
55. Composed
56. Woodland deities

DOWN

1. Secured, in a way
2. Medication container
3. Agnew, once: abbr.
4. Aged
5. Highway
6. Damascus native
7. Wailed: Irish
8. Held or Moffo
9. Common contraction
10. Yes: Spanish
11. Repeats
12. Responds
17. Actress Francis
20. Alluring aura
22. Dancing party
24. Skilled
26. Fourth estate
28. Sooner than: poetic
30. Put into action
33. Imperturbable ones
34. Parisian attraction
35. Briny
36. Groups
37. Flammable material
38. Inures
41. Resin
44. Strip of wood
45. Sicilian volcano
48. After zeta
49. Was positioned
52. Journalist's mentor: abbr.
54. Possessive pronoun

Solution is on page 390

ACROSS

1. Smoked meat
4. French cap
9. Toddler
12. Employ
13. Tusk material
14. Actress Gardner
15. Expressed gratitude
17. Stationery
19. Observed
20. Ore seekers
21. Melancholy music
23. Endures
24. Cooking fat
25. "Cools one's heels"
26. Afternoon: abbr.
28. Singleton
29. Foot woes
30. Edgar Allan —
31. You and I
32. Work boat
33. Soak up, as ink
34. Taut
35. Rips
36. Sea robber
38. College club, for short
39. Worship
40. Teased
43. Under the weather
44. Sneak attacks
46. Be mistaken
47. Kin: abbr.
48. Bed linen
49. Beam

DOWN

1. Lean-to
2. Hardwood tree
3. Use a ruler
4. "Ten-speeds"
5. Tied, as a score
6. Fishing gear
7. Sound of hesitation
8. Office workers
9. Records
10. Above
11. Sailors
16. Lack
18. Picnic intruders
20. Pine Tree State
21. Puff
22. Alley
23. Immense
25. More than bad
26. Needy
27. N.Y. baseball team
29. Horse gaits
30. Serving dish
32. Bruin
33. Lima, for one
34. Fairy tale creature
35. Have faith
36. Duo
37. Not busy
38. Lose color
40. Ascot
41. Notable period
42. Parched
45. Sigh of satisfaction

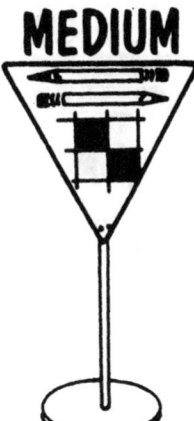

MEDIUM

Solution is on page 391

ACROSS

1. Enjoy a book
5. Has lunch
9. Not many
12. Mystery writer Gardner
13. Jogging gait
14. Actress Gardner
15. Oxeye —, flower
17. Soap, for example
19. Retain
21. Information
22. In general
25. Word with "home" or "boat"
28. Father, to some
29. Elms and oaks
31. Play a part by means of gestures
32. Pixie
34. Pertaining to a sea force
36. Beret, for example
37. Plant part
39. Hinder
41. That man
42. Direction marker
44. Sideways
46. Adorn
48. Alaska city
49. Mistake
52. Baseball teams
55. Charged atom
56. Quiz answer, perhaps
58. Bristle
59. Payable
60. Pay close attention to
61. Influence (someone)

DOWN

1. Scarlet
2. Historic age
3. Identical
4. Sahara or Gobi
5. "— tu, Brute!": Latin
6. Rainbow
7. Revealed secrets
8. Geyser output
9. Overly zealous
10. Pre-holiday night
11. Armed conflict
16. Long (for)
18. Tiny particle
20. Implore (with "with")
22. Musical drama
23. Conspicuous bravery
24. Flat and even
26. Nebraska city
27. Drive back
30. Evil One
33. Word with "hunter" or "teller"
35. Pretend: 2 wds.
38. Ripped
40. Negligent
43. Area = length × —
45. Extend (a subscription)
47. Nothing more than
49. Auction offer
50. Baseball's Gehrig
51. Regret
53. Greek letter
54. Speak
57. Actor Asner

MEDIUM

Solution is on page 391

ACROSS

1. Cartoonist Arno
6. Ruddy
12. Disintegrate
13. Restricted
15. Arum plant
16. Part of USNA
17. Whitney's invention: 2 wds.
19. Man's nickname
20. Initials for Queen Elizabeth
21. Plunder
22. — Hari
23. Swiss capital
24. Tribal emblem
25. Coating on brass
28. City on the Tagus
29. Nautical command
30. Drover's concern
31. Volume
32. Average
33. Mongrel
36. *Douceur*
37. Preserve
39. Imposing structure
41. Ship's crane
42. Brings to mind
43. Sheeplike
44. Name from the Big Band era
45. Witch's town

DOWN

1. Clingstone
2. Fluff
3. Cuspid
4. Prepare copy
5. Fragrant
6. Lidded container
7. Lawful
8. Muscat's land
9. Free (of)
10. Say again
11. Lowered in rank
14. Forceful, energetic person
18. Ibsen heroine
22. Cast
23. Cold Swiss Alps wind: French
24. Awesome storms
25. Glib talk
26. Dodged
27. Mexican port
28. Grid group
30. Dissent from an established belief
32. Twin crystal
33. Carp
34. Italian commune near Venice
35. Biblical juniper
37. Wire measures
38. Volcanic rock
40. Distant

Solution is on page 391

BIBLE CROSSWORD   MEDIUM

by RUSS CARLEY

Bible references in this puzzle are from the King James Version. You'll find it stimulating to solve, and may discover you know more about the Bible than you think you do.

ACROSS

1. With the jawbone of an — . . . have I slain a thousand men. *Judg. 15:16*
4. Now Jacob had pitched his — in the mount. *Gen. 31:25*
8. —, my daughter! thou hast brought me very low. *Judg. 11:35*
12. I heard , . . the —se of thunder. *Rev. 6:1*
13. The north wind driveth — rain. *Prov. 25:23*
14. He . . . — them farewell. *Acts 18:20, 21*
15. — entered into the ark. *Luke 17:27*
16. Remem— the sabbath day, to keep it holy. *Ex. 20:8*
17. Let his children be fatherless, and his wife a —. *Ps. 109:9*
18. Thou hast made him a little lower than the —. *Ps. 8:5*
20. He was — . . . and went away grieved. *Mark 10:22*
21. Adam called his wife's name —. *Gen. 3:20*
22. The harvest of the river, is her —. *Isa. 23:3*
26. As your fathers did, — do ye. *Acts 7:51*
28. Condescend to men of low —. *Rom. 12:16*
30. Cain — Abel
31. What shall — (2 wds.) give in exchange for his soul? *Matt. 16:26*
33. Bela, the son of —z
34. I have dreamed a dream, and there is none that can —rpret it. *Gen. 41:15*
35. The — Testament
36. Their spot is not the — (2 wds.) his children. *Deut. 32:5*
38. Have mercy — me, O Lord. *Matt. 15:22*

39. My Father is — than I. *St. John 14:28*
41. — kingdom of heaven is at hand. *Matt. 3:2*
43. Jesus — born in Bethlehem. *Matt. 2:1*
44. From — come wars and fightings among you? *James 4:1*
47. He shall — himself . . . as a shepherd putteth on his garment. *Jer. 43:12*
50. Every eye shall — him. *Rev. 1:7*
51. —id, slayer of Goliath
52. They shall — together like lions. *Jer. 51:38*
53. Thou shalt not — false witness. *Matt. 19:18*
54. Sir, come down — my child die. *St. John 4:49*
55. Vengeance is — ; . . saith the Lord. *Rom. 12:19*
56. Having —, hear ye not? *Mark 8:18*
57. They . . . cast him into the — of lions. *Dan. 6:16*

DOWN

1. Our fathers did eat m— in the desert. *St. John 6:31*
2. They — forgat his works. *Ps. 106:13*
3. He hath laid — against us. *Mic. 5:1*
4. The writing was . . . of God, graven upon the —. *Ex. 32:16*
5. Thy — and thy she goats have not cast their young. *Gen. 31:38*
6. Straight is the gate, and —row is the way. *Matt. 7:14*
7. Faith, hope, chari—. *I Cor. 13:13*
8. Come into my house, and — there. *Acts 16:15*
9. The — cannot leave his father. *Gen. 44:22*

10. Why make ye this —, and weep? *Mark 5:39*
11. A time to rend, and a time to —. *Eccl. 3:7*
17. He that wavereth is like a — of the sea. *James 1:6*
19. And the —ing and the morning were the first day. *Gen. 1:5*
20. — (2 wds.) liberty them that are bruised. *Luke 4:18*
22. Take thee a barber's —. *Ezek. 5:1*
23. The sons of Judah were Er and O—. *Num. 26:19*
24. God hath shewed it — them. *Rom. 1:19*
25. The Garden of —
26. Paul . . . prayed, and — praises unto God. *Acts 16:25*
27. An — is the tenth part of an ephah. *Ex. 16:36*
29. She maketh herself coverings of —try. *Prov. 31:22*
32. Stand in —, and sin not. *Ps. 4:4*

34. Good were it for that man — (2 wds.) had never been born. *Mark 14:21*
36. He should not — long in the place. *Hos. 13:13*
37. He saved —; himself he cannot save. *Matt. 27:42*
40. Men . . . are not — of them. *Luke 11:44*
42. On the seventh day God — his work. *Gen. 2:2*
44. They that — soft clothing are in kings' houses. *Matt. 11:8*
45. Take — of him; and . . . I will repay thee. *Luke 10:35*
46. Reward her — as she rewarded you. *Rev. 18:6*
47. I took . . . the bracelet that was on his —. *II Sam. 1:10*
48. Isaac dwelt by the well Lahai-—. *Gen. 25:11*
49. They — the ship aground. *Acts 27:41*
50. The — of Galilee
53. Let him — crucified. *Matt. 27:22*

Solution is on page 391

MEDIUM

ACROSS

1. Aeons
5. On vacation
9. Owns
12. Immediately following
13. Lawyer's concern
14. Single
15. There are ten in a century
17. Without company
19. Spring flower
20. Out of order
21. Many times
23. Hits (against)
24. Future plant
25. Jests
26. Myself
28. Young boy
29. Imposed a tariff
30. Entertainer, Doris —
31. Either
32. Domesticated
33. Nip
34. Fixed charges
35. Comforted
36. Liquid measures
38. Lend a hand
39. Join together
40. Cushions
43. That thing's
44. Precipitation
46. On the ocean: hyph. wd.
47. Foot digit
48. Luge
49. Something owed

DOWN

1. In addition
2. Golly!: slang
3. Like a child on Christmas Eve
4. Gazed fixedly
5. High cards
6. Existed
7. "— You Like It," Shakespeare play
8. Longed (for)
9. Creel items
10. Actress Bancroft
11. Beheld
16. Confused clamor
18. Ship's diaries
20. Used the oven
21. Norway's capital
22. Terror
23. Emulates Holmes or Ali
25. Actor Stewart
26. Spouse
27. See 11-Down
29. Tears to shreds
30. Discard (with "of")
32. Sharp tasting
33. Romantic song
34. Pay increase
35. Thin fish
36. Resign
37. "Do — others . . ."
38. Rear
40. Fruit-filled pastry
41. Spider's product
42. Took a chair
45. Mr. Jolson

Solution is on page 391

234

ACROSS

1. Grow older
4. Twinkler in the sky
8. Talon
12. Speak; utter
13. Helper
14. Pit; cavity
15. Jacket parts
17. Simpletons
18. Marry
19. Hearing organs
20. Musical sounds
23. Makes unhappy
26. Gorillas
27. Goes out with
28. Not off
29. Encountered
30. Shoe parts
31. Foot digit
32. Hesitation sound
33. Devil
34. Thorny flower.
35. — off, recited easily and rapidly
37. Small restaurant
38. Decays
39. Fishing gear
40. Alda and Ladd
42. School assignments
46. Go by car
47. Not any
48. Summer zodiac sign
49. Golf pegs
50. Slices
51. Lair

DOWN

1. Donkey
2. "My — Sal"
3. Seeing organ
4. Rescues
5. Bound
6. Paid notices
7. Do's follower
8. Harmonious combinations
9. Not tight
10. Everyone
11. Man's nickname
16. Female sheep
17. Loses color
19. Consumed
20. More docile
21. Musical drama
22. Openwork fabric
23. Tossed greens
24. Hangman's loop
25. Show scorn
27. — on, loves to excess
30. Seasons
31. Heavy weight
33. Rocks
34. Frees (of)
36. Swap
37. Medicinal amounts
39. Lease
40. Actor Carney
41. Fib
42. "Skip to my __"
43. Not young
44. Born
45. Male offspring
47. Raleigh's State: abbr.

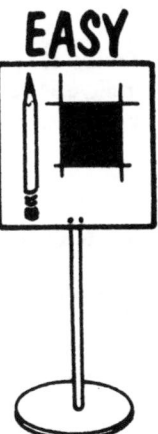

EASY

Solution is on page 391

SHANEANIGANS   HARD

by TED SHANE

You'll find zany definitions in this crossword by Ted Shane, so please look out for traps. For example, the definition for 1-Across is "A stick-up on the ocean," and the answer is MAST. The clues are sly, so be careful.

Solution is on page 392.

ACROSS

1. A stick-up on the ocean
5. 1/10ify
13. The butter half of a yodeler's yodel
14. Noodle-stuffer
15. What Mactavish Jr. hopes to get out of his great-grandad's kilt
16. His wife turned out to be a salty character
17. Add on term and they'll eventually bring the house down
18. What plunging necklines on TV just can't get any
20. Remark that'd make a cat laugh
21. How Boston got its start
23. What a racket among backward people
24. Man involved in a court-ship?
25. DH$_2$Oify (as flood waters)
27. What men do who think they can buy their wives minks for $200
28. Mr. Hogg's well-known daughter
31. Since Castro, these have been on the most-wanted list: 2 wds.
34. The eternally possessive female
35. Mr. Pinch's well-known daughter
36. Bird of genus *epluribusunum*
37. What brides never say during the ceremony but grooms do after
39. Three letters from Cyrano
40. It means goodbye in singletalk
41. Things to avoid flying into
43. The nylon of the '90's
45. O, the pity of it!
46. This keeps the head warm
47. Cried Sigrid when her boyfriend was cut in two: "Half — is better than none!"
50. Tourist-luring view

52. Lair-conditioned home with built-in bars
53. Her breath comes in short pants and snickers
54. Wise students don't guess, they do this

DOWN

1. Shave Ma Nature
2. It's brown as a beery
3. Stamp on even the most fragile packages
4. Place to run to from Niagara
5. Took the carets out of a literary stew
6. esroh yb tneW
7. Choice thing a butcher likes to give his help in salary
8. Frozen: simplified spelling
9. This place is filled with tourists, lobsters and Republicans seeking this kind of chance
10. Dudsing
11. What the Indian did in as he walked the warpath
12. This turned to Gaelic as the Irish kept talking through the centuries
19. You can roast them all you like but they'll still be our favorite dogs
20. 1890 cuddle coupés
21. Kind of ache the classical conductor had (he took Brahmso-seltzer for it)
22. It causes the wind to whistle thru Carnegie Hall
24. Broadway sign meaning "Tickets for this show can be obtained for $100.00 a pair at the scalpers"
26. Peacockish, purse-proud and plutocratic

27. drac laer A
29. It sure keeps farmers on the hop
30. Disoriented in the Pacific
32. Kind of port sailors will drink in a storm
33. Would you say two people marrying in a rowboat were united in holy this?
38. Ginebriate
39. The more it gets down in the mouth the more of a stinker it becomes

41. Wrapped in goggle-eyed wonder
42. This occupies a jai place in Latin America
43. Kind of light actors like to see themselves in
44. Personal zing
46. Man's most expensive bad habit
48. Time past (but not pastime)
49. The number of capitalists you find in the capitalist system
51. This is just about about

HARD

ACROSS

1. Mud dauber
5. Craze
8. Tennis great
12. Bread spread
13. Mrs. Lennon
14. Stop!
15. Memento
17. Vain types
18. Cougar
19. Hotel patron
20. Clan symbol
23. Sphere
25. Poet Khayyám
26. Semitic deity
27. Function
30. Sham splendor
32. Deal with
34. Baseball's Mel
35. Defects: slang
37. Majors, et al.
38. Shade of yellow
40. Cultivates
41. Division of the U.K.
43. Help
45. Dismounted
46. Day's close, to Browning
50. Nap
51. Two "fins"
52. Aphrodite's son
53. Prophet
54. Outer district
55. Strong emotion

DOWN

1. Cooking pan
2. Sudsy brew
3. Find out
4. Baseball hitters, at times
5. Froth
6. Capital of Turkey
7. Female rabbit
8. Appalling
9. Noted jockey
10. Beer ingredient
11. Orient
16. Aggregate
19. Festival
20. All, to Caesar
21. Neglect
22. Tease
24. Meals
26. Depressed
28. Fight
29. Hardy heroine
31. Declines
33. Hubbub
36. Carved out
39. 39.37 inches
40. Swamp
41. Crams
42. Lily genus
44. Yield
46. Summer, in Paris
47. Author Levin
48. Track down
49. Suffix for "in the style of"

Solution is on page 392

ACROSS

1. In favor of
4. Footfall
8. Box in an exhibition
12. Fuss
13. Tiny skin opening
14. A Great Lake
15. Army men
17. Marries
18. Walk on
19. Distress signal
21. Matching group
22. Ran into
24. Very wise man
26. Offer, as a price
29. Male sheep
31. Desires
34. Corrosive
36. Paving substance
38. Halt
39. Satan
41. Show agreement
43. Pig pen
44. Matinee —, popular actor
46. Wager
48. Sleeping place
50. Gratuity
52. Lost color
56. Follow orders
58. Woo with music
60. Not any
61. Peasant
62. Decade number
63. Terminates
64. Snow toy
65. No matter which one

DOWN

1. Swift
2. Aroma
3. Actor's part
4. Web spinner
5. Foot digit
6. Goes wrong
7. Mexican monetary units
8. Stitch
9. Gifts
10. Assistant
11. Remainder
16. Water barrier
20. Carpenter's tool
23. Make lace
25. Fuel
26. Not good
27. Frozen water
28. Stockholder's gain
30. Person
32. Small child
33. Secret agent
35. Accomplished
37. Steal from
40. Parking area
42. Protect
45. Speech impediments
47. Sunbather's goal
48. Doggy tidbit
49. Black: poetic
51. Use a paring knife
53. Information
54. Biblical garden
55. Declare untrue
57. Affirmative!
59. Fish eggs

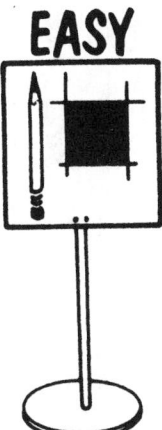

EASY

Solution is on page 392

239

EASY

ACROSS

1. Desires
6. Dinner course
11. Add more to a heap: 2 wds.
12. Cleverly avoid
13. West Point student
14. On the ocean
16. State prosecutor: abbr.
17. Lode loads
18. Fruit rind
19. Heavy weight
20. Disfigure
21. Far down
22. Triumphs
23. Actor Asner
24. Brooches
25. Free (of)
26. Leaseholder
28. Trustworthy
31. Frost, as a cake
32. Assigned piece of work
33. Friendly greeting
34. Clock front
36. One of a pair
37. Crash (into)
38. Exist
39. Butter squares
40. Put on the payroll
41. — and behold!
42. Controversial contraction
43. Opposing teams
44. Strike hard
46. Filled (a truck)
48. Relieves
49. Come into

DOWN

1. Broader
2. Pub drinks
3. Tennis court feature
4. As far as
5. Adders and cottonmouths
6. Witnessed
7. Actress Gardner
8. California city, for short
9. — to, make larger: 2 wds.
10. Campus bigwigs
11. July 4 event
13. Celestial body
15. Drink slowly
18. Transmitted
19. Ocean movement
21. Eat out
22. Deliberate eye movement
24. Stride
25. Garden beauty
27. Pleasant
28. Easter bonnets
29. Divided
30. Clocks, as a race
32. Tell tales
34. Untrue
35. Fragrance
36. Adult male
37. Bus passenger
39. Crusted desserts
40. Conceal
42. Had lunch
43. Used a chair
45. Happens
47. By

Solution is on page 392

ACROSS

1. Mr. Wiesel
5. Cake ingredient
9. Fuss
12. Judge's bench
13. College group
14. Make a slip
15. The two
16. Soften
17. Ineffectual person
18. Cultivate
20. Pilgrims
22. Slalom
24. Cook's aid
26. Spanish coins
28. Indian State
31. Forest ox
32. Extinct bird
34. Mrs. Chaplin
35. City on the Loire
37. Journalism's Janet
39. Extension
41. Alphabet sequence
42. More musty
44. Actor Wallach
46. Kimono accessory
47. Pitfall
49. Ms. Korbut
52. Clumsy one
53. Quote
54. Sped
55. Compass point
56. Hebrew letters
57. Disclose

DOWN

1. Wane
2. Vientiane native
3. 1941 Ellen Glasgow novel: 4 wds.
4. She loved Narcissus
5. Newt
6. Steinbeck work (with "The") : 3 wds.
7. The late Mr. Nasser
8. Miss Stevens
9. MacKinlay Kantor's Pulitzer winner
10. Sullen
11. Advantage
19. Is, to Pierre
21. Unstable particle
22. Young oyster
23. Gambling game
25. Noah's son
27. Like some seals
29. Again
30. Engels' associate
33. Winglike part
36. Tattle: slang
38. Pub order
40. Uncanny
42. Satellite
43. Scottish port
45. Gallery
48. Foot
50. Coagulate
51. Shoemaker's item

HARD

Solution is on page 392

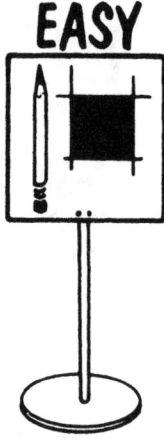

EASY

ACROSS

1. Leg's front part
5. Droops
9. Afresh
13. Deckhand's mop
17. Send a telegram to
18. Drop heavily
19. What butchers sell
20. Dip out, as water
21. Fuss
22. Labor Day month
24. Judge's mallet
25. One-cent coins
27. Very chilly
28. Most recent
29. Also
30. Roofing piece
31. Roy Rogers' wife
32. Moves, as a bird's wings
35. Necklace part
36. Truly
40. Ornamental trim
41. Formal dance
42. Uses asphalt
43. Regret
44. Female sheep
45. Child's toy
46. Auctions
47. Mr. Reiner
48. Trap
50. Canvas shelters
51. Desert animal
52. Anger
53. Liberates
54. In favor of
55. Startle
58. Slides accidentally
59. Offer marriage (to)
63. Deep affection
64. Chairs
65. Library loan
66. Moving truck
67. Mr. Vigoda, of acting
68. Tremble
69. Still; quiet
70. Tear; pull apart
71. Ship's window
73. Had on, as clothing
74. Musical groups
75. Jumps
76. Decline in power
77. Drink, like Fido
78. Frightens
81. The —, the cream of the crop
82. Snowy seasons
86. Residences
87. Getting ready (for)
89. Payable
90. Region
91. Harvest
92. Sleeveless garment
93. Make eyes (at)
94. Fender mishap
95. Hen products
96. Soon after
97. Robert or Oliver

DOWN

1. Exchange
2. Conceal
3. Press (clothes)
4. Compass point
5. Swiftness
6. Swiss mountains
7. Received
8. Exceptional
9. Walk at a leisurely pace
10. Requirement
11. Corn spike
12. Dieter's concern: abbr.
13. Lists of proposed candidates
14. Ocean movement
15. Fruit drinks
16. Waist ornament
22. Wrongdoings
23. Form
24. Strong winds
26. Back of the neck
28. Country roads
30. Recount
31. Peace symbols
32. Escape from danger
33. Grassy area around a house
34. High playing cards
35. Large bundle
36. Stops
37. Streetcar: British
38. Entice
39. Scream
41. Use a drill
42. Window sections
45. Without light
46. Oozes
47. Pond fish
49. Pleasant
50. Stale; hackneyed
51. Do a chef's work
53. Small quantity, as of snow
54. Out of
55. Smack
56. Tramp
57. Above
58. Closes, as an envelope
59. Rod
60. Baking chamber
61. Beach "floor"

62. Concludes
64. Stores
65. Unfurnished
68. Cobblers mend these
69. Get in touch with
70. Engrossed (in)
72. Menace
73. Stinging insect

74. Loud, sudden noise
76. Cries
77. Flaxen cloth
78. Food fish
79. Apple center
80. Prayer word
81. Boast

82. Dry, as dishes
83. Border
84. Govern
85. Start of a plant
87. Wooden pin
88. Cheerleader's shout
91. In —, concerning
93. Either . . . —

Solution is on page 392

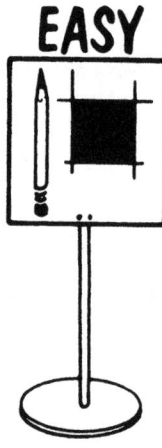

EASY

ACROSS

1. Guided
4. Plant fluid
7. "With it": slang
10. Encountered
13. Spoken
15. Uses a spoon
17. Challenges
19. Painful
20. Fence entrance
21. Claw
22. Worship
23. Jack rabbit
24. Summer shoes
26. Frequently
28. Jogs
30. Urgent, as a need
31. Tiresome people
32. Leading actor
33. At that place
35. Stunned
36. Cats
39. Not tall
40. Proofreader's mark
41. Resided
42. Tease: slang
44. Upper limbs
45. Keeps away from

46. Eye cosmetic
47. Walk about in shallow water
48. Bambi's mom
49. Pierces with a knife
50. Females
51. Founded (on)
52. Authors
54. Legal suits
55. Fixed prices
56. Beavers' products
57. Zoo enclosures
58. Ripped
59. Pares
61. Counterfeits
62. A few
65. Ethical
66. Wants and expects
67. Musical sounds
68. Label
70. Military "hooky-player": abbr.
71. Strong winds
72. Shopping wagons
73. Ice-cream holder
74. Bright color
75. Does a pilot's work
76. Birds' abodes
77. Hermit, for one
78. Good wishes
80. Places for skaters
81. Ripples
82. Frees (of)
83. Fender mishaps
84. Mr. DeBusschere, of basketball
85. Mark, as exams
87. Coal digger
88. Buccaneers
91. Whip, as eggs
92. Sister's daughter
94. Foreigner
96. Tied, as a score
98. A Great Lake
99. Threaded nail
100. Endures
101. Ten-cent coin
102. Number of years in a decade
103. Affirmative reply
104. Used to be
105. Ignited

DOWN

1. Ship's daily record
2. Historic periods
3. Information
4. Not fresh
5. Is sick
6. In favor of
7. Devil's domain
8. Press (clothing)
9. For each
10. Castle's ditch
11. Makes a mistake
12. It follows "ess"
14. Banks, at times
15. Steady, intent look
16. Dozes
17. Old-fashioned
18. Pioneer; colonist
19. Like sheep, after a trim
25. Grime
27. Worry
29. Sudden attack
31. Farm buildings
32. "Lucky" number
33. Toss
34. "Four-bagger"
35. Smears on, as plaster
36. Monetary penalties
37. Clean, as the blackboard
38. Factions
39. Unhappy
40. Sears
41. Citrus fruits
43. Cot
45. Plant stalks
46. Fails to win
47. Nourish, as a plant
49. Stable's compartment
50. Salary
51. Uncovers; exposes
53. Perfect model
54. Baker's creations
55. Wanders about
57. Sleeveless garments
58. Campers' shelters
59. Strength; force
60. Wear away
61. Pleats, for example
62. Separates, as laundry
63. Make amends (for)
64. Country roads

65. Spoil; impair
66. Farm workers
67. Chores
69. Berlin native: abbr.
71. Tends the roses
72. At the middle
73. Desired with envy
75. Deposited (eggs)
76. Baseball-team number

77. Molten rock
79. Shred, as cheese
80. Extend (a lease)
81. Cautions
83. Cuts into cubes
84. Counts calories
85. Actor, Richard —
86. Weather-forecaster's word

87. Simple
88. Leaning Tower of —, Italian sight
89. Wicked
90. Half: prefix
91. Wager
93. Slippery
95. Statute
97. Tennis-court feature

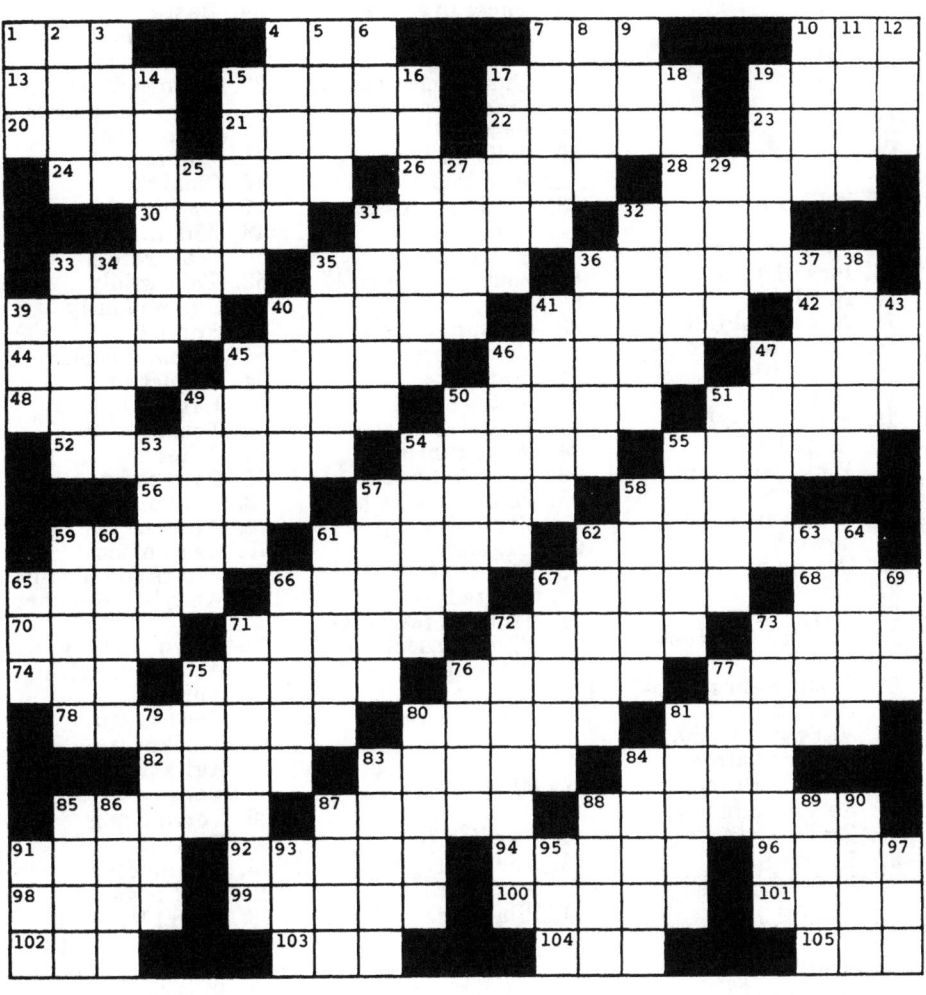

Solution is on page 393

HARD

ACROSS

1. "Manon" or "Lulu"
6. Israeli seaport
10. Bewilder
14. Ancient object
15. Skimmer part
16. Paradise
17. Vertical
18. Eugene —, U.S. labor leader
19. Word with "tip" or "pigeon"
20. Large spring flowers
22. Get-up-and-go
23. Cheer
25. Large stone
26. Carried in a tumbrel
29. Uncle Sam's country: abbr.
30. Very great amount
31. Charged atom
32. Island: French
33. Serious offenses
35. Begin
37. Proboscis
38. Spud, to some
40. Wapiti
41. Finding device
42. Network
44. Plus
46. Not itinerant: abbr.
49. Boxing blows
51. Watchful times
55. Black-backed gull
56. Notable period
57. Hail!
58. Triumphant cry
59. Corroded
60. "Never — Wolf"
61. Physician, for short
62. Pup's doctor, for short
63. Turn
65. Lively
66. Vane reading
67. Foot lever
69. Those over there: archaic
71. Doled (out)
74. Ump's relative, for short
76. Pastoral
80. Split, in a way
81. Was told
83. Fictional sea captain
84. Soft metal
85. Soup vegetable
86. Sniggler's catch
88. Solemn promise
89. Very hard
91. Water
92. Sharp curve
93. Writer Sarton
94. Make confused
96. Ripening agent
98. Pennsylvania port city
99. Urgency
102. Stop that!
103. Existed
104. Tinker's teammate
105. Flying insect
106. Propensity
107. Posed again

DOWN

1. Swedish coin
2. For each
3. A tusker
4. Pilaf base
5. Emoters
6. Surrender (a right)
7. Small stream
8. Barbecued treats
9. Print measures
10. Discourage
11. Passage, as of a law
12. Last letter
13. Object
21. Denials
22. Criticize unfavorably
23. Reddish-brown
24. Large continent
26. Camp bed
27. Lioness of "Born Free"
28. Pronghorn
31. Annoys
34. Baste
36. Woe is me!
37. Short letter
39. Turned away
41. One who chooses
43. Forbidden
45. Piquant
46. Cicatrix
47. Oz dog
48. Aid, in a way
50. Wall recess
52. Talk wildly
53. Subsequently
54. Surfeit
57. Summer cooler
64. Mimicked
65. Urgent request
68. Tract
70. Sister
71. Gym pads
72. Way out
73. Apartment; flat
75. Be at often
77. Alters completely
78. Andy's radio partner
79. Down periods
81. Attention-getting word
82. God: Latin
85. Thickness
87. Agitated state: slang
90. Terra firma
91. Foreign
94. Unhindered
95. Roof edge
96. Naval VIP: abbr.
97. Excessive sentimentality: slang
98. Recede
100. Musical syllable
101. Adjective ending

Solution is on page 393

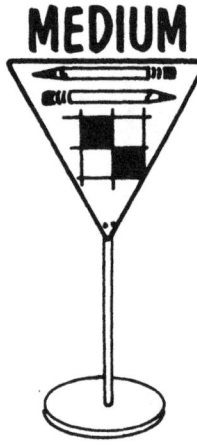

MEDIUM

ACROSS

1. Cook's garment
6. Small table
11. Lean-to
15. Food fish
19. Loud cry
20. Wait close by anxiously
21. Vaulting aid
22. Lima's country
23. Coyote State: 2 wds.
25. Came in last
26. Train track
27. Social insects
28. Portent
29. Author
31. Small whirlpool
32. Affirmative reply
33. Part of speech
34. Decree
35. Lifetimes
37. Towel word
38. Small horse
39. Forefather
43. Ski straight down a slope
46. Sharp flavor
47. Piccolo's kin
48. Fussy excitement
49. Intoned song

50. Actuality
51. Niagara sight
52. School dance
53. Reddish brown
54. Young horse
55. Become unwoven
56. Bizarre: French
57. Skill
58. Eating implement
59. Lure
60. Shack
61. Musical introduction
63. Stingy person
64. Moreover
68. Employ
69. Desires
70. Singing voice
71. Metallic mineral
72. Stop
75. Jockey's outfit
76. The two
77. Certain
78. Hodgepodge
79. Blustering fellow
80. Greater amount
81. Sat (for pictures)
82. Alphabet letter
83. Musical groups
84. Irritate
85. Funny movie
86. Emotions
88. Highland Scot
89. Gardening tool
90. Official grade
91. Zoo enclosure
92. Citrus fruit
93. Spoil
96. Batters' goals
98. Layers
101. Prong
102. Auction
103. Blue-pencil
104. Frost
105. Certain edition of a foreign author's work
108. Floating ice sheet
109. Aware of: 2 wds. (slang)
110. Indian tent
111. Had dinner
112. Watch over
113. Abound
114. Correct
115. F'rock

DOWN

1. Ore analysis
2. Call, for short
3. Puts to flight
4. Six make an inning
5. To the — degree, to an extreme
6. Private eye: slang
7. Keepsake
8. English river
9. Lacy fabric
10. Sketch
11. Bowler's challenge
12. Owl's cry
13. Otherwise
14. Takes away
15. Binges
16. Racing advantage: 2 wds.
17. Dry
18. Rightfully
24. Portals
30. Beam
33. Bird's home
34. Baptismal bowl
36. Golly!: slang
37. Look for
38. Agreement
39. Bowling lane
40. Invalid
41. Scent
42. Eternal City
43. Discarded metal
44. Whirring sound
45. Urgency
46. Conversation
47. Act of kindness
50. Golfer's shout
51. Countenances
52. Greens shot
54. ZIP —
55. Takes five
56. Yours and mine
58. Circuit breaker
59. Small and unimportant
60. Silence!
62. Abundant, as vegetation
63. Shopping areas
64. Destiny
65. Home
66. Made a mistake
67. Slender; fragile
69. Untamed region

70. Dull person
72. Cook
73. Facility
74. Declaration
75. Crooned
76. Roll (of cloth)
77. Indefinite amount
79. Basketball attempt: 2 wds.
80. Distance measure
81. Prod
83. Storage box
84. Boat race
85. Desert animal
87. Endured
88. Garfield, for one
89. Washed lightly
91. Billiards shot
92. Flaxen cloth
93. Pine Tree State
94. Lily plants
95. Tears; rips
96. Weight
97. Inactive
99. Musical sound
100. Be important
101. Recording ribbon
102. Agitate
106. Radiation dosage
107. Append

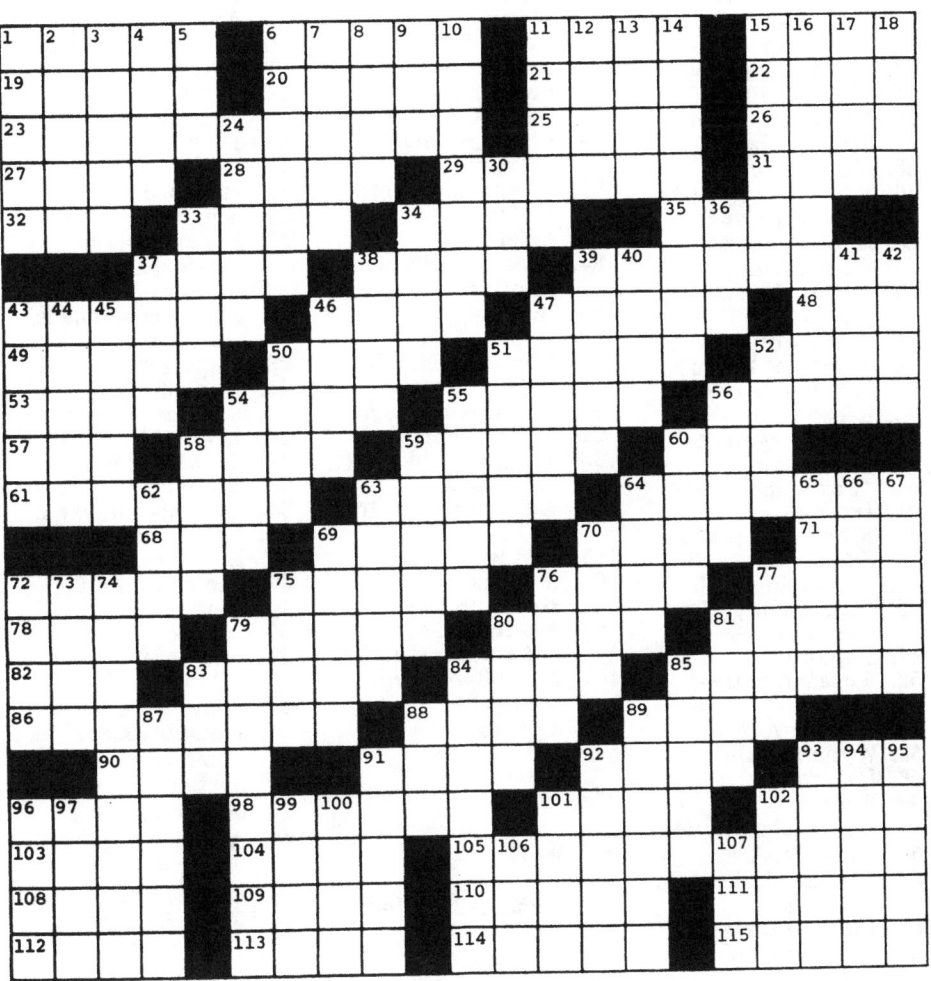

Solution is on page 393

SPECIAL CHALLENGER CROSSWORD

"THE NAME'S JAMES"   **by LOUIS SABIN**

Here is a real toughie for you. We have omitted giving you such helps as "2 wds.," "hyph. wd.," and "slang"; but in the spirit of fair play, all abbreviations and foreign words are so indicated.

ACROSS

1. Emulate Cicero
6. Proportionate
13. Like schooners, e.g.
19. Talisman
20. Fumigating device
21. Slanted
22. President, President, author
25. Knickknacks
26. Printer's measures
27. More deprived
28. Bidding expert Culbertson
29. Arthur Marx's cognomen
31. Samovars
32. Friend of Camus and de Beauvoir
36. Recto's opposite
37. School organization: abbr.
38. "Farm" performer
41. *Inter* —
42. Flowerless plant
43. Spades or hearts
44. "Pinocchio" fish
45. Biographer, pilot, singer
51. Deplore
52. Yucatán native
53. Delight
54. Actress Adorée
55. Wynn and Sullivan
56. *Posadas*
57. Budges
58. Autoist destinations
59. Grain husk
60. Crimean tribesman
61. Whist, e.g.
62. Cotton fabric
65. Treated ham, e.g.
66. Claudia — Johnson
67. Crony
70. Expect
71. Shipworm, e.g.
72. Chosen
73. "A Chorus Line" song
74. Actor, actor, song writer
78. Part of HOMES
79. Danube feeder
80. Fishing reel: Scottish
81. Temporary home
82. 1/100 of a yen
83. At all
84. King David's composition
86. Quickly
88. Wise
90. Runs like Nevele Pride
91. Palindrome word
92. Novel segment
95. Margin
96. High rank
101. Actor, actor, actor, actor
105. Red wine
106. Michelangelo Buonarroti, e.g.
107. AL franchise
108. Financial setbacks
109. Xylophonelike instrument
110. Shabby

DOWN

1. General Bradley
2. Contumelious
3. Came to earth
4. Canopy
5. Star: French
6. Larrigans
7. Federally funded utility system: abbr.
8. NHL great
9. Appraisers
10. In time, to Mehta: 2 wds.
11. Trunk
12. "Put the — on"
13. Tear into bits
14. Pallid
15. Pungs, e.g.
16. Singer Tennille
17. Fencing blade
18. Writer, Earl — Biggers
19. Stereo component, for short
23. Napoleonic marshal
24. Unprofitable
29. Relative of a stilt
30. River through Pisa
32. Cavalry sword
33. Audibly
34. Advances in rank
35. Fancy marble
36. Hindu texts
37. Finishing golf shots
38. Isolated
39. Stairway post
40. Pitches
42. Silver-screen swashbuckler
43. Comic-strip reporter
44. Minos' realm
46. Abu Dhabi or Fujaira, e.g.
47. Turner and Cantrell
48. FES, for example
49. Trojan War epic
50. Chemical salt
57. Indian wrap
58. Court action

59. Pickling solution
60. Skier's christie and telemark
61. Senator with "the right stuff"
62. Wizards: archaic
63. Knowledgable
64. "Mack the Knife" singer
65. "I'm as — as Kansas . . ."
66. Tocsin
67. Sits for an artist
68. As regards
69. Mehta's "slow"

71. Newspaper headlines
72. Deeds of wickedness
75. Tester's substances
76. Tiff
77. Shoshonean
84. Before hostilities
85. Kenyan's neighbor
86. Lithographs
87. Actor Michael
88. Range janglers
89. "— Grows in Brooklyn": 2 wds.
90. Iota preceder
91. Ostrich's cousin

92. 350, in Roman numerals
93. Whole: prefix
94. Garments in 46-Down
96. Novelist Ferber
97. Advantage
98. Require
99. "The Horse's Mouth" author, Joyce —
100. See 26-Across
102. Conway or Holt
103. Border
104. File attachment

Solution is on page 393

DIAGRAMLESS

MEDIUM

This Diagramless is 15 boxes wide by 15 boxes deep.

ACROSS

1. Fashion craze
4. Ungentlemanly gent
7. Yawn
8. Possesses
11. Declare to be true
13. Indy 500, and others
14. Buchwald or Carney
15. Pertaining to the Vatican head
17. Pub drink
18. Harass
21. Metallic rock
22. Huge and bulky
24. Aimed a finger (at)
26. Wallet stuffers
27. Rescue
28. Stationery
30. Assemblages of buffalo
33. Conifer
34. Compete (with)
35. Fights, cat style
38. Small rock
40. Profits
42. Biblical "you"
43. Bankbook entry

46. Oven-baking pan
50. Make angry
51. Three-legged supports, as for cameras
53. Keatslike poem
54. Rub out
56. Ignited
57. Domesticated
59. Pronounce indistinctly
60. Bandleader Brown
61. Equal
62. Capitol Hill employee: abbr.
63. Dwelling place: abbr.

DOWN

1. Countenances
2. Mimic
3. Predetermine, as by fate
4. Prisoner
5. Actress Gardner
6. Bus terminal
7. Festive affair
8. Jack rabbits
9. Give weapons to
10. Footfalls

12. Infrequent
13. L.A. footballer
16. Guided
19. Finished
20. Biblical flood survivor
23. High female singing voice
25. Jittery
28. Rank under a corporal: abbr.
29. Be on the sick list
31. Racket
32. Call on
36. Cowboy movie
37. Recipe direction
38. Not barefoot
39. Breakfast appliance
41. Quiet
42. Jogs
43. Perish
44. Is mistaken
45. Resounds, as a bell
47. Large, heavy books
48. Paradise
49. Nickname for a "carrot top"
52. Baked dessert
55. Seek charges
58. Fifth or Park: abbr.

Solution is on page 393

1 2 3

253

DIAGRAMLESS

HARD

This Diagramless is 15 boxes wide by 15 boxes deep. Starting box is on page 393.

ACROSS

1. Labyrinth
5. Eagerly excited
6. Carthage queen
7. Actress MacGraw
8. Health resort
11. Coarsely ground grain
13. Titled Britons
15. Luminous intensity
20. Public vehicle
23. "David Copperfield" character
24. Tender to the touch
25. Before: prefix
27. Offspring
28. Hibernia, to poets
29. Forbidden fruit locale
30. Is in the hole for
32. After-tax profit
33. Certain firework: 2 wds.

37. Fight; quarrel
38. Gridiron measure
41. Summer souvenir
42. Round Table title
43. Ocean movement
44. Beer barrels
45. Mine deposits

DOWN

1. Feminine title
2. Nimble-footed
3. Astrologer's concern
4. The self
8. Understand
9. "Zing"
10. Ascended
12. Young boy
13. Made smooth

14. Said under oath
16. The offer is not acceptable: 2 wds. (slang)
17. Block (out), as a sound
18. Buffalo's lake
19. Landlord's income
20. Heavyweight boxing champion of the '30s
21. Put an end to
22. Plant stalks
26. Pass into law
31. Like a fox
34. Post-Depression agency: abbr.
35. Preserve in airtight containers
36. Less difficult
39. Land elevation
40. Adorn
43. Boxing victory: abbr.

Solution is on page 394

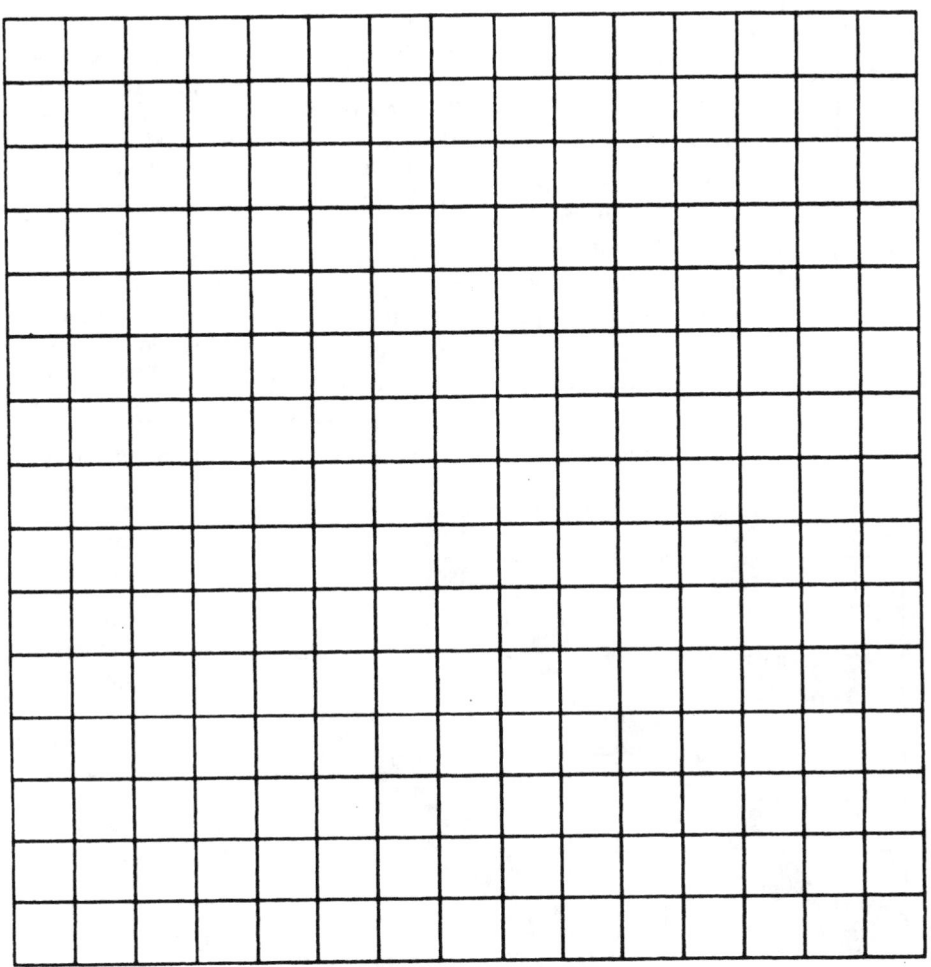

ACROSS

1. Cattle food
4. Pumpernickel or rye
9. Taxi
12. Refrigerate
13. Wash lightly
14. Dollar bill
15. Come down
17. Helicopter or jet
19. Witch
20. Restaurant employee
21. T-bone is one
24. Jack rabbits
25. Cause to slant
26. Takes a "breather"
27. — and fro
29. Give guns to
30. Canoes, etc.
31. Dog's foot
32. Concerning
33. Fife's kin
34. Summon
35. High shoes
36. Raggedy Ann and Andy
37. Not dense or crowded
39. Pod vegetable
40. Tahoe and Erie
41. Dentist's action, at times
45. Grow older
46. "Carmen," for one
48. Regret
49. Cradle or cot
50. Ready cash
51. Picnic pest

DOWN

1. Concealed
2. High card
3. *Oui* or *sí*
4. Smash; burst
5. Circle
6. Conclude
7. While
8. Leaves; goes
9. Paint layers
10. Comedienne Meara
11. Brewery product
16. Informal talk
18. Tells a whopper
20. Squander
21. Good thing to "wish upon"
22. Grow weary (of)
23. Shade tree
24. — up, warms over
26. Highway
27. Describing most basketball players
28. "Wise" birds
30. Bloom
31. Buddy
33. Golfer's shout
34. Mine output
35. Oven-cooked
36. Postpone
37. Thick slice (of bacon)
38. Book part
39. Not polluted
41. Ball-point item
42. A Gershwin
43. Convent dweller
44. Receive
47. US mail depot: abbr.

EASY

Solution is on page 394

256

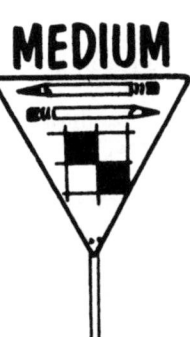

MEDIUM

ACROSS

1. Supply
6. No longer wild
10. Homilies
12. Words of agreement
14. E.T., for one
15. Mailing need
17. Singer Campbell
18. Envy, sloth, etc.
19. Witnessed
20. Sibilant sound
21. Leonine hair
22. French novelist
23. Grotto
24. Actress Black
25. Fright
27. Sups
28. Roebuck's partner
29. Hull
30. Special workshops, for short
31. Rickles, etc.
32. Theater sign: abbr.
35. Here: French
36. Remedy
37. Exceeded 55 mph
38. — bridge, floating structure
40. In front
41. Win (an election) overwhelmingly
42. Prizefight aids
44. Remain
45. Realty proofs

DOWN

1. Convinces
2. Tests
3. Prophecy
4. Guidry or Darling
5. Printer's measure
6. Russian news agency
7. Quantity: abbr.
8. Criterion
9. Hires
10. Wise man
11. Jellyfish's lack
13. Attach by stitching: 2 wds.
16. Number from "A Chorus Line"
18. Be frugal
21. Defaces
22. Hall-of-Famer Aaron
23. Shipment from Detroit
24. Chocolate candy
25. Manatees: 2 wds.
26. Presidential group
27. Sand hill
28. Loses traction
29. Antlers
31. Twosome
32. Shell out
33. Interprets
34. Betting factor
36. Facsimile
37. "For want of a nail the — is lost"
39. Daytime reception
40. Expert
43. Memorable Sullivan

Solution is on page 394

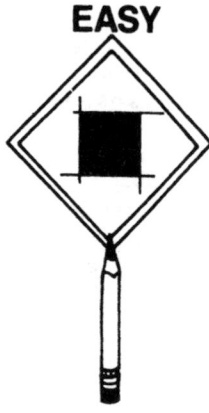

EASY

ACROSS

1. Fair; even
5. Give a smack to
9. Pest on Fido
13. Melt
17. Mr. Preminger of film-directing fame
18. Angelic arc
19. Falls behind
20. Whet
21. Sheep's cry
22. Tying, as seat belts
24. Lying face downward
25. Screams; screeches
27. Care for
28. Oozed
29. Baseballer Knight
30. Relax
31. Occupies a chair
32. Wide necktie
35. Sunset direction
36. Sooner State
40. Bank deal
41. Garden implements
42. Ruffle
43. Skillet
44. Shade tree
45. "The Farmer in the —"
46. In an imperfect way
47. Surprise invasion
48. Look at
49. Sprite
50. Desert animal
51. Red-berried evergreen
52. Short-lived fashion
53. Card game
54. Hope or Newhart
55. Church singing group
58. Employed
59. Pliable metal
60. Country lodge
63. In this place
64. Money houses
65. Dairy product
66. Female deer
67. George Gershwin's brother
68. Pennies
69. "— out the barrel"
70. Party giver
71. Denver's State
73. Vend
74. Cotton bundles
75. — up with, tolerates
76. Surface (a street)
77. Soap shape
78. Emphasize
81. Govern (over)
82. Interval of rest
86. Publish (a book)
87. Certain photographs
89. Lubricate
90. Relieve (a pain)
91. Pod vegetables
92. Wrongdoings
93. Hooting birds
94. Changed the color of
95. Fairy-tale monster
96. Whirlpool
97. Destiny

DOWN

1. Employment agency's offerings
2. Beehive State
3. Play the leading role
4. — and fro
5. Unsteady, as hands
6. Young girl; miss
7. Height: abbr.
8. Female rhymester
9. Spark-making stone
10. Arrive at O'Hare
11. Omelet item
12. While
13. Remove grain from wheat
14. Croquet wicket
15. Actress Meara
16. Pesky plant
22. Daring act
23. Bird's shelter
24. Flower part
26. Press, as clothes
28. Foolish
30. Partner of "rod"
31. Great ability
32. Beerlike beverages
33. Shoe bottom
34. — to, recovered consciousness
35. Howling animal
36. Judge's cry in court
37. October birthstone
38. Post (a letter)
39. Griffith or Williams
41. Contained
42. Widely known
45. Term of affection
46. Oven-cooks
47. Steal from
50. Bottle stoppers
51. Horn sound
52. For shame!
53. Variety of bean
54. Comedian Cosby
55. Stylishly smart
56. Decorated soldier
57. Spoken

58. Clock pointers
59. Cultivate (the soil)
60. False god
61. "Schnoz"
62. Butterfly snares
64. Throbs
65. Burrowing animal
68. Pie shell
69. Car gear for backing up
70. Stringed musical instrument
72. Unlocked
73. Pepper's partner
74. Food fish
76. Pocketbook
77. Flagmaker Ross
78. Drove (a car) too fast
79. Serving platter
80. Ascend
81. Bellow
82. Orange peel
83. Hawkeye State
84. Cause to tip
85. Otherwise
87. Wooden pin
88. Assist
91. River of Italy
93. — course, certainly

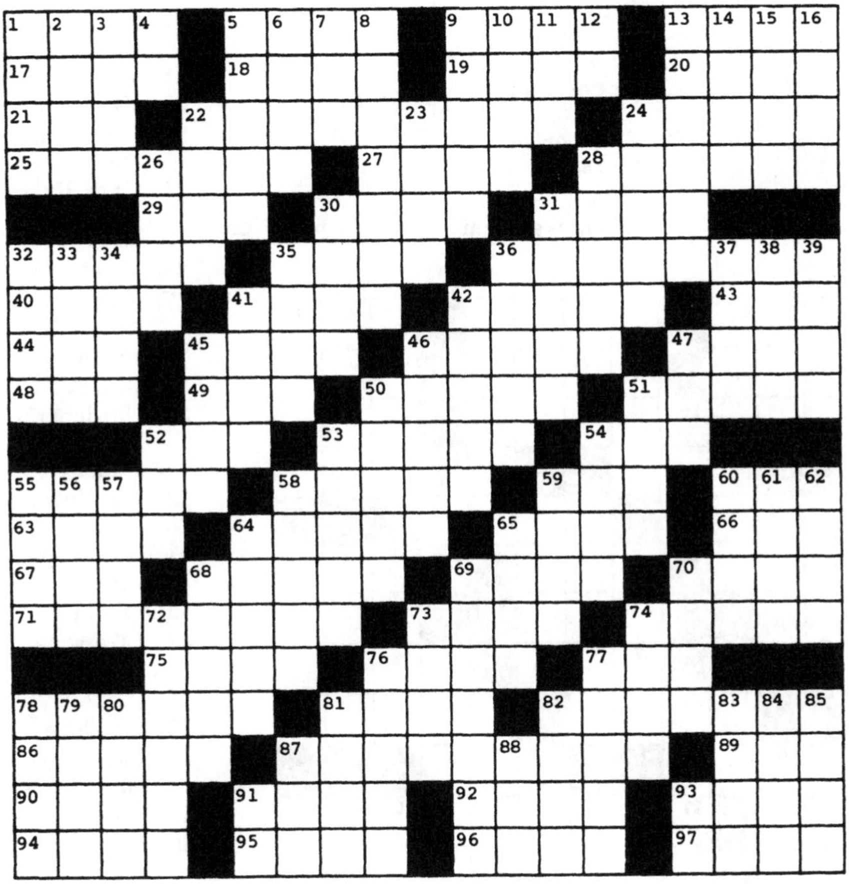

Solution is on page 394

MEDIUM

ACROSS

1. Rind
5. Emcee Parks
9. Girl of song
12. Roof overhang
13. Poker bet
14. Hatchet
15. Feigned
17. Convene
18. One way to get to the base runner
19. Does a household chore
21. "Thou shalt not — ..."
24. Knight and Charles
26. At any time
27. Opposite of a "rave"
28. Summertime refreshers
32. Profit
33. Keatslike poem
34. Rah: Spanish
35. Horse gait
37. Golfing norm
38. Light, pink wine
39. Consumer
41. Displayed concern
42. Orb
45. Prohibition
46. Laceration
47. Imperils
53. Fifth or Park: abbr.
54. Papal name
55. N.Y. canal
56. Entertainer Vereen
57. Fairly flew
58. Wrath

DOWN

1. Get-up-and-go
2. Musical perception
3. Eden dweller
4. Part of a monogram
5. Thrill: slang
6. Finale
7. Map abbreviation
8. Presidential nickname
9. Enact (a law)
10. Take one's leave
11. Acquires
16. Break bread
20. World power: abbr.
21. 1/100th dollar
22. Finished
23. Presidential "no"
24. Gary Burghoff role in M*A*S*H
25. Mime
27. Tug-of-war need
29. Portal
30. In addition
31. Gardener's purchase
36. Clumsy boat
38. NYC athlete
40. Oozes
41. US neighbor: abbr.
42. "Collar"
43. Like some wires
44. Candid
45. Hairless
48. Part of a baby's day
49. Owing (to)
50. Pitching stat: abbr.
51. Tractor-trailer
52. Call on

Solution is on page 394

ACROSS

1. You need "this" to tango
4. Char
8. — Little Indians
11. Globe, for one
12. Surfer's quest
13. Cover with asphalt
14. Cryptic
16. Webster's dad
17. Johnny or Rosalind
18. Magazine extra
20. Partially melted snow
22. Confront
23. Candlestick, for one
24. Donate: 2 wds.
28. High card
29. Like some jackets
30. Regret
31. Answers
33. "Georgy —"
34. Floor coverings
35. Essential to life
36. Refer indirectly (to)
39. Belonging to me
40. Martin or Jones
41. "— in Blue"
45. Bewilder
46. Citrus fruit
47. Enemy
48. Heaven
49. Time period
50. Boggy land

DOWN

1. Actor Poston
2. Cleverly humorous
3. Dims
4. Windshield-wiper sound
5. Every
6. Ms. Gardner
7. Eases
8. Story
9. Always
10. Nearest in place
13. Fettucine or linguine
15. Duty
19. Require
20. Shadowbox
21. Wedding-gown trimming
22. Looks after
24. With extreme care
25. Cancel: 2 wds.
26. Atmosphere
27. Shout
29. Noisy
32. Trim, as bushes
33. Cotton-fiber cleaners
35. Snake
36. Includes
37. Roof problem
38. Slothful
39. "I Remember —"
42. Hurry
43. A female deer
44. Desire

HARD

Solution is on page 394

261

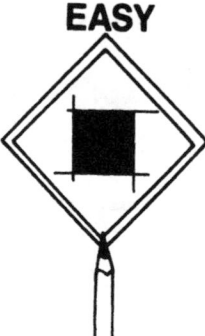

EASY

ACROSS

1. Building site
4. Record on a cassette
8. Hacks
12. Ms. Lupino
13. Sour substance
14. A Great Lake
15. "Tea — Two"
16. Ran into
17. Chalkboard
18. Uses transparent paper to copy
20. Drinks slowly
21. White — a sheet
22. Roads
25. Glasgow resident
28. Go quickly
29. At home
30. Skillet
31. Kitchen and den
32. A Gershwin
33. One
34. Wild west Army posts
35. Pace
36. Flag features
38. "Don't — mad!"
39. Pub brews
40. Starts (a garden)
44. Buckets
46. Exist
47. Notable period
48. Otherwise
49. Woe is me!
50. Slippery fish
51. Mimicked
52. Beaver constructions
53. Sandra or Ruby

DOWN

1. Raise
2. Scent
3. Scarlett O'Hara's home
4. Domesticates
5. High cards
6. Deep hole
7. McMahon or Sullivan
8. Aided
9. Rub out
10. Sharp humor
11. Observe
17. Fathers
19. Feline
20. Plant stalks
22. Leopard's features
23. Whitewall
24. Easy task: slang
25. Health resorts
26. Not able to: contraction
27. Atop
28. Painful spots
31. Strong cords
32. That thing
34. Packed to the limit
35. Red or Baltic
37. Hoist, as a flag
38. Make holy
40. English baby-buggy
41. Require
42. Oak or elm
43. Bargain event
44. Green — soup
45. Swiss mountain
46. Southern State: abbr.
49. Paid notice, for short

Solution is on page 395

ACROSS

1. Mild
6. Sphere
11. Word with "eye" or "ocean"
12. Boxers' "souvenirs": slang
14. Friend, in Madrid
15. Envelop: 2 wds.
16. Possessive pronoun
17. Unpoetic language
19. Fuss
20. Does the town: 2 wds.
22. Recipe direction
23. Express scorn
24. Clark Gable role
25. Teapot feature
27. Hesitate
28. Bias
29. Truth
30. Split rattan
31. Catcher's screen
35. Miss Gardner
36. Dull finish
37. Mr. Parseghian
38. What tyrants do
40. Bumper sticker
42. Behaved underhandedly
43. Join
44. Looked surprised
45. Falk or Fonda

DOWN

1. Blue devils
2. Boundary
3. Candy flavoring
4. Like some ions: abbr.
5. Resigns: 2 wds.
6. Apparition
7. Reside
8. Single
9. Scolds
10. Learned
12. Seeker of new talent
13. Tennis, e.g.
18. Source; origin
21. Word with "tele"
22. Closes
24. Achieved: 2 wds. (slang)
25. Toiling
26. Cure-all
27. Agreement
28. Oodles
29. Destined
31. With—breath
32. Unspoken
33. Speak pompously
34. Less brilliant
36. Create
39. Faucet
41. Compass point

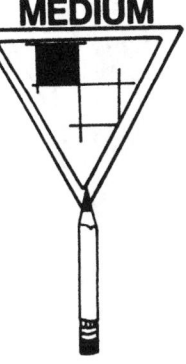

MEDIUM

Solution is on page 395

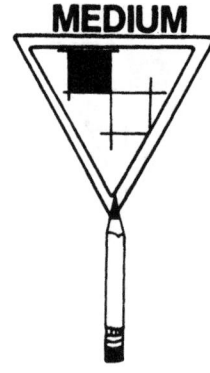

MEDIUM

ACROSS

1. Sweet potato
4. Engagement
8. Quarrel
12. Her
15. Always
17. Prophetic sign
18. Messenger
19. Remain
20. Locations
22. Color slightly
23. Press clothing
24. Emotional or mental condition
25. Removed from office
27. Marathon
29. Sums
31. Governed
32. Lions' nape hair
33. Storm
34. Afternoon gathering
35. Trousers
36. Frighten
38. Portions out
41. Horror-film actor, Vincent —
42. Coagulate
43. Cuff
47. Angered
48. Hag
49. Want badly
50. "— Maria"
51. Prevaricate
52. Glow
53. Serious
54. Jabs
56. Summer cooler
58. Common Danish pastry
59. Turn back to
60. Put forward, as a question
61. Mark test papers
62. Example
63. Revolutionary rider
66. Incline
67. Best liked
71. By oneself
72. The things there
73. Devil's domain
74. Expire
75. Clock setting in Calif.: abbr.
76. Use a loom
77. Captivated
78. Child's toy
79. Golf pegs
81. — of Capri
82. Hotel employee
83. Davis or Standish
84. Sticky stuff
86. Valleys
87. Distress signal
88. Secret writing
89. Scrooge
90. Sword handles
92. Pastry shop
94. Kiln
95. Summer shoes
97. Nuclei
98. Land measure
100. Military "lights out"
102. Slow-moving mollusk
104. Dollar bills
105. Bellow
106. Theater sign
107. Ocean movement
108. Marry
109. Dunce
110. Declare untrue
111. Gross minus costs

DOWN

1. Affirmative vote
2. Eager
3. Measuring device
4. — on, liked to excess
5. In the center of
6. Five pairs
7. Way in
8. Seasonings
9. Peels
10. In the past
11. Canvas shelter
12. Not fresh
13. Sombreros
14. Look at
16. Generally supposed
19. Phases
21. Shoe bottoms
24. Sheriff's I.D.
26. Baltic, for one
28. Poker stake
30. Speak eloquently
32. New England State
35. Lying face down
36. Drudge
37. Sheltered bay
38. Factory
39. A Great Lake
40. Abound
41. Self-esteem
42. Lifting device
44. Como or Mead
45. Opposite of 110-Across
46. Nuisance
48. Pursue
49. Unrefined
52. Sleeping sound
53. Vine fruit
54. Mexican dollars
55. Above
57. Candid; frank
58. Ordinary writing
59. Poe's bird
61. Mitt
62. West Point student

63. Engrossed
64. Otherwise
65. Cast one's ballot
66. Fine-grained rock
67. Phonies
68. Graven image
69. Flooring square
70. Snakelike fish
72. Trial
73. Healthier
76. Older and —

77. Gifted
78. Far off
80. Wheel radials
82. Flower urn
83. Shapes
85. Fruit drinks
86. Distract
87. Transgression
88. Was concerned
    (for)
89. Righteous

90. Rash
91. Murdered
92. Tibia
93. Word with "back"
    or "train"
95. Twirl
96. Lateral surface
97. Bovine animal
99. Dove sound
101. Chopping tool
103. Allow

Solution is on page 395

HARD

ACROSS

1. Unite
4. Destiny
8. Scrutinize
12. High card
13. Pongids
14. Ripped
15. Aromatic
17. Poker stake
18. Food fish
19. Saved
21. Dillon
23. Dined
24. First "Tonight Show" host
27. Family member, for short
29. Musician Clark
32. Brags
34. Paper handkerchief
36. Recede
37. Garden tool
39. Wide-mouthed pitchers
40. Have debts
42. Be concerned
44. Chewy candies
47. Rents
51. Spring flower
52. Showing no profit
54. Color lightly
55. Assistant
56. Mouse's kin
57. Rim
58. Sketched
59. Time periods: abbr.

DOWN

1. Blow gently
2. Beige
3. College official
4. Distant
5. Separate
6. Principles
7. Superlative endings
8. Begin
9. Talk
10. "Laugh-In's" Johnson
11. Want
16. Bingo, et al.
20. Less arduous
22. Choir's offering
24. Presidential nickname
25. Tennis stroke
26. Toiling
28. That thing
30. Possessive pronoun
31. For sure!
33. Thus
35. Expand
38. Filled pastry
41. Use foolishly
43. Stage whisper
44. Quote
45. Dry
46. Mild oath
48. Weird
49. Russian ruler
50. Speedy planes: abbr.
53. Novel

Solution is on page 395

ACROSS

1. Have creditors
4. Postage item
9. Dove's call
12. Diamond State: abbr.
13. Command
14. Uncooked
15. Actress, Sandra —
16. Fashion craze
17. Oak nut
19. Thunder sound
21. Winter storm
22. Satisfies
24. Made a choice
27. Birch or willow
28. Jury
29. — and behold!
30. Fishing pole
31. Arrives on shore
32. Kitchen utensil
33. Morning: abbr.
34. Conserves
35. Record (music)
36. Street events
38. Blisters
39. Helps
40. Coin opening
41. Grin
43. Robin Hood's drink
44. Wedding-announcement word
47. Moray
48. Fast
50. Building wing
51. Printer's measures
52. Goblet features
53. Wheel edge

DOWN

1. Strange; unusual
2. Tiny
3. Chose (by vote)
4. Couches
5. Snare
6. Use an abacus
7. Myself
8. Trots spiritedly
9. Throng
10. Paddle
11. Possess
18. Spiral
20. Robert E. —
21. Transmits
22. Sandal feature
23. Fragrance
24. Copenhagen residents
25. Use a ladder for love's sake
26. Lavishes love (on)
28. Surfaces (a road)
31. Climbing aids
32. Business associate
34. Go on a cruise
35. Also
37. Railroad tracks
38. Toboggans
40. Slender
41. Look at
42. Males
43. Large monkey
45. Mr. Wallach
46. Graceful tree
49. — home, not out

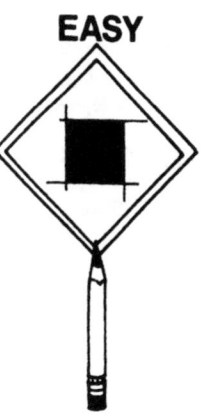

EASY

Solution is on page 395

BIBLE CROSSWORD MEDIUM

by RUSS CARLEY

Bible references in this puzzle are from the King James Version. You'll find it stimulating to solve, and may discover you know more about the Bible than you think you do.

ACROSS

1. They — him with grass like oxen. *Dan. 5:21*
4. — saith the Lord, thy redeemer. *Isa. 44:24*
8. Brother of Jacob
12. How long will it be — they believe me? *Num. 14:11*
13. Now abideth faith, —, charity. *I Cor. 13:13*
14. I have suffered the — of all things. *Phil. 3:8*
15. Thou hast made summer and —. *Ps. 74:17*
17. He that shall — unto the end . . . shall be saved. *Matt. 24:13*
19. — restoreth my soul. *Ps. 23:3*
20. Thou shalt not bear fa— witness. *Rom. 13:9*
21. I will — you out of their bondage. *Ex. 6:6*
22. — shall inherit the earth. *Matt. 5:5*
25. Get three behind me, —. *Luke 4:8*
27. — many loaves have ye? *Mark 6:38*
28. Glory to — in the highest. *Luke 2:14*
29. Whose soever sins ye —, they are remitted unto them. *St. John 20:23*
33. The —ts shall melt with fervent heat. *II Pet. 3:10*
35. —as had a quarrel against him. *Mark 6:19*
36. It came to pass in the month —. *Neh. 2:1*
37. The birds of the — come and lodge in the branches. *Matt. 13:32*
38. Put it . . . upon the great — of their right foot. *Ex. 29:20*
39. The birds . . . have —. *Matt. 8:20*
41. Jesus — his peace. *Matt. 26:63*

42. Thou — my beloved Son. *Mark 1:11*
45. My beloved is like a — or a young hart. *Song 2:9*
46. My God, why hast thou forsaken —? *Matt. 27:46*
47. He shall be buried with the — of an ass. *Jer. 22:19*
49. Solomon's builders and — builders did hew them. *I Ki. 5:18*
53. The Garden of —
54. Wipe away all tears from their —. *Rev. 7:17*
56. The — of Galilee
57. We remember . . . the —s, and the onions. *Num. 11:5*
58. The angel Gabriel was — from God unto . . . Nazareth. *Luke 1:26*
59. Go to the —, thou sluggard. *Prov. 6:6*

DOWN

1. Many are called, but — are chosen. *Matt. 22:14*
2. —, the family of the Erites
3. He shall be cast into the — of lions. *Dan. 6:7*
4. The word is nigh —, even in thy mouth. *Rom. 10:8*
5. The Lord spake unto Moses and Aaron in mount —. *Num. 20:23*
6. Rise — and walk. *Luke 5:23*
7. — thou this woman? *Luke 7:44*
8. The —er shall serve the younger. *Rom. 9:12*
9. The fathers have eaten — grapes. *Ezek. 18:2*
10. —el, the family of the Asrielites
11. With their tongues they have — deceit. *Rom. 3:13*
16. — will be done. *Matt. 6:10*
18. Now is our salvation — than when we believed. *Rom. 13:11*

20. The — cannot leave his father. *Gen. 44:22*
22. It . . . appeareth for a little time, and — vanisheth away. *James 4:14*
23. God sitteth upon the throne of his —ness. *Ps. 47:8*
24. Thy — and they she goats have not cast their young. *Gen. 31:38*
25. Of a truth thou art the — of God. *Matt. 14:33*
26. Father of Abner
28. From Abraham to David are fourteen —tions. *Matt. 1:17*
30. Beholdest thou the — . . . in thy brother's eye? *Matt. 7:3*
31. She had made an — in a grove. *I Ki. 15:13*
32. They — unto it a lace of blue, to fasten it. *Ex. 39:31*
34. — shall not live by bread alone. *Matt. 4:4*
35. Hath God cast away — people? *Rom. 11:1*

37. I— no pleasant bread. *Dan. 10:3*
40. The Lord put them under the — of his feet. *I Ki. 5:3*
41. She opened — eyes. *Acts 9:40*
42. Cain rose up against — his brother. *Gen. 4:8*
43. Though I be — in speech, yet not in knowledge. *II Cor. 11:6*
44. A good — bringeth not forth corrupt fruit. *Luke 6:43*
46. There went up a — from the earth. *Gen. 2:6*
48. I will not with — and pen write unto thee. *III John 13*
49. A — gathereth her chickens under her wings. *Matt. 23:37*
50. King of Judah
51. There came wise — from the east. *Matt. 2:1*
52. I saw thrones, and they — upon them. *Rev. 20:4*
55. Prepare — the way of the Lord. *Matt. 3:3*

Solution is on page 395

HARD

ACROSS

1. Imitate
5. Taste with zest
10. Mary Jane feature
15. Jogging gait
19. Melt
20. Barter
21. June birthstone
22. 60 minutes
23. Whet
24. Similarity
26. Price
27. Unit of work
28. Walking stick
29. Row
30. Opposed
32. Finery
34. Slopes
36. Largest continent
37. "The — in Winter," Hepburn film
38. Auctions
39. Bunches
43. Milk-producing farm
45. Stiff
46. Plants of a region
47. Experienced person, for short
48. Frees
49. Type of cap
50. Pine Tree State
51. Conceit
52. Fruit drink
53. Bowling lane
54. Auto style
55. Trite
57. Earth's great circle
59. Satellites
60. Rancher's concern
61. Viscous
62. Bearlike animal
63. Lacking light
64. Flight of steps
67. Election districts
68. VIPs: 2 wds.
72. Sheriff's group
73. Spotted horse
74. Large handbags
75. Metallic mineral
76. Fixed routine
77. Loses color
78. Ancestors
79. Nova
80. High card
81. Uses a drill
82. "In God We Trust" is one
83. Shut
84. Hair-raiser
86. Percussion instrument
87. Acid
88. Form
89. Mass. port city
90. Discovers
93. Vichyssoise ingredient
96. Collection of sayings
97. — in, implode
98. Swerve
99. Eager
100. Strategic delay: 2 wds.
105. Peak
106. Loyal
107. Long-plumed heron
108. Deduce
109. Escape
110. That woman's
111. Slender
112. Conjecture
113. Trial

DOWN

1. Volatile anesthetic
2. Task
3. Kitelike aircraft: 2 wds.
4. Be in debt
5. Exert to the utmost
6. Gladiatorial-combat site
7. Ornamental vessel
8. Lyric poem
9. Sleep phenomenon
10. Slapping sounds
11. Rips
12. Hurried
13. Curved portion
14. Enjoyment
15. Menace
16. Laugh loudly
17. Scoreboard column
18. Kilmer "honoree"
25. — up, crammed
28. Satiate
31. Passport endorsement
33. Ventilates
34. Shrewd
35. Dismounted
36. Solitary
38. Temptress
39. Shears
40. Occurrence
41. Royal
42. Shoulder wrap
43. Liquid amount
44. Assistant
45. Team race
46. Animals of a region
49. Short sounds
50. States of mind
53. Revere
54. Type of apartment, for short
55. Farm buildings
56. Aleutian island
58. Rainbow
59. Markets
60. Bird enclosures
62. Sections of window glass
63. As aforesaid
64. Mother Goose thin man

65. Feel
66. Fall flower
67. Broader
68. High shoes
69. "Easy Rider" vehicle
70. Memorable periods
71. Withered
73. Peeled
74. — pole
77. Adherent

78. Judge's garment
79. Veer
81. Spot
82. Lombardy capital
83. Pigeon coop
85. Likenesses
86. Dressing table
87. Cuts apart
89. Satisfied fully
90. Women given knighthood

91. Domesticates
92. Sugary
93. Trodden way
94. Monster
95. See the sights
97. Restaurant
101. Lifetime
102. Anger
103. Musician's job
104. African antelope
105. Day time: abbr.

Solution is on page 396

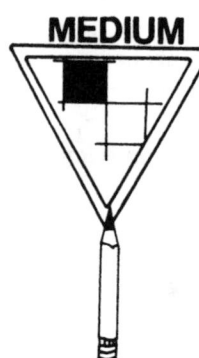

MEDIUM

ACROSS

1. City of Light
6. The latest thing!
9. Health club
12. Mrs. Bunker
13. Beer
14. Tavern
15. Inquisitive
16. Honest
18. ⅝ mile: abbr.
19. Printing: abbr.
20. Meeting place
21. James Bond, for one
23. Slim
25. "— Sir with Love," 1967 film
26. Big-man Bunyan
27. Movie spools
30. Visitors like E.T.
32. Word with "vegetable" or "flower"
33. Denise on "The Cosby Show"
34. Pigs
35. Negative answer
36. Mythical monsters
38. Carpenter's tool
39. NY canal
41. "You — There!," TV oldie
42. Laugh sound
43. Primers
45. Animal claw
48. Male
49. Actor Vigoda
50. Unattached
51. Southern State: abbr.
52. Laver or Stewart
53. — down, diminished

DOWN

1. Sty
2. Fuss
3. Dangerous
4. List entry
5. Bashful
6. Light blue, for one
7. Put in a straight row
8. Family room
9. Harpooned
10. Knitting stitch
11. Biblical brother
17. Boston-based TV sitcom
19. Along with
21. Pierce, as with a knife
22. Horseback game
23. December visitor
24. Lugs
26. Looked (at)
28. Songstress Horne
29. Winter precipitation
31. Gary's State
32. Disappeared
34. — around, roughhoused
37. "Mata Hari" actress
38. Beauty parlor
39. Ms. Bombeck
40. Authentic
42. Nimbus
44. Lend an —, listen
45. Make lace
46. United
47. Actor Beatty

Solution is on page 396

ACROSS

1. Drilling tool
4. Take a — at, try
8. Play divisions
12. Fruit drink
13. Story
14. Woody plant
15. Inflict pain
17. Jazzman Basie
18. Rave
19. Skillets
20. Incline
22. Batter's goal: 2 wds.
25. Actor Nolte
26. Salaries
27. Physician: abbr.
28. Dollar bill
29. Bakery selections
30. Crusted dessert
31. You and I
32. Rescued
33. Ghosts' cries
34. Broke suddenly
36. Owl sounds
37. Require
38. Sixty minutes
39. Storms
41. Alphabet characters
44. Tucked in
45. Put on the payroll
46. Drink slowly
47. Belonging to that woman
48. Pagan god
49. Plaything

DOWN

1. Baseball club
2. Marriage vow: 2 wds.
3. Patio
4. Daring feat
5. Small pie
6. Pub brew
7. Exist
8. Makes amends
9. Mash; squeeze
10. Decimal base
11. Harden, as cement
16. Armored vehicle
17. Court actions
19. Called publicly
20. Blizzards
21. Flax cloth
22. Used an oven
23. Simpleton
24. Ringlet
26. Fluttered
29. Sleeveless garments
30. Most needy
32. Drives too fast
33. Boxing contest
35. Wrath
36. Traveler's stopover
38. Medal-of-honor winner
39. College cheer
40. Actor Vigoda
41. Pot cover
42. River: Spanish
43. Secret agent
45. Informal greeting

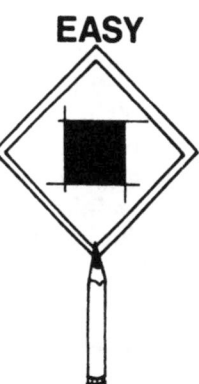

EASY

Solution is on page 396

PUNANAGRAMS

by MEL TAUB

Punanagrams are tricky but fun to solve. Definitions may be jokes or puns on the word wanted, or an anagram of the word itself. Generally there's a straight definition as a clue, too. For example, the answer to 5-Down is DARED. *Adder* is the anagram, with "Challenged" as an additional clue. Roman numerals may be used; the words YOU, ARE, EYE, SEE, etc., might stand for U, R, I and C, respectively; "energy" could stand for the letters N, R, G, or "any" for N E. Consider the definitions from all angles and you will find they do make definite sense. And, have fun!

ACROSS

1. 'Taint hot
6. Meals give folks in USSR pep
13. Where Ida sat during ball games
14. Musical group allows for these poetic forms
16. Make an offer t' finisher?
17. A place to store tent rope
18. Kind of ire?
19. Eye —'n' nose 'n' throat, almost
21. Area for an escort
22. Owe friend a gem
24. Side that fades
26. I let them put it on a floor
27. The beast wrote in Greek letters
29. Why is Leo so relaxed?
32. 50, that is
33. When he errs, sea captain uses them
35. Hairdo for wee pups
37. Assume sea-going man went to this school
38. Who I lost in Asia
39. Furnish a p-period
43. Gag isn't used when putting on play
47. Old car in Brazil, I hear
48. 1,000 Romans stop to dance
50. They go for ye ladies here
51. Liberal fellows like Carney, et al.
53. Tight, as instructed, so to speak
55. Follower of Major, when in the mood
56. You'll find them, sir, at a round-up
59. See if leaving Siegfried becomes grating
61. Something of value Ryan got out of Germany
62. E. European resident of Empire State capital?
64. Author who elates readers
66. Story of a Swiss patriot may be revealing
67. He never said No to Venus
68. De sky in de saying?
69. Sees at the onset

DOWN

1. Loftier, esp. tree
2. Is able to say good-bye to music
3. Not even 500 Romans do
4. What creditor has on Neil
5. Challenged adder
6. A boon to seer or hearer
7. It may run out of coffee
8. Bad tips put him in the hole
9. Study rope
10. Choose or select, almost
11. Could it repel the beholder?
12. He squeals; lies, too

13. It could be sort of a light
15. Peter's favorite actress
20. 'E calls " 'ello!"
23. Girl with nothing but rope
25. For Rousseau, a sure loss, but not much in France
28. Who I mess with on highways
30. Patton's not going to quarrel
31. Try a literary form?
34. Put T. on the ballot, shortly
36. Bet a wad, e.g.
39. Where Noah gazed at rara avis
40. Replied and put in jeopardy
41. Fit to drink? It may be a plot
42. Little one who makes Al complete

43. For purist, it goes right to the point
44. Men, i.e., go for her
45. In a sense, I'm prepared for retribution
46. They're underground, so G-men can't find them
49. It may attract T-man, e.g.
52. Place where horses may act evasively
54. 'Taint pygmy
57. Ain't for
58. Anna's King said "I am without aid"
60. How odd — a real joint
63. A 51-year-old Roman boxer
65. Realtor loses rare piece of property

Solution is on page 396

275

ACROSS

1. Countenance
5. Piscine fea-
   ture
8. Black-tongued
   dog
12. Eager
13. Sci-fi item, for
    short
14. Conceal
15. Popular music
17. Stopped
19. Nothing
20. Coal distillate
21. Troupe mem-
    ber
24. Habit
27. Steep, rugged
    rock
28. Caliber
29. Soak
31. Silent
32. Weight unit
33. Mongrel
34. Sixth sense,
    for short
35. Enticement
36. Rattan, e.g.
37. Ability
39. Soiree
40. Boy
41. Human being
42. Musical work
45. Appropriates
49. Common metal
50. Baseball stat,
    for short
52. Nursery color
53. Redecorate
54. Hankering
55. Tibetan crea-
    ture

DOWN

1. Distant
2. Lifetime
3. Gear tooth
4. Yule drink
5. Combustible
   material
6. Supposition
7. Musical work
8. Map
9. Towel word
10. Lyric poem
11. Marry
16. Freshen, in a
    way
18. Alleviated
21. Peak
22. Pastry item
23. Florida city
24. Certain sports
    area
25. Movie award
26. — McKinley
28. Limiting line
30. Victim
32. Fold
36. Awning
38. Grassy plain
39. Cushion
41. Principal
42. Baronet's title
43. Metallic min-
    eral
44. Signal assent
46. Dessert choice
47. High explo-
    sive, for short
48. Hit the slopes
51. Exist

Solution is on page 396

ACROSS

1. Mobile's State: abbr.
4. Prohibit
7. Like Satan
11. Mr. Linden
12. Elliptical
14. Dig for coal
15. Catch up with
17. Await decision
18. Pleasure boat
19. Sunrise direction
21. Ancient
23. Employees look forward to this
27. Ocean, to poets: 2 wds.
31. Bell's creation
32. Unusual
33. Sign of assent
35. Deborah Kerr role
36. Advantage
38. Early settler
40. Expressed consent
42. Soft earth
43. Durocher and namesakes
45. Tries out
49. Beverage choice
52. Raze: 2 wds.
54. Golf club
55. Heroic tale
56. Miss Farrow
57. Oboe, e.g.
58. "Sawbuck"
59. Urge (on)

DOWN

1. Sailor's call
2. Volcanic rock
3. Mr. Guinness
4. Cruet
5. Miss Gardner
6. Lawn tool
7. Carrying away nothing: hyph. wd.
8. Compete
9. Stopover
10. Conducted
13. Jump
16. New England State: 2 wds.
20. Tree product
22. Lair
24. Finished
25. Miss Baxter
26. 365 days
27. Waiter's need
28. Possess
29. Notable times
30. Cork's sound
34. Dark
37. Mr. Marvin
39. Exceeded
41. Specks
44. Do an usher's work
46. A few
47. Small branch
48. Obstacle
49. Churchill's title
50. Raw metal
51. Buck's mate
53. Mature

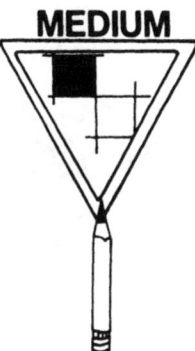

MEDIUM

Solution is on page 396

EASY

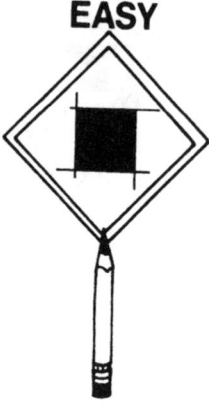

ACROSS

1. Flower support
5. Wish
9. Shadowbox
13. Contraction
14. Merit
15. Blacksmith shop
16. Gorilla
17. Proofreading symbol
18. Worship
19. Leased
21. Bosc, for one
23. Actor Danson
24. Gauge
25. Prohibits
26. Hive insects
27. Crowbars
26. Car fuel
30. —la-la
33. Lion's ruff
34. Eroded (metal)
37. O'Hare, for one
39. Companions
40. Accomplish
41. Study of plants
42. Wave
43. Gun the engine
44. Climbing plant
45. Cab fee
46. Grape plant
47. Stockings
49. Out of danger
50. Skillet
51. Likely (to)
52. Domesticated
53. Plane garage
56. Musical tone
57. Pierce
59. Mother
60. Complete
62. Corn spikes
63. Baseball's Guidry
64. Shade giver
65. Leak
66. Play roster
67. Lofty
69. Slave
70. — Francisco
71. Everyone
72. Leaning tower city
73. Steel worker
76. Mate of 59-Across
77. Vaulter's aid
78. Baseball field
79. Flee
81. Severs
82. Doctors: abbr.
83. Singleton
84. Writer
86. Concluded
88. That, and no more
89. Brother's daughter
93. Choose
94. Army group
95. Rides a bike
96. Wants
98. Pondered
100. Distress signal
101. Actor Welles
102. Location
103. Heredity unit
104. Rank
105. Allows
106. Cheers: Spanish

DOWN

1. Wasp group
2. Indian shelter
3. Happening
4. —, myself, and I
5. Commander
6. Paddle
7. Get ready
8. Comes in
9. Turf
10. File a complaint
11. Concur
12. Marsh grasses
15. Distant
17. Rite
20. — Aviv, Israel
22. Equally
25. Twisted
26. Sport fish
28. Differ
29. Shore bird
30. Bill
31. — de Janeiro
32. Painter
34. Unusual
35. Paradise
36. Peace symbol
38. Tar
39. Unadulterated
42. Eatery
43. Chime
45. Notoriety
46. Wind indicator
47. Rabbit's kin
48. Candid
49. Rational
50. Butter pieces
52. School semester
53. Angel's instrument
54. Andy's pal
55. Throw a tantrum
57. Medicine tablet
58. Fence piece
61. Narrate
63. Haphazard
65. Medicinal amount
66. Tranquil
67. Record
68. Woe!

69. Floor square
70. Spicy
72. Pontiff
73. Accompanying
74. Terminate
75. Pathways: abbr.
77. Window glass
78. Obligation

80. Competitive game
81. Civilization
84. Beast
85. Shed
86. Contributor
87. Musical production
88. Running
90. Artist's stand

91. Lookalike
92. Winding curves
94. Armed service
    branch: abbr.
95. Pod vegetables
97. Fawn's mother
99. Established
103. Leave

Solution is on page 397

ACROSS

1. Foolish one: slang
4. Condition
9. Possessive pronoun
12. Lyric poem
13. Heathen
14. Society-page word
15. Feeling
17. Old hand; for short
18. Expert
19. Observe closely
21. Malice
24. Certain relatives
28. Another possessive pronoun
29. Mushroom part
30. Pack away
31. Corn spike
32. Exist
33. Single
34. Sour
36. Flushed
37. Raised
38. Good wishes
40. Sheriff's band
41. Mr. Onassis, to friends
42. Express disapproval
43. Likely
45. Ravage
51. Falsehood
52. Remove any sign of
53. 2,000 lbs.
54. Conducted
55. Ranked
56. Female sheep

DOWN

1. Distress signal
2. Fruit drink
3. Enclosure
4. Zest
5. Docile
6. Grow older
7. Shade of brown
8. Join
9. Whitney and Bell
10. Golf gadget
11. Established
16. Makes lace
20. Sure!
21. Use a cutting tool
22. Tranquility
23. Watered
24. Peels
25. Mimicked
26. Musical sounds
27. Stockholm native
29. Member of the deck
35. Patriotic women's group: abbr.
37. To —, besides
39. Passenger
40. Modeled
42. Foundation
43. Everyone
44. Dessert choice
46. Notable age
47. Tank
48. Consumed
49. Pull
50. Compass point

Solution is on page 397

MEDIUM

ACROSS

1. Craze
4. Idle notion
8. Blackhearted
12. Pay dirt
13. Unctuous
14. Hawaiian goose
15. National Guard members
17. Head: French
18. Facility
19. Lethargy
21. Break down (a sentence)
23. Pronoun
24. One of the seven deadly sins
25. Related series
29. Caviar
30. Center of attention
31. Bullfight cry: Spanish
32. Example
34. Betelgeuse, for one
35. City in Latvia
36. Sycophant
37. Magnificent
40. Check
41. Continent
42. Columbus' sponsor
46. Church season
47. Artifice
48. Ages and ages
49. Playing card
50. Expensive
51. Filthy place

DOWN

1. In favor of
2. Exist
3. Merits
4. Less good
5. Busy place
6. Island: French
7. Friedan's "The Feminine —"
8. Main course
9. George Bush, e.g.
10. Preposition
11. Sly look
16. Posing no difficulty
20. Blame
21. Persian elf
22. At another time
23. Birthplace of Mohammed
25. Canary
26. Persons of great reputation
27. Dressed
28. Weird
30. Bazaar
33. Agreement between nations
34. Tender
36. Potato
37. NaCl
38. Consumer
39. Evergreen
40. House: Spanish
43. "Peggy — Got Married"
44. Fortune
45. Some

HARD

Solution is on page 397

SPECIAL CHALLENGER CROSSWORD

by JOHN M. SAMSON

Here is a real toughie for you. We have omitted giving you such helps
as "2 wds.," "hyph. wd.," and "slang"; but in the spirit of fair play,
all abbreviations and foreign words are so indicated.

ACROSS

1. Third World, e.g.
5. Machine-shop items
10. God of the under-world
15. Harvest
19. Oar: Italian
20. Fictional Mr. Heep
21. "— -porridge hot . . ."
22. Start of a Shakespeare comedy
23. Divisible by two
24. Ropelike vine
25. Chose (to)
26. Jumping bug
27. Photos of yore
29. Gold measure
31. Unimpaired
33. Race-track fence
34. Twentieth century art patron
35. Hook's henchman
36. Like Polly Flinders' clothes
39. Part of VCR
40. Glade
44. See 1-Down
45. Athenian lawgiver
46. Laughing
47. Free from taboo, in Tahiti
48. "Dies —"
49. Harsh-voiced parrot
50. Tempus —
51. Fanatic group
52. Lobster trap
53. Fountain treat
54. Bates, of "Psycho"
56. Florentine painter
57. Somnambulate
60. Couturier name
61. Personal conduct
62. One's daily bread
63. Zeal
65. See socially
66. Profession
69. Genu
70. One's forte
75. Maleficent acts
76. Abandon
78. Keynes' field: abbr.
79. Actress Mary, from Scotland
80. Trunk article
81. Conclusive
82. Bittern, e.g.
84. Precise; proper
85. JFK abbreviation
86. Splits
87. Arroyo
88. Cara or Ryan
89. Capital of Chile
91. "Sesame Street" denizen
92. Like some nickels?
93. Protagonist
94. "Tribute" playwright
95. Four gills
96. Bondman
99. "De Profundis" poet
100. Save
104. Solarium, e.g.
105. Cheer up
107. Criticize mercilessly
109. Home of baseball's champs
110. Transept end
111. Cut in two
112. Wipe out
113. Denary numbers
114. Military meal
115. Shabby
116. Mel's TV locale
117. Cloy

DOWN

1. Western author, with 44-Across
2. A son of Jacob
3. Cracked mirror, e.g.
4. Penitent
5. Ambo
6. Historian Durant
7. Wedge-shaped inlets
8. Tawny
9. Try to blackmail
10. Portuguese port
11. Compensate
12. Suffragette Carrie
13. Employ
14. Lees
15. Roof support
16. Actress Raines
17. Scot's name
18. Trial college boards: abbr.
28. Ivy League school
30. Sun disk
32. Shipshape
34. River at Yuma
35. Slaughtered
36. Junk, caravel and clipper
37. Word of mouth
38. Emulate Cicero
39. Outspoken
40. Prop for Groucho
41. Bury
42. He was in "Extreme Prejudice"
43. U. of Florida athlete
45. A Peace Nobelist of 1978
46. Hearsay
49. Greenskeeper's need
50. Cold: Spanish

282

51. Capital of Crete
53. Espionage agents
55. More peculiar
56. Lustrous fabric
58. Colosseum official
59. Dorothy's home
61. City in Georgia
64. Lively dance
65. Hunter's lure
66. Boundaries
67. Peronista heroine
68. Red Sea island
69. A Japanese sport
71. "Hostess with the mostest" Mesta

72. Enticed
73. Threefold
74. Site of San'a
76. "Aussie" wild dog
77. Bellowed
81. Intrepid
83. Nobelist Wiesel
84. Dissents
86. Cambodian coin
87. Mortarboard wearer
88. Charged atoms
90. River at Henley
91. Queen of whodunits

92. "The Lion in —"
94. Positioned on
95. Group of deputies
96. Coal carrier
97. Motto of Rhode Island
98. Polar explorer
99. Breaker
100. Actor in "Brian's Song"
101. Actress Perlman
102. Outlet
103. Facilitate
106. Jamie — Curtis
108. Mouth: prefix

Solution is on page 397

DIAGRAMLESS

MEDIUM

This Diagramless is 15 boxes wide by 15 boxes deep.

ACROSS

1. Definite article
4. Serving dish
5. No longer original
6. Statute
9. Form
10. — off, start a play in hockey
11. Stairway part
12. Accomplish
14. Frosted, as a cake
15. Ill-mannered people
16. Window sections
18. Roof edge
19. Cuts with the teeth
20. Before: poetic
21. Gentleman: Spanish
22. That woman
25. Dutch flower
26. Pack closely, as cargo

27. Telephone salutation
28. Subdivision of a play
29. Valuable fur
30. Negative response
32. Apple center
33. Mr. Carney and namesakes
34. Summer TV fare
36. Opposite of 30-Across
37. Aircraft-detecting device
38. News article
39. Animal enclosure

DOWN

1. Stumble
2. Detested
3. Organ of sight
4. Snares
5. At that place
6. Shoestrings

7. High cards
8. Marry
9. Heating apparatus
10. Of better quality
11. Fly aloft
13. Judgement
15. Honey-making insect
17. Upon
19. Chime, for one
21. Pouts
22. Strict
23. Sharpen
24. Female sheep
25. Canvas shelters
26. Clean by rubbing vigorously
27. Employ
28. "Go away!": slang
29. "Merry" month
31. Speak pompously
35. Paradise
37. Tear (apart)

Solution is on page 397

DIAGRAMLESS   EXPERT

This Diagramless is 21 boxes wide by 21 boxes deep.
Starting box is on page 407.

ACROSS

1. Plat parcel: 2 wds.
5. Contend (with)
6. Incident
8. Dispatcher
10. Calyx leaf
12. Gaiter
16. Additional clause
18. Great Lakes acronym
20. Café
22. Word with "smoke" or "fire"
23. Respected
27. Hodgepodges
29. Market location
33. Loan shark's act
34. Bear's order to his broker
35. "G.W.T.W." setting
36. Stupid
37. Husky burdens, often
42. Brightly colored bird
44. Star: suffix
45. Barracks picture
46. Very, with "so"
47. Objects
50. Subordinate to
51. Site of Knossos
52. Put to sea
55. Fate; doom
57. Valuable find, for short
58. Gives way
60. Reddish-brown hue
61. Spent
63. Musical farmer's locale
64. Clearheaded
66. Stile, e.g.
69. Part of a teapot
70. Border
71. Drowse

DOWN

1. "Snake eyes"
2. Nil, to Lendl
3. Starts the bidding
4. Warmhearted
7. Lukewarm
9. Word on a tire
11. ". . . — me your ears"
12. Pretense
13. Lech Walesa, e.g.
14. Stockpile
15. Concise
17. Remounts, out West
19. Refinery
21. Levitates
24. Smallest of a litter
25. Gaelic
26. Batik processor
28. Bondservant
29. Gawk
30. Game of "It"
31. Regions
32. Range ropes
37. 'Tater
38. Salesman's "spiel"
39. Companion to "odds"

40. Opera highlights

41. Dash

43. Lepidopterist's tool

48. Stuck in the mud

49. Incline

51. Site of Nicosia

53. Wickedness

54. Negotiate (with)

56. Hardware item

59. Denominations

62. Infant wear

65. Electron tube

67. Bearskins, sometimes

68. Galley notation

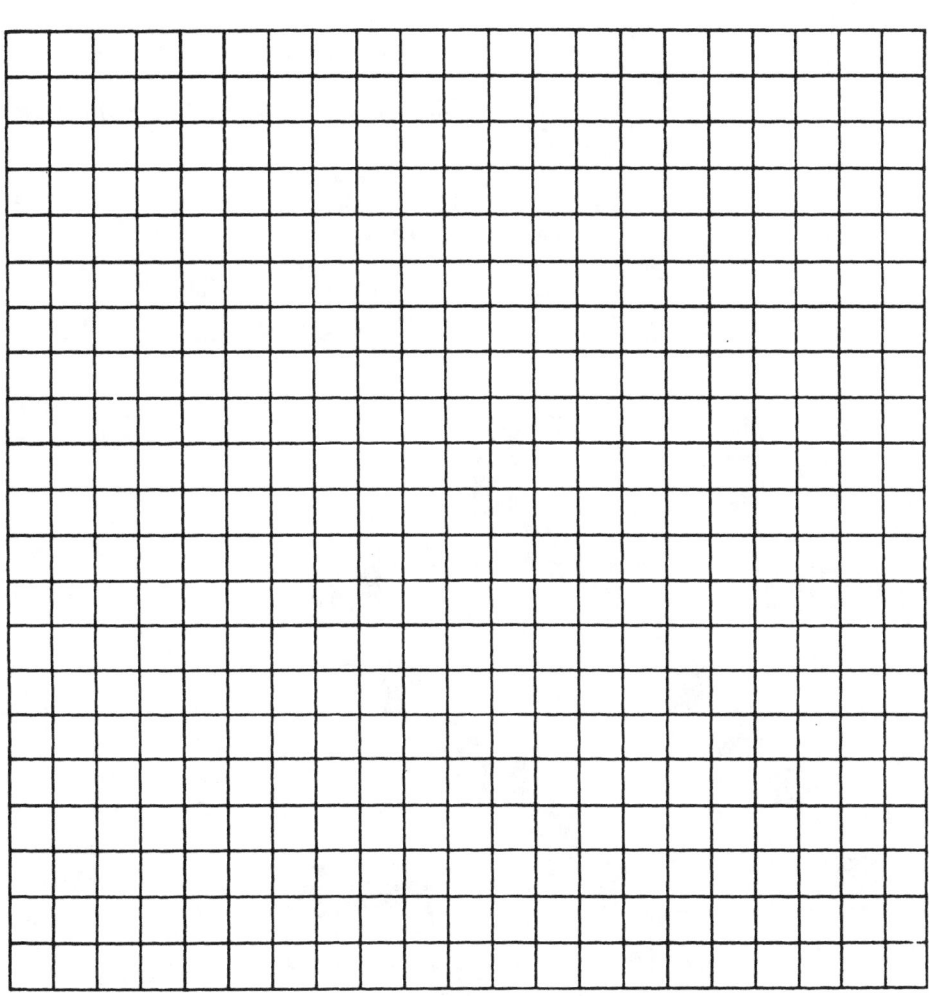

Solution is on page 398

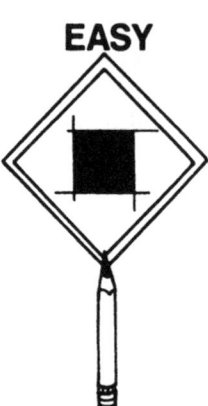

EASY

ACROSS

1. Wager
4. Cabbage dish, for short
8. Wound mark
12. Actress Gardner
13. Ripped
14. Cab
15. Oil-well tower
17. Longed (for)
18. Writing fluid
19. Actress Turner
20. Loud kiss
23. Performed a certain circus act
26. Fork part
27. Dull people
28. Baton Rouge's State: abbr.
29. Have lunch
30. Phonies
31. Very small amount
32. Morning: abbr.
33. Musical sounds
34. Dry, as a dish
35. Iguanas and chameleons
37. Salaries
38. B.P.O.E. members
39. Chum
40. Judge's garments
42. Cancel: 2 wds.
46. Deserve
47. Fill a suitcase
48. Female deer
49. Darn!
50. Carney and Linkletter
51. Morning moisture

DOWN

1. Wicked
2. The first woman
3. Paving substance
4. Strong, unpleasant smell
5. Tress
6. Noah's boat
7. You and I
8. Bee "bites"
9. Panama or Erie
10. Chopping tool
11. Get — of, eliminate
16. Oriental grain
17. Book leaves
19. Fishing baits
20. Shoplift
21. Florida city
22. Picnic pest
23. Funny stories
24. Wed secretly
25. Social engagements
27. Musical groups
30. Eating utensils
31. "The — is up!"
33. Natural ability
34. Room divider
36. Striped animal
37. Strolls
39. Treaty
40. A bright color
41. Boat paddle
42. Automobile
43. Strange; unusual
44. Enemy
45. Opposite of many
47. Ma's mate

Solution is on page 398

ACROSS

1. Presidential nickname
4. Child's summer resort
8. Begone!
12. Chum
13. Length x width
14. Ocean surge
15. Gathers: 2 wds.
17. Caesar, for one
18. Conducted
19. Unadorned
20. School group
23. Dispatch: 2 wds.
26. Tortoise's adversary
27. Bed boards
28. Not on your life!
29. Had lunch
30. Reads briefly
31. Brooch
32. Augusta is its capital: abbr.
33. Petty quarrels
34. Fence door
35. Get ready
37. Puts in order of preference
38. Rural road
39. Male sheep
40. Mako, for one
42. Invents: 2 wds.
46. Detest
47. Change position
48. Put in service
49. Potato buds
50. Performs (a deed)
51. Travel guide

DOWN

1. Likely (to)
2. Lamb's cry
3. Antlered animal
4. Lawsuits
5. Desertlike
6. Chess pieces
7. Mr. Kettle
8. Dueling weapons
9. Portrait-bearing gem
10. Ms. Gardner
11. "Sawbuck"
16. Differently
17. Talks wildly
19. Pinto and lima
20. The winner: slang
21. Tardier
22. Exist
23. List of candidates
24. Join together
25. Musical sounds
27. Frighten
30. Paddle (a child)
31. Butter square
33. Certain tires
34. Olympic event
36. Perk up
37. Garden tools
39. Critic's favorable review
40. That girl
41. Dried grass
42. Dairy sound
43. Total
44. Yankeeland: abbr.
45. Brisk energy
47. Physician: abbr.

EASY

Solution is on page 398

ACROSS

1. Chats: slang
5. Snow runner
8. Pierce
12. Revise
13. Skirt edge
14. Hawkeye State
15. Presidential "no"
16. Newspaper employee
18. Chick's cry
20. Pesty plants
21. Slanted
24. Egg producer
25. Even
26. Wet earth
27. "Demon" drink
30. Finished
31. Small child
32. Heal
33. Can material
34. Race unit
35. Suspends
36. Chest bone
37. Flat-bottomed boats
38. Safe spot
41. Identical
42. Nome natives
44. Rim; border
48. Final
49. Cooking vessel
50. Film "spool"
51. Washington bills
52. Woolly mama
53. Search for

DOWN

1. Minister's title: abbr.
2. Citrus cooler
3. Cherry seed
4. Plug
5. Grate
6. Hold on to; retain
7. Little demon
8. Warning signal
9. Carry; haul
10. Filled with wonder
11. Soap units
17. Was in debt
19. Snaky fish
21. Mailbox opening
22. Son of Jacob
23. Baking chamber
24. Crude cabin
26. Swab
27. Ladder step
28. Exhort
29. Army meal
31. Dinner bill
32. Professions
34. Chain unit
35. Son of Noah
36. Relaxes
37. Stitch loosely
38. Angel's "headgear"
39. Actor Alda
40. Flower holder
41. Wintry flakes
43. Mimic
45. Actress, Ruby —
46. Golly!
47. Mooselike deer

Solution is on page 398

ACROSS

1. Knock sharply
4. Ring-shaped island
9. Certain chess pieces: abbr.
12. Mine find
13. Magna —
14. Laughter sound
15. Affirmative reply
16. Explosive
17. Prepared
19. Appropriated for oneself
21. Recreation spot
22. Pointed weapon
24. Room "topper"
27. Young salmon
28. Lifting machine
29. Word of choice
30. Biblical beast
31. Coastline
32. In the style of: 2 wds.
33. Has being
34. Type of wrap
35. Thicke, of "Growing Pains"
36. Jewish month starter: 2 wds.
38. Embed
39. Ranks
40. Grain enclosure
41. Actor's platform
43. "Exodus" hero
44. Everyone
47. Vigor
48. Poe's bird
50. One of the Stooges
51. Linear measurements: abbr.
52. Winter weather
53. Supped

DOWN

1. Judge Bean
2. Exist
3. Annoys
4. Thespian
5. Combat vehicle
6. Leftover scrap
7. Military officer: abbr.
8. Actress Day
9. Yellowish-brown
10. A Lincoln son
11. Timid
18. Perry's creator
20. Rower's need
21. Ms. Bailey
22. Toledo's country
23. Out of fashion
24. Tiara
25. Pitcher Ryan
26. Give (permission)
28. Tumult
31. April weather
32. CSA member
34. L.A. weather
35. "The Greatest"
37. Envelops
38. Patterned cloth
40. Algonquian Indian
41. Watch covertly
42. Turner or Mack
43. Hail!
45. Fortune
46. Confederate commander
49. Mr. Pacino

Solution is on page 398

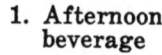

ACROSS

1. Afternoon beverage
4. Hopping insects
9. Sleeping place
12. Canoe paddle
13. Smallest amount
14. Fruit drink
15. Gift
17. Stove
19. Allow
20. Place for a ring
21. Sugary
24. Searches (for)
25. Magic stick
26. Melodies
27. All right
29. To — fro
30. Villages
31. Enthusiast
32. "— and My Girl"
33. Christmas plant
34. Freshwater fish
35. Short letters
36. Not as good
37. Fires a gun
39. Automobile
40. Use up needlessly
41. Ragged clothes
45. Malt beverage
46. Lift up
48. Maple-tree contents
49. Affirmative reply
50. Very thin, as fabric
51. Timid

DOWN

1. Spinning toy
2. Spike of corn
3. "Roses — red"
4. Group of ships
5. Christian fasting period
6. Dine
7. While
8. Cords
9. Gun sounds
10. Border
11. Antlered animal
16. Child's winter vehicle
18. Picnic pests
20. Amusing
21. Moved in water
22. Decrease
23. Conclude
24. Wolf sounds
26. Shoe bottoms
27. Large shade trees
28. Leg joint
30. Staggers
31. Evergreen tree
33. Owl's cry
34. Opposite of starboard
35. Organs of smell
36. Basic thirst quencher
37. Swing from side to side
38. Healthy
39. Assignment for Sherlock Holmes
41. Bind
42. Curvy letter
43. Cheer sound
44. Secret agent
47. Expression of delight

Solution is on page 398

ACROSS

1. Clasp; grip
5. Fur scarves
9. Sorrowful
12. Toward shelter
13. Curved door-way
14. Historic period
15. Not standing
17. Lifted
19. Integrity
20. Back part
21. Exhort
23. Kingdom
27. Add
31. Dogwood
32. And not
33. Stage play
35. Long fish
36. Frank
38. Winter storm
40. More recent
42. Not false
43. Chicago team
45. Indian prince
49. Inconstant
52. Capital of Montana
53. Mine product
54. Facility
56. Aroma
57. Golly!
58. Remain
59. Color slightly

DOWN

1. Minced-meat dish
2. Butter substi-tute
3. Thin
4. Roundabout way
5. Immoral
6. — else!
7. Pain
8. Cut, as wool
9. Place
10. Exist
11. Mom's mate
16. Went wrong
18. Worry
20. Seasons again
22. Clothing
24. Region
25. Ogle
26. Pinochle term
27. Privy to: 2 wds.
28. Slangy nega-tive
29. Ship's company
30. Moslem prince
34. Sky-blue
37. Place for a choker
39. Fanatic
41. Command-ments
44. Thrash
46. "Return of the —," movie
47. Soon, to poets
48. Deer
49. Obscuring mist
50. Anger
51. Average grade
52. Attention-getting word
55. Continent: abbr.

MEDIUM

Solution is on page 399

BIBLE CROSSWORD   MEDIUM

by MARILYN WING

Bible references in this puzzle are from the King James Version. You'll find it stimulating to solve, and may discover you know more Bible than you think you do.

ACROSS

1. —, and it shall be given you. *Matt. 7:7*
4. Maintain good works for necessary —. *Titus 3:14*
8. — what I am. *I Cor. 15:10* (2 words)
11. Mine enemies and my —s came upon me. *Ps. 27:2*
12. — . . . prepared an ark. *Heb. 11:7*
13. Within . . . an half — of land. *I Sam. 14:14*
14. Take . . . the t— from him, and give it unto him which hath ten talents. *Matt. 25:28*
16. Their — was as the torment of a scorpion. *Rev. 9:5*
18. The king . . . hired masons and carpenters to — the house. *II Chr. 24:12*
20. — them about thy neck. *Prov. 6:21*
21. They spar— like the colour of burnished brass. *Ezek. 1:7*
23. As the birds that are caught in the —. *Eccles. 9:12*
27. The servant is — from his master. *Job 3:19*
30. Prophets . . . — with their teeth. *Mic. 3:5*
32. They hanged Haman on the —lows. *Esth. 7:10*
33. — us not into temptation. *Matt. 6:13*
34. Be of good ch—; thy sins be forgiven. *Matt. 9:2*
35. The beasts go into —, and remain. *Job 37:8*
36. Thine ox and thine — may rest. *Ex. 23:12*
37. Where I am, there ye may be —. *St. John 14:3*
38. The children's teeth are set on —. *Jer. 31:29*
39. There were seven — to go up to it. *Ezek. 40:26*
41. Yet shall he be brought to the grave, and shall remain in the —. *Job 21:32*
43. Thou anointest my head with —. *Ps. 23:5*
45. We are the clay, and thou our —. *Isa. 64:8*
49. Cast thy burden upon the Lord, and he shall — thee. *Ps. 55:22*
53. Ye shall not shout, nor make any —. *Josh. 6:10*
54. Whether —ent or absent, we may be accepted. *II Cor. 5:9*
55. Hast thou not . . . curdled me like ch—? *Job 10:10*
57. Thou art a wise —. *I Ki. 2:9*
58. Our word toward you was not — and nay. *II Cor. 1:18*
59. He should not — long in the place. *Hos. 13:13*
60. They have mouths, — they speak not. *Ps. 115:5*

DOWN

1. The noise was heard — off. *Ezra 3:13*
2. The dove found no rest for the — of her foot. *Gen. 8:9*
3. The Lord will preserve him, and — him alive. *Ps. 41:2*
4. I . . . stayed there — now. *Gen. 32:4*
5. God — loved the world. *St. John 3:16*
6. If any man hunger, let him —. *I Cor. 11:34*
7. Elisha said, Shoot. And he —. *II Ki. 13:17*

8. He casteth forth his — . . . : who can stand before his cold? *Ps. 147:17*
9. Gather the wheat into my b—. *Matt. 13:30*
10. They — Moses and Aaron, who stood in the way. *Ex. 5:20*
13. Prayer ending
15. Thou wast — and bare. *Ezek. 16:7*
17. They shall — from the dead. *Mark 12:25*
19. Rebel not against the Lord, nor — against us. *Josh. 22:19*
22. Where thou —, will I die. *Ruth 1:17*
24. With us are both the gray-headed and very — men. *Job 15:10*
25. All Israel shouted . . . so that the earth — again. *I Sam. 4:5*
26. I am the Lord, and there is none —. *Isa. 45:5*
27. Creatures ran and returned as . . . a —h of lightning. *Ezek. 1:14*
28. They may — from their labours. *Rev. 14:13*
29. Take thine —, eat, drink, and be merry. *Luke 12:19*

31. The Philistines were gathered . . . into a —. *II Sam. 23:11*
35. Forgive us our debts, as we forgive our —rs. *Matt. 6:12*
37. The churches of — salute you. *I Cor. 16:19*
40. I set before the sons . . . — full of wine. *Jer. 35:5*
42. The love of — is the root of all evil. *I Tim. 6:10*
44. A false witness will utter —. *Prov. 14:5*
46. They prepared —er and stones to build the house. *I Ki. 5:18*
47. Was not — Jacob's brother? *Mal. 1:2*
48. The veil of the temple was — in twain. *Matt. 27:51*
49. The son of Nun sent . . . two men to — secretly. *Josh. 2:1*
50. Now are we s— that thou knowest all things. *St. John 16:30*
51. The — of Galilee
52. Cast the — on the right side of the ship. *St. John 21:6*
56. What I —y unto you I say unto all. *Mark 13:37*

Solution is on page 399

ACROSS

1. State executives: abbr.
5. Emmets
9. Doze (off)
12. Cut and splice (film)
13. Brusque
14. Where: Lat.
15. Arizona town
16. Canal of note
17. River: Spanish
18. Adherent: suffix
20. "The Fairie Queen" author
22. Marsh gas
25. Trevino or Majors
26. Mr. Wallach
27. Filipino Moslem
29. Eden dweller
32. Pewter ingredient
33. Current fashion
35. Defunct basketball league: abbr.
36. Droops
38. Dry; barren
39. Come down with
40. "Collar"
42. English satiric painter, 1697-1764
44. Keenly
47. Aussie bird
48. California's Big —
49. City in Ohio
51. Icelandic epic
54. Overhead railways
55. Completed
56. Selves
57. Dined
58. Greeley's direction
59. Smell

DOWN

1. Jewel stone
2. Pindaric work
3. Home health care provider: 2 wds.
4. Hidden booty
5. Part of a royal flush
6. Children's poems: 2 wds.
7. Outing
8. Sword: poetic
9. Remained annoyed: 3 wds.
10. Drama award
11. Famous fashion designer
19. Knitted pomponned hats
21. Teachers' organization: abbr.
22. Shea Stadium athletes
23. Director Kazan
24. Part of N.B.
28. Medley
30. Be accessory to
31. High school subject
34. Advantage
37. Met, as a legislature
41. Underneath
43. Moslem leader
44. On "the briny"
45. Religious sect
46. Not taped
50. Learned skill
52. "Meet John —"
53. Query

Solution is on page 399

296

ACROSS

1. Tic — toe
4. Word with "hopper" and "roots"
9. Mr. Linkletter
12. Pie — mode: 2 wds.
13. Metal fastener
14. Golfer Trevino
15. Put back
17. Wear away
19. Musical sound
20. Extend across
21. Stay on one's feet
23. Marionettes
26. A Great Lake
27. Tiresome ones
28. That thing
29. Moving truck
30. Showed concern
31. —-la-la
32. Mr. Sullivan
33. More painful
34. Look closely (at)
35. Irritates
37. Group of students
38. Fuse together
39. Basketball player's target
40. Moist, sticky substance
42. Eskimo's spear
45. Atmosphere
46. Stare angrily (at)
48. Number of wheels on a bicycle
49. Solidify
50. Alleviates
51. Matched collection

DOWN

1. Paving substance
2. Pub brew
3. Ahab or Nemo
4. Magnificent
5. Cereal grass
6. Wide street: abbr.
7. Compass direction: abbr.
8. Pressed down (on the brakes)
9. Without company
10. Primary color
11. Golf peg
16. Solitary
18. Knocks sharply
20. More confident
21. Number of dwarfs in "Snow White"
22. Swap
23. Skin openings
24. Becomes weary
25. Famous actors
27. Uncovered
30. Destination for some high-school grads
31. Pekoe brewers
33. Plant stalk
34. Drop heavily
36. Spin
37. Apple centers
39. Rabbit's kin
40. Droop
41. Fib
42. Owns
43. Be indebted to
44. Negative word
47. California city: abbr.

Solution is on page 399

ACROSS

1. Illuminating device
5. Secret agent
8. Mop (the deck)
12. At a distance
13. Golf peg
14. Scarlett O'Hara's home
15. Stanley —, auto
17. Ali Baba and the — Thieves
18. Scottish cap
19. Shopping area
20. Ticket taker
23. Woods
26. Clarinet accessory
27. Rescued
28. Mr. Jolson
29. Summer fruit drink
30. Airport boarding areas
31. Boxing term: abbr.
32. — Scala, opera house
33. Ceramic squares
34. Ooze
35. Tangled
37. Some horses
38. Chums
39. Drone
40. There are 52 in a deck
42. Moves clumsily
46. Medicinal plant
47. "— Casey," TV doctor
48. A Great Lake
49. On needles and —
50. Wager
51. Engrossed

DOWN

1. — Vegas
2. Rearward, on a ship
3. Actress West
4. Chattered
5. Flower part
6. Part of MPH
7. "Oh, come all — faithful . . ."
8. Put aside
9. Blemishes
10. Mr. Linkletter
11. Body of water
16. Stain
17. Transportation costs
19. Relocates
20. Russian mountains
21. Roofed auto
22. "— Haw"
23. Destined
24. Spoken for
25. Feeds (the pigs)
27. Supermarket special events
30. Fish parts
31. Hot beverage
33. Swaps
34. Sad; melancholy
36. Pinafore
37. Liquor
39. Stalk
40. Bottle top
41. Noted boxing champion
42. Confederate general
43. Baseball stat: abbr.
44. Tear
45. Group of objects
47. Gun pellet

Solution is on page 399

ACROSS

1. — Angeles
4. Celebrities
9. Mr. Lincoln, to pals
12. Consume
13. Spring flower
14. Young boy
15. Period of note
16. Frozen water
17. Aromas
19. Combat vehicle
21. Jungle "king"
22. Broken-arm support
24. Art dealer's establishment
27. Whistle blast
28. Desert animal
29. Laugh sound
30. Actor Howard
31. Bestowed love (on)
32. Evergreen
33. While
34. More painful
35. Small lake
36. Arms
38. Shows concern
39. Autos
40. Gasp for air
41. Rage
43. Newsman Rather
44. Employ
47. Hearing organ
48. Idolize
50. Fall month: abbr.
51. Woman's name
52. Sound qualities
53. Ram's mate

DOWN

1. Actor Majors
2. Boat paddle
3. Depot
4. Bee bite
5. Nip's "pal"
6. Pub brew
7. Newport's State: abbr.
8. Went bad
9. By oneself
10. Exclude (from)
11. Sullivan and Asner
18. Toy baby
20. Small insect
21. More crippled
22. Sipping aid
23. Not tight
24. Fence doors
25. Drama, "Watch on the —"
26. 36-inch units
28. Foot ailments
31. Welcome rug's kin
32. Chinese-cookie insert
34. Practice boxing
35. Cooking vessel
37. Oak nut
38. Walking sticks
40. Peel
41. Baltic, for one
42. Beige
43. Actor Johnson
45. Plant seeds
46. Actress Arden
49. Perform

EASY

Solution is on page 399

PUNANAGRAMS

HARD

by MEL TAUB

Punanagrams are tricky but fun to solve. Definitions may be jokes or puns on the word wanted, or an anagram of the word itself. Generally there's a straight definition as a clue, too. For example, the answer to 35-Across is DISMAYS; *Miss Day* is the anagram, with "Fills with apprehension" as an additional clue. Roman numerals may be used; the words YOU, ARE, EYE, SEE, etc., might stand for U, R, I and C, respectively; "energy" could stand for the letters N, R, G, or "any" for N E. Consider the definitions from all angles and you will find they do make definite sense. And, have fun!

ACROSS

1. Vandalizes the Hearsts
8. Oklahoman drops off Kohn at Texas shrine
13. Arizona town antedating Sir Walter?
14. Sm. oral phenomena
16. If it's 5, Ron sure is exceeding the limit
17. Beard associated with tiaras
18. See att. to settle this
19. Is he from Siberia? No sir!
21. Don't ever observe cry
22. Hank around Stanley
23. Sounds like malicious manner
24. It's a long way from Lima
25. Hit's below the hankle
26. Who goes with d' uncle?
28. Heathen finds it appalling to lose pill
29. Trying to get isn't
31. He & Ellen are Greek
33. Kind of ante?
34. Does my abandoning Marty make me a deserter?
35. Fills Miss Day with apprehension
39. Did he find singing a strain?
43. Not much air up there
44. A fellow insurance man
46. It's in one of 261 rowboats
47. Showed we left wearing boots
48. It's polite to leave a lot of money
49. Buffalo man with fish? Why?
50. Kind of snip?
51. Get a load of him!
52. Where Luigi met Al at two
54. Act 5 owes all to book
56. Man Arnie met in Erivan
58. Let Ida be followed
59. Terms not to be confused with tranquility
60. Comes close to snare
61. Notice leaf oozing?

DOWN

1. On Wall Street you may find him
2. Source of income for Al Stern
3. A p-power of d-decision
4. He knows what plaids cost
5. Shoved down the middle
6. The start of eternity
7. 'Taint bus
8. A big pipe with force
9. It comes out of l' mine
10. He's the rage from Algeria
11. Rub with the same gas
12. Neither a little nor a lot of bird
13. Get Streep ready beforehand
15. He had his base in ancient Italy

20. She's listed under the B.
23. Ruffian may gum up the works
24. Where Mathilda hid out
26. Money down the drain in Jordan
27. Hadroit fellow?
28. Is Ellen apt to grow one?
30. Mated in the zoo
32. — Copland (Irish-American composer?)
35. He posted an edict
36. With whom to have a chat in Greek
37. This fellow, to her, is not too tall
38. Spoke from the dais
39. Ming's predecessor?

40. Factories, a lot, go in for this
41. Shine during a tirade
42. Nordics such as Ryan
45. Shows malicious satisfaction to those who go last
48. Lops D off dawdles and goes slowly
49. An ace of Crete capital
51. Rave in court
52. Hungarian masquerading as emir
53. Kind of tress?
55. Back of a secret sect's cab?
57. — bucks (money made by shad fishermen)

Solution is on page 400

ACROSS

1. Arrest (a criminal)
4. Hula —, '50s fad
8. Open-handed blow
12. Put in service
13. Biblical name
14. Goodbye, to a Briton: hyph. wd.
15. Movie house
17. Discharged (a gun)
18. Garden tools
19. Wedding band
20. Revolves
22. Perils
25. Reside
26. Is fond of
27. Near
28. Pub brew
29. Skeleton parts
30. — a la mode
31. "Show Me" State: abbr.
32. Good reviews
33. Remedy amount
34. Hits
36. — down, watered
37. Above
38. Chums
39. Book leaves
41. Gather
44. Always
45. Hammer or saw
46. Prosecute
47. Armed conflicts
48. Wide-eyed birds
49. Visualize

DOWN

1. Pecan
2. Fire remnant
3. Busy place
4. Detests
5. Lyric poems
6. Canoe paddle
7. Afternoon: abbr.
8. Wasp bites
9. Big
10. Lunched
11. Cushion
16. First-rate: 2 wds.
17. Speeding penalties
19. Pronged garden tools
20. Shuts noisily
21. Aviator
22. Eats in style
23. Elevate
24. Spirited horse
26. Sweetheart
29. Makes cookies
30. Own
32. Comedienne Joan
33. Child's "baby"
35. Pilot's "OK"
36. Corridors
38. Swimming site
39. Church seat
40. Actress Gardner
41. Dairy animal
42. Actor's signal
43. Golf mound
45. As far as

Solution is on page 400

ACROSS

1. Otherwise
5. Thick head of hair
8. Pillow cover
12. Direct
13. Feeling of fear and wonder
14. Villain's adversary
15. Statuette
17. Rainbow goddess
18. Is able to
19. Sunflower State
21. Golf score
24. Rescue
25. Ground
26. Garden hose, for one
27. — for, choose
30. Cry of surprise
31. Misty moisture
32. Hawaiian food
33. Shack
34. Butter alternative
35. Ringlet
36. Agitate
37. Speed
38. Strikes (out)
41. Waterproof boot
42. Hautboy
43. Tongue twister, for one
48. Floating ice sheet
49. Skill
50. Simple
51. Hiker's shelter
52. Fishing snare
53. Banyan

DOWN

1. Sprite
2. Maui garland
3. Droop
4. Inferred from data
5. Chief
6. Possess
7. Baby's hiding game
8. Luster
9. That woman's
10. Diva's song
11. Velvety plants
16. Beam of light
20. Declare positively
21. Dull: slang
22. Honolulu's island
23. Small fly
24. Terrific!
26. Charm
27. Musical work
28. Harbor
29. Mah-jongg piece
31. Ballot
35. Seal of approval
36. Popular Halloween costume
37. Sombrero
38. Attic
39. Competent
40. Before long
41. Golf stroke
44. Metal mineral
45. Distant
46. Employ
47. Cleaning-fluid ingredient

MEDIUM

Solution is on page 400

ACROSS

1. Opening; break
4. Summit
7. Gift topper
10. Lubricate
11. Reverent wonder
12. Clock information
13. Idealist
15. Characteristic
16. High cards
17. Smallest amount
18. Prices
20. Heavy metal
21. Woe is me!
22. Ocean
23. Paradise
27. Males
28. Faucet
29. Before: poetic
30. Cooking vessels
32. Skill
33. Huge continent
34. Skinny
36. Armada
37. Eating utensil
39. Ale's kin
40. Sharp end
41. Voted into office
44. Sound quality
45. Guided
46. Make a mistake
47. Picnic pest
48. Physicians: abbr.
49. Dawn to dusk

DOWN

1. Supreme being
2. Broadcast
3. Nice
4. Domesticates
5. Is in debt
6. For each
7. Partiality
8. Leave out
9. Moist
12. Swap
14. Behaves
15. Afternoon affair
17. Jumped
18. Live in tents
19. Bread spread, for short
20. Gain knowledge
22. Discoloration
24. Marooned
25. Great Lake
26. Tidy
31. Small rock
33. Actor Guinness
35. Torrid
36. Nourishes
37. Anon
38. Quart part
39. Ran, as dye
40. School organization: abbr.
41. Shade tree
42. Notable time
43. Arid

Solution is on page 400

ACROSS

1. Overactor: slang
4. Egyptian month
8. Kettle
11. Caesar's last question: 3 wds. (Latin)
14. Deplore
15. Admiration
16. Tree-to-be
18. "— a girl"
19. Stuff
20. Stadium
23. Most lofty
26. Reading matter
27. Espouse
28. Division word
29. Wooden strip
30. "A Chorus Line" number
31. "Animal —," Orwell work
32. 43,560 square feet
33. Witticism
34. Ancient Greek theaters
35. Clam
37. Beer and ale
38. Demeanor
39. Clamor
40. Blouse
42. Nuptial
46. Favorite
47. Plenty
49. Some
50. Mother of Castor and Pollux
51. Peg

DOWN

1. ". . . he done — wrong"
2. Ingested
3. Catskills, e.g.: abbr.
4. Circle parts
5. Situate
6. Towards
7. Mollusk "product"
8. Leisurely walk
9. Possessive pronoun
10. Knockout number
12. Not settled: 4 wds.
13. Alpha follower
17. Sierras' State
19. West Point student
20. Mythical strongman
21. Respond
22. Hand or foot, e.g.
23. Caruso was one
24. Scatter
25. Tony Musante TV role, and others
27. Wives
36. Mercury, e.g.
37. Hitchcockian menace
39. Actor Andrews
40. Baden-Baden, for one
41. Female lobster
42. Slander
43. Blasting material: abbr.
44. Ungettable serve
45. Mr. Majors
48. "To — or not . . ."

Solution is on page 400

ACROSS

1. Car for hire
4. Baby carriages, in London
9. Dried fruit
12. Fuss
13. Like a king
14. "We — the World"
15. Fabric; cloth
17. Foolish one
19. Comfortable
20. Treats with contempt
21. Assert
23. Funny stories
24. Had on
25. Valleys
26. Scale tone
28. — and outs, details
29. "Iliad" author
30. Film, "12 Angry —"
31. Possessive word
32. Prehistoric dwellings
33. Rapid
34. Highway divisions
35. Stallion, for one
36. Smarts
38. Boxing match
39. Prods
40. Playing tenpins
43. Anger
44. Customary
46. New: prefix
47. Senator Kennedy, to friends
48. Fence supports
49. "Blue"

DOWN

1. Felix or Garfield
2. Summer beverage
3. Freight-train units
4. Award
5. Depend (on)
6. Grow older
7. Pa's mate
8. Raincoat
9. Carnivals
10. Press (clothes)
11. Obtains
16. Carry
18. Female deer
20. Shoe parts
21. Move through water
22. Theater award
23. Actor Garner
25. Birds of peace
26. Minus
27. Poker stake
29. Ends a phone call: 2 wds.
30. Actors Sheen and Mull
32. Walking stick
33. Unpleasant
34. Enjoyed
35. Roars, as with laughter
36. Barbecue rod
37. Ripped
38. Canoe, for one
40. School vehicle
41. Teachers' group: abbr.
42. Deity
45. In order (that)

Solution is on page 400

306

ACROSS

1. Paid out (money)
6. Certain geometric figures
12. Red or green
13. Not public
15. Knowing
16. Countess's title
17. Forward
18. Allow
19. Prepares (copy)
21. Macadamia —
22. Sketched
24. Dollar bill
25. Spouse
26. Talk wildly
28. Stopwatch
29. "Hash mark"
32. Silly mistakes: slang
33. Hackneyed
34. Used up
35. Speed contest
36. Paid athlete, for short
37. Log float
41. Fruit drink
42. Shallow dish
44. Falsehood
45. You and I
46. Conduct
47. Oak nut
49. Stillness
51. Adjusted, as a piano
52. Lariat loops
53. Plant beginnings

DOWN

1. Burn with steam
2. Energy
3. Overjoy
4. Neither's partner
5. Oak or maple
6. Broken-bone support
7. Speechify
8. Pot covers
9. Climbing plant
10. Elected prosecutor: abbr.
11. Stronger
14. Comes into
20. Finished
21. Title
23. Inscribe
25. Underground worker
27. Gorilla
28. Cargo weight
29. Soda-sippers
30. Auto down payment, sometimes: hyph. wd.
31. Paddy crop
32. Overshoe
34. Exam marks
36. Location
38. Unattended
39. Discharged, as a gun
40. Oversees, as a flock
42. Ballpoints
43. Has lunch
46. Lion's name
48. Actor's signal
50. Behold!

Solution is on page 401

EASY

ACROSS

1. Jumps, bunny style
5. Prayer-ending word
9. Did the crawl or sidestroke
13. Cabbage salad
17. Grew older
18. Mislay
19. It "marches on"
20. Evergreen tree
21. Dublin's country: abbr.
22. Wife of 87-Across: 2 wds.
24. Aircraft
25. Put back, as funds
27. Telegram
28. Dreaded
29. Frozen water
30. Pillar
31. Occupies a chair
32. Incline; slope
35. Shopping wagon
36. Sooner State
40. Gasoline holder
41. Falseface
42. Overflow
43. Jar cover
44. Dined
45. Sunrise direction
46. Cries
47. Repair
48. Modern
49. Garfunkel or Carney
50. Baked —, Boston dish
51. Library items
52. Invite
53. Cures
54. Cut with an ax
55. Bread spread
58. Chicago football team
59. "— pleasures and palaces . . ."
60. Partner of "tucker"
63. Spoken
64. Longs for
65. Scores a victory
66. Fruit-juice drink
67. Point a gun (at)
68. Farm buildings
69. Relax
70. Heap (on)
71. Cornhusker State
73. Daring deed
74. Runner's distances
75. Picnic pests
76. Wharf
77. Box for coal
78. Umpire's call
81. Liberate
82. Most peppery
86. Golf clubs
87. U.S. Chief Executive
89. Automobile
90. Piece of plumbing
91. — off, begins a golf game
92. Singer, Jerry —
93. Buckeye State
94. Drove (a car) too fast
95. Dinner for Dobbin
96. Finishes
97. Pleat; tuck

DOWN

1. Tresses
2. Fairy-tale monster
3. Chick's sound
4. Coyote State: abbr.
5. "Wonderland" girl
6. Greater amount
7. Curvy letter
8. NBC, for example
9. Begin
10. Broad
11. Alcott girl
12. Myself
13. Splatter (water)
14. One who stretches the truth
15. Actress Meara
16. Pesky plant
22. Actuality
23. Shopping memo
24. Blossom segment
26. Chain part
28. — in, acts as a substitute
30. Bygone time
31. Omits
32. Hall-of-Famer Musial
33. Tardy
34. Afresh
35. Players in a play
36. Unlocks
37. Margarine
38. Costly fur
39. Sums up
41. N.T. book following Matthew
42. Closes (an envelope)
45. Simple to do
46. Has on (clothes)
47. Cut the grass
50. Throbs
51. Hospital needs
52. Everything
53. Hair dye
54. Household tip
55. Comedienne Rivers
56. Great Lake
57. Baby sheep
58. Kennel sounds
59. Light rain
60. Arrestee's release money
61. Not busy
62. "Busy" insects
64. Squander
65. Feeble

68. Money houses
69. Get
70. ½ quart
72. — cats and dogs, poured
73. Enemies
74. Baseball glove

76. Clothe
77. Canine treats
78. Drinks slowly
79. Stumble (over)
80. Lasso
81. Worry (over)
82. Contained

83. Resound
84. Travel via ship
85. Trampled (on)
87. Soup choice
88. Newsman Rather
91. In the direction of
93. — course, certainly

Solution is on page 401

ACROSS

1. Coarse person
5. Boast
9. Listened to
14. Coil
16. Unimportant matters
18. Small dog
20. Tell tales
21. Rat or mouse
22. Specimen
23. Play part
24. Calls forth
26. Domiciles
28. Vat
29. Scream
31. Natural gift
32. Makes an exchange
33. Broad
34. Garment's joining part
36. Cardinal number
37. Begin
38. Pattern
39. Terrycloth item
41. Junkets
42. Healed
43. Quick-witted
45. Jeer at
46. Brooches
47. Bedroom adjunct
48. St. John and Ireland
49. Hide
52. Plunders
53. Zoo enclosures
54. Dry up with heat
55. Scottish river
57. Donkey
58. Methods
59. Concoct, as a plan
60. Spring month
61. Tiny
62. Arbor
63. Sorceress
64. Hogs
66. Used a colander
68. Be equal to
69. Sounded loudly
70. Produced (offspring)
71. Trench
72. Excited
73. Trueheart's beloved
75. Squeeze
76. Seashore
77. Newly made
78. Hunt illegally
79. Sticky stuff: slang
80. Aid
83. Succulent
84. Color slightly
85. Hold firmly
87. Loam
89. Little demon
90. Fraud
91. Played the coquette
93. Alphabet letter
94. Perfect example
96. Is of value to
98. Tyro
100. Goes to bed
101. Center
102. Interlaces
103. Abounds
104. Alphabet letters
105. Worn-out horses

DOWN

1. Sets some distance apart
2. Small
3. Scrap of leftover food
4. Indonesian isle
5. Fractured
6. Bus passenger
7. Streets: abbr.
8. Card game, for short
9. Curses
10. Historic periods
11. Provide with weapons
12. It causes violently disturbed water
13. Deceived
14. Remain
15. Make a loan
16. Garden tool
17. Crosswise
18. Lure; entice
19. Mutineer
25. Elector
27. Paddles
30. Tardiest
32. Shocks deeply
33. Less good
35. Relocates
37. Human beings
38. Chew steadily
40. Drenched
41. Stories
42. Sure thing: slang
43. Concluded
44. Not as constrictive
45. Zoo creature
46. Portico
47. Talon
48. Satiated, as from overindulgence
49. Capture
50. Has high regard for
51. Inclined
53. Intimidated
54. Repair, in a way
56. Watched closely
58. Cash
59. Fasten with a hook or knot
62. Tree
63. Be on the lookout
64. Messy stuff
65. Squanders

67. Disconcert
68. Chop finely
69. Constrictor
71. Explanatory draw-
ing
72. Sit on a perch
73. Brass instrument
74. Interval of relief
75. Corn bread

76. Ribald
77. Aviator
78. Fresh-water game
fish
79. Questions relent-
lessly
81. Affectionate
82. Fragments
84. Domesticates

85. Move smoothly
86. — up, kept in
88. Marvin and Majors
90. Shape; outline
91. Wither
92. Dejected
95. Bind
97. Namely: abbr.
99. By way of

Solution is on page 401

ACROSS

1. New York City and Boston
6. Type of war plane
12. Prods
17. Kindly; gracious
18. Small hollow
19. Pastel color
20. Sticks with the status quo: 4 wds.
23. Iroquoian
24. Opinion, as of the law
25. Egyptian port
26. Barbarian
27. Asian battleground, for short
28. Hastened
29. Popular TV chef
31. Bunyan's bovine
32. Arid plains
34. Pomander-ball spice
35. Be bested
36. Atmosphere
37. "Blue — Shoes
38. Pull along
39. Not quite up to full measure
42. Rails
43. Smoke screen: hyph. wd.
47. Dessert-cart treat
48. More wan
49. Educated; cultured
50. West Indies export
51. Justices of the peace
53. Abyss
54. Set apart
56. Sharpens
57. Distance measure
58. Scans
59. Summits
60. Fruit drink
61. Opposing view
62. Weepy
63. Female rabbit
64. Whirl
66. Foundation
67. Murky condition
71. Run before the wind
72. Caruso, for one
73. Take —, take a break
74. Biblical name
75. Sesame-seed oil: var. sp.
76. Blockhead
77. Went head first
78. Yarn
79. Genuine: 6 wds.
84. More cunning
85. Baltimore team member
86. Diver's maneuver
87. Convenient
88. "Advise and Consent's" Pidgeon
89. Join, as a group

DOWN

1. Look towards obliquely: 2 wds.
2. Neither late nor early: 2 wds.
3. Ascent
4. Shooting marble
5. Unexpected success
6. Shaped into bundles
7. Mineral combinations
8. Some adults
9. Ghostly cry
10. Hard to pin down
11. Entertain
12. Pleased
13. Word with "olive" or "corn"
14. Hawaiian greetings
15. Europe's "blue river"
16. View
17. Narrow valleys
21. Alkaline substances
22. Secreted
28. Barbecue bar
29. Get rid of emotional tensions: 3 wds.
30. Coal scuttles
31. Viny retreat
33. Gasp
34. Heals
35. Adores
37. Dense
38. Carries
39. Airplane runway
40. Sufficient reason
41. Arthurian garb, often
42. Wise men
43. Quotes
44. Swift
45. Beneficial; advantageous
46. In Italy, he's *Pietro*

48. Communion plate
49. Tall and lean
51. Bricklayer
52. Bellows
55. Clearheaded; rational
57. Carriage; manner
59. Argentinian money
60. Approach
62. Trumpet fanfare

63. Branch off
64. Bell-shaped perennial
65. Arrive: 2 wds.
66. Author, Saul —
67. Aria performer
68. Sir Galahad's mother
69. Weld
70. Guide
71. Hide away (jewels)

72. Also
73. Vestibule
76. Walleyed pike
77. Valley
78. "Twerp": slang
80. Espoused
81. Nothing
82. Speck
83. One of the twelve tribes of Israel

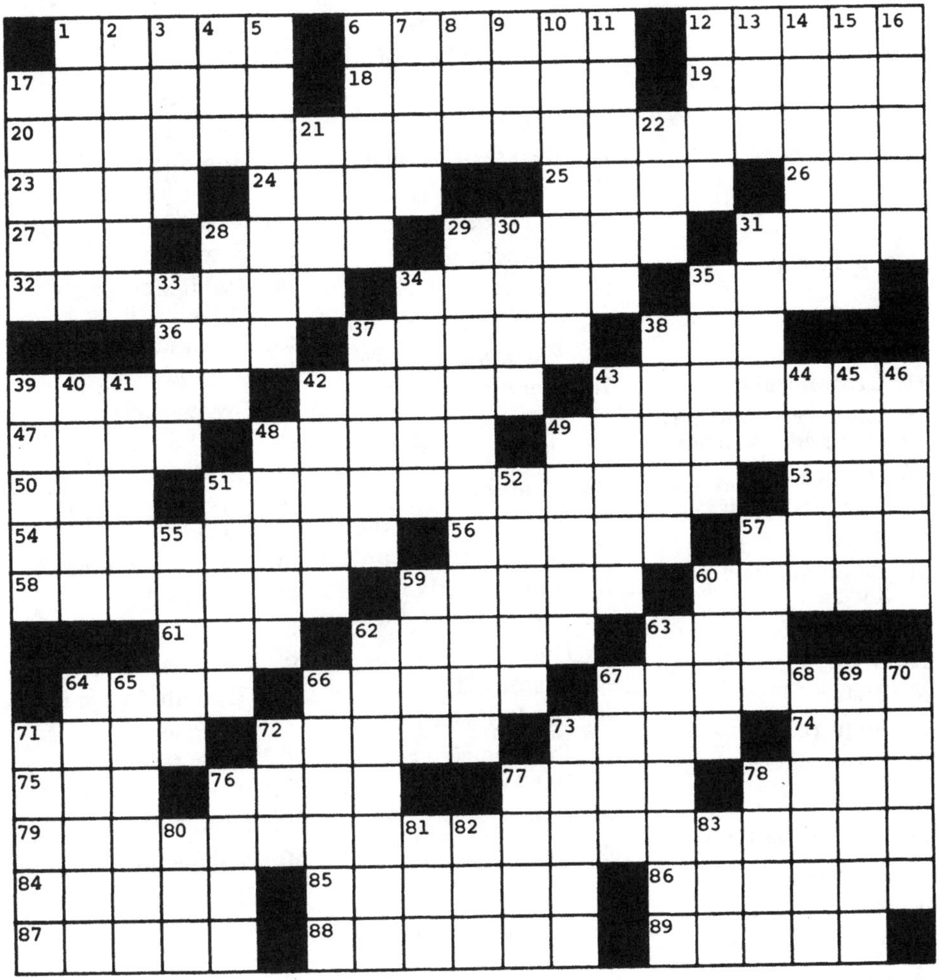

Solution is on page 401

ACROSS

1. Declare
6. Sheer fabric
11. Crew members
16. Element common to coal and diamonds
17. Display
18. Portuguese city
20. Sum
21. Complain loudly: 3 wds.
23. Utter defeat
24. Branding devices
26. Bitter
27. Acquired
28. Filing device
29. Go away!
30. Campus building
31. Enormous
32. Huron and Erie
34. Act the coquette
36. Chess piece
37. Persian fairy
38. Imposing dwelling
40. Mongrel
41. Nearly
43. Grove
44. Stringed instruments
48. Meadows
49. Left, on a ship
51. Stringed instrument
52. Pile
53. Roast
54. In a rage: 3 wds.
56. Hindu garment
57. Avail oneself of
58. Yearn
59. Concise
60. Beasts of burden
61. Combining
63. Old —, alumnus
64. Without risk
66. Support
67. Chatters
69. Woman's nickname
70. Smudge
73. Delineates
74. City on the Nile
76. Small lake
77. Time of prosperity
78. West German capital
79. Mild expletive
82. Scrap
83. Noisy
84. Displayed
86. Donkey's call
87. Create noisy confusion: 3 wds.
90. Land
92. Despot
93. Helices
94. Gave temporary use of
95. Clans; tribes
96. Presently
97. Causes to go

DOWN

1. Pacific island group
2. Rabble-rouser, perhaps
3. Border upon
4. Large amount
5. Lure
6. Fortune-telling card
7. Algerian port
8. Eye part
9. — Vegas
10. Ugly thing
11. Bored expression: hyph. wd.
12. Mimic
13. Negative word
14. Stabilizing parachute
15. Straight man
16. Vehicle
19. Frequently
22. Legal wrong
25. Grate
29. Equipment for the slopes
30. Man's nickname
31. Injured
33. Ascended
34. Plants of a region
35. Ultimate indignity: 2 wds.
36. Witty retort
37. Satisfy
39. Dwelling
40. Evil spells
41. Snapshots holder
42. "The — of the Shrew"
44. Open spaces

45. A selfish purpose to promote: 4 wds.
46. Very seldom
47. Thorny
50. Qualm
51. Throng
55. Warms
56. Up to now: 2 wds.
58. Wharf
62. Happy
63. Metric measure
65. Related
67. Outgrowth
68. Barge
70. Gambler
71. Certain eels
72. Complete
73. Gloomy
75. Chronicles
77. Watercraft
78. Officious
80. Roof overhang
81. Looked at
83. Season for fasting
84. Slide
85. Island dance
86. Grain husks
88. Fool: slang
89. Speak lovingly
91. Fish eggs

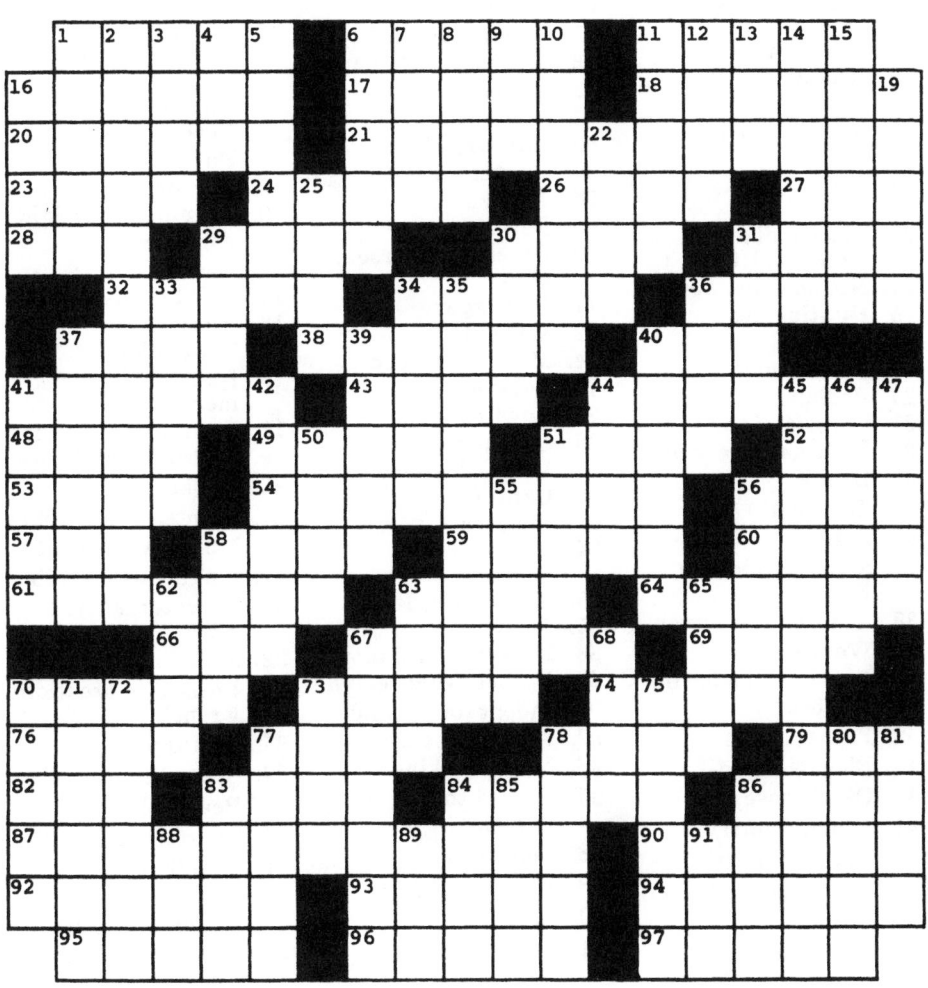

Solution is on page 401

SPECIAL CHALLENGER CROSSWORD

"PUN & PENCIL"   **by LOUIS SABIN**

Here is a real toughie for you. We have omitted giving you such helps as "2 wds.," "hyph. wd.," and "slang"; but in the spirit of fair play, all abbreviations and foreign words are so indicated.

ACROSS

1. Plausible excuse
6. Radiator
12. Boys'-night-out party
16. Enjoys a meerschaum
17. Unmask
18. New Hampshire flower
20. Singing party invitation?
22. The Omni and Freedom Hall
24. Not smooth: abbr.
25. Hunting dogs
26. Threefold
28. Genetic monogram
29. Bedlam
31. *"Prosit!,"* for one
32. Believer, of a kind
33. Dilute
34. Toughen
36. Fold
37. Swiss theologian, Karl —
38. Alfie, on the screen
39. Warrants
41. Queen of the ice in the '30s
42. Pantry
43. Blackbirds
44. Dig discovery
45. Island country
46. Actor Charles
49. Edison contemporary
50. Initiate
53. Dancer Jeanmaire
54. Honkers
55. Strops
56. Subway unit
57. Up in years
58. Holy snakes!?
60. Actor Sean
61. General Houston
62. Macbeth, for one
63. Miffed
64. — blanche
65. Literary theft
67. Dowitcher, e.g.
68. Trunks
69. Pershing's men
70. Greeley, Jefferson, et al.
71. Outrigger
72. Wise guy
74. Metric measure
75. Careless
79. Bowling venue
80. Courage
81. Voice of a dove
82. Caption
83. Spheres
84. He lies in Red Square
85. Kriss Kringle
87. Activity
88. Entertainer Zadora
89. French wine region
90. Indonesian island
92. Altar response
93. Nine of a kind
95. Forced to sing in Camelot?
98. Bell town
99. Encroach upon
100. Lineup
101. Tommy's gun
102. More orderly
103. Links-legend Sam

DOWN

1. In love
2. — Alamos
3. DDE's namesakes?
4. Attack
5. Carbon 14 and uranium 235
6. Charge against Luther at Worms
7. Put forth
8. Mirrors
9. Formidable weight
10. Abstruse
11. Revise
12. Point of view
13. Flag
14. Toby filler
15. Indian railroad men?
16. Lourdes destination
19. Incisor's neighbor
20. Hooked up
21. Slanted type: abbr.
23. More levelheaded
27. Singer, — Kabbible
30. — water, stayed afloat
32. SE Florida town
33. Patisserie creation: French
35. A Muppet
37. Starr caller?
38. Peaceful periods
40. Sportscaster Scully
41. "Siddhartha" author
42. Shimmery fabrics
44. Hall of Fame shortstop
45. Baccaratlike game

46. Understand
47. Stately
48. Guatemalan music men?
49. Itsy-bitsy
50. Tale of adventure
51. Epic segment
52. Shore birds
54. Mountain-bike essential
55. Plenty
58. Questionable
59. Snoop

60. Heaven: French
62. Pastels
64. Take in, by vote
66. Stations: French
67. Squelched
68. Chorus syllable
70. Polish additive
71. Cabal, e.g.
72. Declivity
73. Place for slips
74. Cosmetic base, often
75. Sub chaser's tool
76. Decked out (in)

77. Breaking pitch
78. Judean king
80. Author Mehta
81. Type of RV
84. Tempted
85. Glove fabric
86. Pyromaniac's crime
89. Hair like Cher's
90. Ruthian blast
91. Caama
94. Snack
96. Juan's wife
97. Actress Hagen

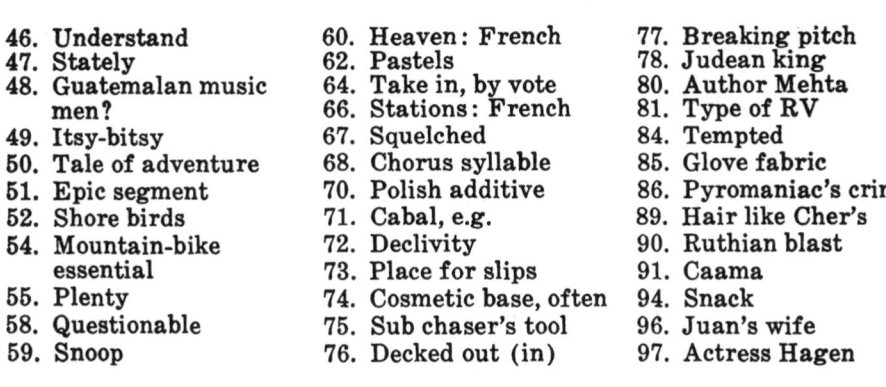

Solution is on page 401

DIAGRAMLESS

MEDIUM

This Diagramless is 15 boxes wide by 15 boxes deep.

ACROSS

1. Wealthy
5. Allow
8. Keep after school
10. Overjoyed
12. Novel's plan of action
14. Arm joint
15. Ripped
17. Venomous snake
18. Pecans and almonds
20. Red or Black
23. — up, absorb
24. Vigoda or Burrows
27. Footed vase
28. Sicilian volcano
29. Adjustor
32. Finest
35. Inquire
36. Hostel
37. Dine
38. — Moines
39. Teen detective, Nancy —
41. Heifer
44. Require
46. Sand hills
48. Page
50. Combat
51. Trimmed, as shrubs
53. Lyrical poem
54. Jog

DOWN

1. Primary color
2. That thing
3. Tam-o'-shanter, for one
4. Sword handle
5. Peggy, Pinky, or Brenda
6. Songstress Fitzgerald
7. Dinner checks
8. Lawn moisture
9. Midday
11. Lid
13. Have faith in
16. British prep school
19. Healthful spot
20. Mopes
21. Noted period
22. Prefix meaning "against"
24. Museum offering
25. "Let It —," Beatles hit
26. Mild oath
28. Sea eagle
30. Employ
31. Atop
32. Cot or four-poster
33. Merit; deserve
34. Construction metal
40. Cry
41. Slice
42. Aware of: slang
43. Fuse metals together
45. Move suddenly and fast
46. Father
47. Envision
49. Animal hair
50. Wager
52. Negative reply

Solution is on page 402

DIAGRAMLESS

MEDIUM

**This Diagramless is 15 boxes wide by 15 boxes deep.
Starting box is on page 407.**

ACROSS

1. Fan; devotee
5. "Milky" stone
6. Went by plane
10. Leather band
12. Desert green spots
14. Gregarious
16. Sewing need
19. Scottish Gaelic
20. Belonging to us
21. Snare
22. — symbol, sign of one's social position
24. Minor
25. Set
26. French capital
27. Worth
30. Carried
31. Light, narrow boat
32. Butter portion
33. Visit often; frequent
34. Privileges

37. The — of Capri
38. Foot digit
39. Memorable periods
41. Figure of speech
43. Wealth
46. Frozen rain
47. Inclined (to)
48. Utters
49. Sea eagle
50. Writing table

DOWN

1. Employer
2. As far as: 2 wds.
3. Mockery; comedy
4. Talents; knacks
6. Concentrate (on)
7. Den
8. Curvy letter
9. Cowboy movie
11. Time gone by
13. Quick raid

15. Group of sports teams
16. Spiritual nature
17. Rodents
18. Secret agent
23. Golf peg
24. Golf score
26. Commotion
27. Leaps over
28. Strengthens and tempers
29. Parking area
30. Sack
31. Instance
32. Wharf
33. The man
34. Plant parts
35. Journey
36. Hallowed
38. He and she
40. Coastline
42. Pod vegetable
44. Austrian river
45. Look for

Solution is on page 402

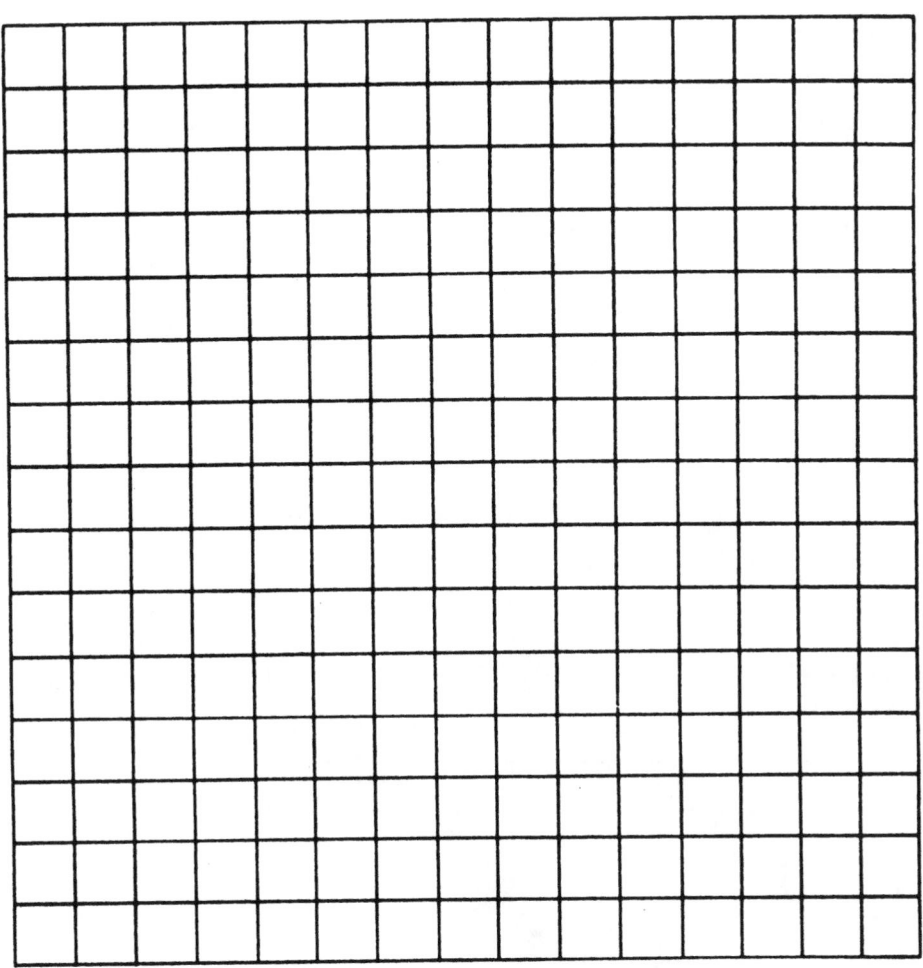

ACROSS

1. Paving substance
4. — on one's nerves, irritate
9. Ancient
12. Dublin's country: abbr.
13. Synthetic fabric
14. Pod vegetable
15. Use a ruler
17. Sleep vision
19. Corn-bread cake
20. — an ear, listens
21. Change, as car gears
23. Board game for two
25. Salad fish
26. Ice (a cake)
27. Casual greeting
29. Omelet item
30. Chicken shelters
31. Owned
32. You and I
33. Less good
34. Corn husk
35. Tills the soil
36. Classroom adhesive
37. Porch step
39. Show-biz flop: slang
40. Act the author
41. Teeter-totters
44. Breeze
45. Pie shell
47. Short sleep
48. Plaything
49. Tepees
50. Thirsty

DOWN

1. Funnyman Conway
2. "You — My Sunshine"
3. Autumn farm chore
4. Hog's sound
5. Uncommon
6. Popeye's "yes"
7. — and fro
8. Going on forever
9. Unlocks
10. Guide the way
11. Hoover and Grand Coulee
16. Parlor piece
18. Relax
21. Boil slowly
22. Gigantic
23. Cranky
24. Comedian, Bob —
26. Shape; mold
27. Sentry's shout
28. Not busy
30. Accurate
31. Wife's mate
33. Stay behind
34. Overacting actors: slang
35. — tale, child's story
36. Rhymesters
37. Wallop (a housefly)
38. Threesome
39. Better than better
41. Solar energy source
42. Declaration of Dec. 8, 1941
43. Secret agent
46. Scale tone

Solution is on page 402

ACROSS

1. Singer Davis
4. Buffalo's kin
9. Health resort
12. OPEC concern
13. Love
14. Actor Linden
15. "Death Wish" actor, Charles —
17. Bell's invention, for short
19. Travel by sea
20. Mix (with a spoon)
21. Topic; subject
23. Pupil
26. By —, without understanding
27. Actress Keaton
28. Ames' State: abbr.
29. The thing's
30. *Chili con* —
31. Actor Gibson
32. Exist
33. Store events
34. Step
35. Chosen by vote
37. Examples
38. Young lady, Scottish style
39. Wagon
40. Unaccompanied
42. Word with "Chinese" or "magic"
45. Quick swim
46. Road sign
48. Operated
49. Lyric poem
50. Rival
51. Stitch

DOWN

1. Unruly crowd
2. Atmosphere
3. Places to hang clothes
4. Jazz great, Count —
5. False god
6. Male heir
7. Either
8. Uranus' neighbor
9. Coastline
10. Pot's "pal"
11. Pub brew
16. Identify
18. Conceal
20. Musial and Kenton
21. Clan
22. Traveler's lodging
23. Fathered
24. Brother's daughter
25. Stories
27. Evans and Robertson
30. Child's marble: hyph. wd.
31. Skilled craftsmen
33. Glance at quickly
34. Portion
36. Marry secretly
37. Lollypop, for one
39. Serene
40. Fuss
41. Cap; cover
42. Actress Remick
43. Film, "Norma —"
44. Opposite of SSE
47. At home

Solution is on page 402

ACROSS

1. "Steppenwolf" author
6. Accumulate
11. Printing tool
12. Leave abandoned
14. Absent
15. Building part
17. — and behold!
18. Machinist's group: abbr.
19. Thick steel rope
20. King: French
21. Next year's senior: abbr.
22. Golf score
23. Without
24. Homeric epic
26. Battle of the —
27. Secondhand
28. Trickle down, as water
29. Corny
31. In fine —, healthy
34. Soon
35. Tribal divisions
36. Never!
37. Operated (a machine)
38. Basketball position
39. NOW issue: abbr.
40. For example: abbr.
41. Fellow, in London
42. Of the ear
43. Environment
45. Foul odor
47. Cowboy competition
48. Pentateuch

DOWN

1. Sportscaster Cosell
2. Dutch cheese
3. Firmament
4. NYC borough: abbr.
5. Betrothed
6. Stroll
7. Masculine
8. 100 square meters
9. Thus
10. Goodbye: 2 wds.
11. Bluegrass instrument
13. Clamor
16. Skillfully
19. "— at the Bat"
20. Norton's neighbor Kramden
22. West German city
23. Satisfies
25. Canadian territory
26. Trademark
28. Most beloved
29. Seraglio
30. Wild ass
31. Excessive criticism
32. Make more rewarding
33. Household pest
35. N.Y. governor
38. Adhesive
39. Sicilian volcano
41. Offer
42. Above: poetic
44. Perform
46. Until

Solution is on page 402

ACROSS

1. Tree juice
4. Depend (on)
8. Numbered musical work
12. Knot
13. Great Lake
14. Traditional knowledge
15. Summer drink
16. Carter or Ford, at one time
18. Answered
20. Myself
21. Also
22. One of the evergreens
26. Unaccompanied
29. Used to be
30. Neither's partner
31. Flag support
32. "Sly" creature
33. Slugger Musial
34. Zsa Zsa's sister
35. Long period of time
36. Cite
37. Repeal
39. Pool stick
40. Musical tone
41. Los Angeles team
45. Pharmacy
49. Last letter
50. Small amount
51. Aid in wrongdoing
52. Sprinted
53. First garden
54. Snares
55. Total up

DOWN

1. Heavenly body
2. Assistant
3. Chick's sound
4. Complain; fret
5. Made a mistake
6. Fibbed
7. Affirmative reply
8. More aged
9. Poet, Edgar Allan —
10. Vase
11. Place (down)
17. Rascals
19. Country road
22. Musical horn, for short
23. "Do — others . . ."
24. Paint layer
25. Sea eagle
26. Mimic
27. Adore
28. Norwegian man's name
29. Was victorious
32. Enemy
33. Petitioned legally
35. — out, makes (a living) with difficulty
36. Silences
38. Church instrument
39. Gem weight
41. Dressing gown
42. Poet Pound
43. "— all about it"
44. Transmit
45. Game cube
46. Scepter
47. Shoshonean Indian
48. Beach-goer's goal

Solution is on page 402

ACROSS

1. Ignited
4. Cabbage salad
8. Reach across
12. Wedding vow: 2 wds.
13. Assistant
14. Ripped
15. Neither's "partner"
16. Guided
17. Squander
18. Ran away to wed
20. — and needles
21. Has life
22. Makes unhappy
25. 2:15 or 4:45, for example
28. Floor squares
29. Exclamation of surprise
30. Ballad
31. Passenger
32. Also
33. Mr. Jolson
34. More rational
35. Color; hue
36. Wants
38. The Keystone State: abbr.
39. Pub orders
40. Horse's pace
44. Word with "scuba"
46. Owns
47. Have life
48. Level
49. Wagon
50. — Tin Tin
51. Bird's home
52. Towards shelter
53. Picnic pest

DOWN

1. Queue
2. False god
3. Bull: Spanish
4. Bargains
5. Fibbed
6. Total up
7. You and I
8. Gets up
9. Sheriff's gang
10. Mr. Linkletter
11. Wedding announcement word
17. Broader
19. Lemon meringue is one variety
20. More faded
22. Lateral edges
23. Time for lunch
24. Used a pistol
25. Frog's kin
26. At rest
27. Myself
28. Fork prongs
31. More unusual
32. Scale note
34. Without sound
35. Beige
37. Rescues
38. Glue's kin
40. Show concern
41. O'Hara residence
42. The "Emerald Isle": poetic
43. Lease
44. Lair
45. "— got sixpence . . ."
46. Actor Holbrook
49. The Golden State: abbr.

Solution is on page 403

ACROSS

1. Well-cooked, as bacon
6. Part of a place setting
11. Navy constructor
12. Director Joffé
14. Poet, Sidney —
15. Justice Holmes
16. Cow-headed goddess of Egypt
17. Barnyard occupants
19. Australian bird
20. French pronoun
21. Some trees
22. "Swipe": slang
23. Name of film fame
24. Tibia, etc.
25. Doubt
27. Tasteless and insensitive
28. Actress, Irene —
29. Bucket
30. McNally's partner
31. Wound in some way
32. Conceit
35. Dudgeon
36. Swiss river
37. Eastern European
38. Going astray
40. Countable
42. Dedicate
43. Complete agreement
44. Name in the news in 1917
45. Subsequently

DOWN

1. Discontinue
2. Rajah's wives
3. Heronlike wading bird
4. Use one of the senses
5. Treachery; betrayal of trust
6. Boat sections
7. Take it easy
8. Middle Eastern name
9. Inns
10. Hostile ones
11. Cowboy's nickname
13. Thrashes
18. California Army base
21. Transportation cost
22. Kentucky product
23. Impart
24. Hat part
25. Altercation
26. Daunt
27. Meticulous
28. Desiccated
29. Equal footing
31. Uta or Jean
32. Beethoven's "Für —"
33. Florida team member
34. Hot spot
36. Prefix for "thesis" or "septic"
37. Fit of pique
39. Particle
41. — trice, momentarily: 2 wds.

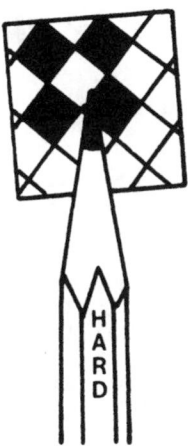

Solution is on page 403

BIBLE CROSSWORD MEDIUM

by MARILYN WING

Bible references in this puzzle are from the King James Version. You'll find it stimulating to solve, and may discover you know more Bible than you think you do.

ACROSS

1. I am not as other men —. *Luke 18:11*
4. Fear came, . . . and trembling which made all my bones to —. *Job 4:14*
9. He caused an east —d to blow. *Ps. 78:26*
12. He . . . rose up, and went his —. *Gen. 25:34*
13. His enemy came and sowed — among the wheat. *Matt. 13:25*
14. Out of the —ry palaces . . . they have made thee glad. *Ps. 45:8*
15. He shall take two he lambs . . . and one — lamb. *Lev. 14:10*
16. I wrote them with —. *Jer. 36:18*
17. Darkness shall — the earth. *Isa. 60:2*
19. He had been there a — time. *Gen. 26:8*
21. — thou not that we perish? *Mark 4:38*
22. — him unto me. *Mark 9:19*
24. Bind me fast with new —. *Judg. 16:11*
25. Jehu — in a chariot. *II Ki. 9:16*
26. The isles tremble . . . : yea, the — that are in the sea. *Ezek. 26:18*
27. He saith . . . Ha, —. *Job 39:25*
29. Ye shall find an — tied, and a colt with her. *Matt. 21:2*
30. A hen doth gather her — under her wings. *Luke 13:34*
31. He shall be cast into the — of lions. *Dan. 6:7*
32. I am as — are. *Gal. 4:12*
33. The tabernacle . . . is fallen down; and I will build again the — thereof. *Acts 15:16*
34. — not thyself because of evildoers. *Ps. 37:1*
35. All of them clothed with all — of armour. *Ezek. 38:4*
36. I bestow all my — to feed the poor. *I Cor. 13:3*
37. Yet was I delivered prisoner . . . into the hands of the —. *Acts 28:17*
39. David took an —, and played with his hand. *I Sam. 16:23*
40. Come into my house and — there. *Acts 16:15*
41. The land is . . . — or lean. *Num. 13:20*
42. He put the broth in a —. *Judg. 6:19*
45. — thee behind me, Satan. *Matt. 16:23*
46. — is the kingdom. *Matt. 6:13*
48. Give ye —, and hear. *Isa. 28:23*
49. They shall see — to eye. *Isa. 52:8*
50. With our flocks and with our — will we go. *Ex. 10:9*
51. She is planted in . . . a — and thirsty ground. *Ezek. 19:13*

DOWN

1. My heart standeth in — of thy word. *Ps. 119:161*
2. Eat not of it —, . . . but roast with fire. *Ex. 12:9*
3. Give not sleep to thine eyes, nor slumber to thine —. *Prov. 6:4*
4. O death, where is thy —? *I Cor. 15:55*
5. Lift up the hands which — down. *Heb. 12:12*
6. Noah . . . prepared an —. *Heb. 11:7*
7. They took a —y, and opened them. *Judg. 3:25*
8. David fled, and — that night. *I Sam. 19:10*
9. The — shall give to their husbands honour. *Esth. 1:20*

10. Flee, save your l—. *Jer. 48:6*
11. They shall wander . . . from the —h even to the east. *Amos 8:12*
18. The sand . . . is upon the sea sh—. *Gen. 22:17*
20. Two are better than —. *Eccles. 4:9*
21. The Epistle of Paul the Apostle to the —sians.
22. Doth the wild ass — when he hath grass? *Job 6:5*
23. The desert shall rejoice and blossom as the —. *Isa. 35:1*
24. The king's sons, being seventy pe—, were with the great men. *II Ki. 10:6*
26. The evil sp— went out of them. *Acts 19:12*
27. Take —, and hearken, O Israel. *Deut. 27:9*
28. Therefore shalt thou plant pleasant pl—. *Isa. 17:10*
30. Wickedness — as the fire. *Isa. 9:18*

31. Water — upon them out of heaven. *II Sam. 21:10*
33. Wide is the gate, and b— is the way. *Matt. 7:13*
34. Christ died — us. *Rom. 5:8*
35. He shall — thee with a rod. *Isa. 10:24*
36. The enemy . . . entered into the — of Jerusalem. *Lam. 4:12*
37. Cast abroad the — of thy wrath. *Job 40:11*
38. Children, — your parents. *Eph. 6:1*
39. Bind him — and foot. *Matt. 22:13*
41. The beams . . . are cedar, and our rafters of —. *Song 1:17*
43. All that handle the — . . . shall come down from their ships. *Ezek. 27:29*
44. Think it not strange concerning the fiery trial which is to — you. *I Pet. 4:12*
47. Whose son is —? *Matt. 22:42*

Solution is on page 403

329

ACROSS

1. Pea shell
4. Shuts noisily
9. Heart of Dixie State: abbr.
12. Anger
13. West Point student
14. Tear
15. Decade number
16. High card
17. Home; residence
19. Shredded
21. Stuff
22. Backbone
24. Short sleeps
27. Sit for an artist
28. Denmark natives
29. Overhead railway
30. C.S.T.'s "kin": abbr.
31. Peeled
32. Zodiac sign
33. Word of comparison
34. Small pies
35. Aid
36. School assignments
38. Taunt
39. — and crafts
40. Fix; darn
41. Wading bird
43. Come in first
44. Genesis woman
47. Noah's craft
48. Expel, as a tenant
50. Pastor's title: abbr.
51. Chorus syllable
52. Storms
53. Ocean

DOWN

1. Deep hole
2. Mine deposit
3. Tooth doctor
4. Frighten
5. Dress trim
6. Fruit drink
7. Myself
8. Began
9. Scent; odor
10. Jar cover
11. Large monkey
18. Prohibits
20. Single
21. Walking stick
22. Pointed weapon
23. Sheriff's group
24. Wagons
25. Fruit rinds
26. Slant
28. Pub game
31. Business associate
32. Guides
34. Bull: Spanish
35. Coop creature
37. Hooded coat
38. Camp shelters
40. Small rodents
41. Sombrero or derby
42. Make a mistake
43. Toupee
45. Victory sign
46. Ms. Gabor
49. Old Dominion State: abbr.

Solution is on page 403

ACROSS

1. Make imperfect
4. Storage tower
8. Burn slightly
12. "The Greatest"
13. Dutch cheese
14. Start again
15. — Tse-tung
16. A "Great" waterway: 2 wds.
18. Winged being
20. "National Velvet" author Bagnold
21. Stair part
23. Resist authority
27. Wild hog
29. Tennis great, Arthur —
31. A Gabor
32. Possessors
34. Fish-eating hawk
36. Marry
37. Molecule component
39. Lubricants
40. Golfing great, Sam —
42. Memorize
44. Sitarist Shankar
46. Royal
49. Andy Williams hit: 2 wds.
53. Health resort
54. Jai —
55. One of Columbus' ships
56. Poet's "always"
57. Slugger Rose
58. Effortless
59. Total (up)

DOWN

1. Mother
2. Actor Thicke
3. River on the Texas/Mexico border: 2 wds.
4. Markets
5. Ms. Lupino
6. L.A. basketball team
7. Sign
8. Unrefined oil
9. That girl
10. Commotion
11. Actor/director Howard
17. Charters
19. Ireland: Gaelic
22. Sunrise direction
24. Waterway between Alaska and Siberia: 2 wds.
25. Mr. Knievel
26. Produces, as an egg
27. Ribbons
28. "— Marshall," TV oldie
30. Residence
33. "M*A*S*H" character
35. Read (over) carefully
38. Singer Newton-John
41. Golfer Palmer, to friends
43. Display
45. Climbing plant
47. Mimicked
48. Bacon fat
49. Chart
50. Bullring cheer
51. Cereal grain
52. Printers' measures

Solution is on page 403

MOVIE-TV CROSSWORD

ACROSS

1. — and Lovers, 1960 British film
5. Kadiddlehopper, Red Skelton role
9. Dance often seen on Magnum, P.I.
13. Greek goddess, Athena —
14. Scarlett —
15. Blame
16. Screen's "Blue Angel": 2 wds.
19. The —, 1978 Burt Reynolds film
20. Compassion
21. Remove bindings
22. Lee J. Cobb's first name, originally
23. Tortoise's fabled competitor
25. — Acres, Albert/Gabor TV oldie
27. Actor, Philip —
28. Producer Hurok
31. Ms. McClanahan of Golden Girls
32. Suiting material
33. Woman's name meaning "joyous"
34. William Powell film, Take One — Step
36. — a Cockeyed Wonder, 1950 Rooney film
37. — Girl, 1980 Katharine Ross TV-movie
39. A Chorus Line number
40. Stockholm native
42. School in the Bay State: abbr.
43. Sullivan and Ames
44. On Your —, 1939 musical
45. Zodiac sign for Brando and Davis
47. Big-band leader Fields
48. King —, 1965 George Segal film
49. Linda Lavin TV role
52. Baseball great Speaker
54. — Wore a Yellow Ribbon
57. Popular "soap": 2 wds.
61. Soon, in Romeo and Juliet
62. Two-door auto
63. Spice used in pickling
64. Superman's girl, Lois —
65. Very large
66. Length times width

DOWN

1. — Time, Next Year
2. Rainer, in The Good Earth
3. A square, to the Fonz
4. Mr. Mineo
5. Mr. Huntley
6. — Sings the Blues
7. Biblical name
8. Ms. West
9. With 50-Down Stormy Weather star
10. Single residence, as an apartment
11. LBJ's daughter
12. Tennis great, Arthur —
14. The — Field, 1979 film
17. Prop used in many Errol Flynn films
18. Lana or Tina —
22. Majors and Meriwether
23. A Man Called —, 1970 Richard Harris film
24. Evita's country: abbr.
25. — Hotel
26. Reigns
27. Mr. — Goes to Town

28. *Miss — Thompson*, Hayworth film
29. Playwright, Clifford —
30. *The Seven Faces of Dr. —*
32. *Black — Squadron*, TV series
34. Enemy
35. Ms. Williams
38. Leave out
41. "— is me!"
45. *—, My Love*, Colbert/Milland film
46. File
47. Play division

49. "I've Got — in Kalamazoo," from *Orchestra Wives*: 2 wds.
50. See 9-Down
51. Part of (a scheme): 2 wds.
52. Ruffian
53. 1948 James Stewart film by Hitchcock
54. Use a spoon
55. Barbara or Alan —
56. Ms. Fitzgerald
58. John Banner's exclamation in TV's *Hogan's Heroes*
59. Bud's partner
60. Ms. Lupino

Solution is on page 403

ACROSS

1. Scarlett's home
5. Burglarize
8. Gem variety
12. Alike, in Paris
13. Bard's word
14. Fury
15. Actor Estrada
16. Lineage
18. Spanish seaport
20. Shifts from a position
21. Den
23. Constellation
24. Delicate work
28. Win over with flattery: slang
31. Nabokov title
32. Volcanic mountain
34. Merino mom
35. Diplomacy
37. Play devil's advocate
39. Narrow inlet
41. Armadillo
42. With arms —
45. Acclaimed
49. Festive gathering
51. Extreme
52. Winged
53. Shut off
54. Move with difficulty
55. Stir up
56. Joan of Arc: abbr. (French)
57. Dagger

DOWN

1. Abound
2. Taj Mahal site
3. Small wading bird
4. Potash
5. Set right
6. Bismuth, e.g.
7. Geological layers
8. Goings-on, in Old Rome
9. Judge, at times
10. Crooked: dialectic
11. Dregs
17. Adverse
19. Infatuated: slang
22. Networks
24. Ample
25. Crete's highest mountain
26. Like weepy types
27. Enclose, in a way
29. Be in the red
30. Very early
33. Theatrical society: abbr.
36. Vocal quality
38. Millers' quantities
40. Finnish city, to Swedes
42. Not in harmony
43. Siva's wife
44. Spheres
46. Diving bird
47. Part of HOMES
48. Instruction to the printer
50. "Nosh"

Solution is on page 404

ACROSS

1. Tropical tree
5. Brooch
8. Pastry
11. Region
12. "Winnie-the-Pooh" character
13. Relate, as a story
14. Genuine
15. Fascinate
17. Like a good drill team: 2 wds.
19. U.S./Canada canals
20. Perched
21. Faucet
23. Student
27. Land measure
28. Treat for Fido
29. "Blow one's stack": 3 wds. (slang)
34. Concept
35. Actress Baxter
36. Resources
38. Openwork fabric
39. Spider's home
42. Consume
44. Alabama city
46. Chinese port
50. October birthstone
51. Small lake
52. Sheep
53. Apollo's mother
54. Put two and two together
55. Affirmative answer
56. Sketched

DOWN

1. French capital
2. Sports edifice
3. Fewest
4. Ale ingredient
5. Get ready
6. Charged atom
7. Negative words
8. Soup morsel
9. Unwell
10. Building wing
13. Difficulty
16. School dance
18. Engrave
22. Nut
24. Hawaiian food
25. Tavern
26. Table support
27. Over: 3 wds.
29. That man
30. Small fish
31. Beverage
32. Foes
33. Toward and within
37. Droop
39. Windshield device
40. Gladden
41. Beneath
43. Pronoun
45. Daring
46. Health resort
47. Mortar trough
48. Also
49. Wonder

MEDIUM

Solution is on page 404

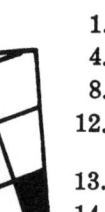

ACROSS

1. Near the stern
4. Minus
8. Nautical word
12. Neither's partner
13. Leave out
14. Musician's gadget
15. Games for searching types: 2 wds.
18. Stanza
19. Ago
20. Antitoxin
23. System of belief
26. Brace
28. Amusement-park offering
30. Society-page term
31. Average
32. Olympic events
33. Neon, e.g.
34. Do a baker's work
35. Helm position
36. Behaves
37. Indian leader
39. O'Neill work
41. Seep
43. Recipient
46. A felony
50. Facility
51. Economist's word
52. Xmas treat
53. Highways: abbr.
54. Members of Congress: abbr.
55. Curve type

DOWN

1. Social insects
2. Knox, e.g.
3. Where valuables are found: 2 wds.
4. Also-ran
5. Flightless bird
6. Part of a salutation, perhaps
7. Level
8. Entertain
9. Labrador retriever: 2 wds.
10. Mel, of baseball
11. Of course!
16. Allege
17. Mythological place
21. Name of a Soviet range
22. Emulated Marceau
24. What ushers do
25. Hodgepodge
26. Wash cycle
27. Play the father-to-be
29. Caribou
32. First-aid item
36. In a frenzy
38. Billy and Pete
40. Washington's successor
42. Abates
44. Son of Seth
45. Brunch order
46. Pronoun
47. Morsel for dobbin
48. Caviar
49. Long, long time

Solution is on page 404

336

ACROSS

"WRITER'S CROSSWORD"
by EUGENE T. MALESKA

1. Proper-noun beginners
5. Carpentry term
9. Stout
12. Army group
13. Father: Arabic
14. United
15. Risqué
16. L'Amour's novels
18. Agent's quest
20. TV's Lorenzo —
21. Five pairs
22. Wrong: prefix
23. The "Say Hey Kid"
25. Typography
30. Autumn month: abbr.
31. Myth
32. Teacher's group: abbr.
33. Play outline
35. Printing instruction
36. Lyric poem
37. Mimic
38. Singing voice
41. Aristophanes work
44. Writer's seminar, for one
47. Peruse
49. Biblical woman
50. The skating Brinker
51. To be: Latin
52. Grant an interview to
53. Rim
54. Olla

DOWN

1. Mongrel
2. Med school course: abbr.
3. It measures 10 characters to the inch: 2 wds.
4. Ancient writing tools
5. Daybreak
6. Aid (a criminal)
7. Writer, John — Passos
8. Author's preliminary summary
9. Mold
10. Tolstoy heroine
11. Hardy heroine
17. Steinbeck's "— of Eden"
19. Printing measure
22. "Venus de —"
23. Author's submissions: abbr.
24. Nuclear Regulatory agency, once: abbr.
25. Peel
26. Hitter's stats: abbr.
27. Curiosity
28. Born
29. Pistol: slang
31. Passing craze
34. Secluded spot
35. Steeples
37. Near; by
38. Inspires with wonder
39. Ageless theme for writers
40. Kilmer honoree
41. Musical piece
42. Church recess
43. Facility
45. That woman
46. Owned
48. Lawn moisture

Solution is on page 404

SPECIAL CHALLENGER CROSSWORD

"MOVIE MAN"   **by LOUIS SABIN**

Here is a real toughie for you. We have omitted giving you such helps as "2 wds.," "hyph. wd.," and "slang"; but in the spirit of fair play, all abbreviations and foreign words are so indicated.

ACROSS

1. Green growth
5. Capital of Saskatchewan
11. Condemn
15. Breakfast staple
17. Ohio-born inventor
18. European iris
20. 1952 film starring 58-Across
22. One of "The Brady Bunch"
24. Masculine nickname
25. Puebla plateful
26. Man of —, Superman's epithet
28. Mr. Hunter
29. Cancel out
31. Role for a boss
32. Legatees
33. Tableland
34. *Año* beginner: Spanish
36. Beatty of "Deliverance"
37. Apple: French
38. Open wagons
39. 58-Across's costar in "Love Me or Leave Me"
41. Cash in Calcutta
42. Happy shout
43. String instrument
44. Batman's "sidekick"
45. Al-Qâhirah
46. "Tiny Alice" playwright and family
49. Stable newcomers
50. Likely to be mistaken
53. Energy type
54. Riyadh native
55. White House employees
56. Goddess of dawn
57. Depot alert
58. Puzzle's subject
60. One of three
61. Bear: Spanish
62. "— in Arms"
63. British WWII vessel
64. Verse pattern in London
65. Blushed
67. Gridlock, e.g.
68. Washing machine cycles
69. Peripheral
70. Frat letter
71. Albacore
72. Poet Dowson
74. Dishonor or disgrace
75. Supporting player in 14-Down
79. Dapper
80. Moe's brother
81. Tomcat
82. More underhanded
83. Cologne complaints: German
84. Desert "steed"
85. Town in Cyprus
87. Famous French magazine
88. Race outcome, at times
89. Fernando or Lorenzo
90. Subjects of many toasts
92. Military expert Marshal: initials
93. Less taxing
95. 1939 film starring 58-Across
98. Fencing move
99. Actor Michael
100. Corrupt condition
101. Noted political cartoonist
102. Sleuth Lupin
103. Actor Richard

DOWN

1. More substantial
2. Scrap
3. Calendar abbreviation
4. Churchill of "Royal Wedding"
5. Staggered
6. Trimming tool
7. Gerard and Hodges
8. Equal: prefix
9. Eric the Red's crew, e.g.
10. Whenever
11. Cupolas
12. Evangelist Roberts
13. NHL great
14. 1955 film starring 58-Across
15. Time: comb. form
16. On the brink
19. California mountain
20. Sought (someone's) attention
21. "Days of Our Lives" veteran actor
23. Disconcert
27. Before, to Byron
30. Seek to prove
32. Pueblo Indians
33. Polynesian language
35. Wickerwork material
37. 1931 film starring 58-Across
38. Spirals
40. Wife's property
41. Stamping grounds for Hope and Crosby?

42. "Roots" author
44. Don Juans
45. West Point attendee
46. "The Maltese Falcon" actress
47. Wandering free
48. 1945 film starring 58-Across
49. In the public eye
50. The last exam
51. French river
52. Anglo-Saxon underlings
54. Fencer's choice
55. Early Greek "mall"
58. Ms. Gaynor
59. Lessen

60. Defendable
62. Harold Robbins best seller (with "The")
64. Tends
66. Sonny and Cher numbers, e.g.
67. MacArthur's promissory verb
68. Origin of the word "robot": abbr.
70. Farm machine
71. "Bewitched" toddler
72. Growing from
73. Of an ethnic group
74. Indonesian island

75. — Sibert Cather
76. Waterproof cloth
77. Forbush of "South Pacific"
78. Fear
80. Engine part
81. NHL job: var. sp.
84. Proofreader's mark
85. — duck
86. Polished
89. Grable's trademark
90. Sharpen, in a way
91. Flight hazard
94. Actress Claire
96. Printing spaces
97. Doctors' organization: abbr.

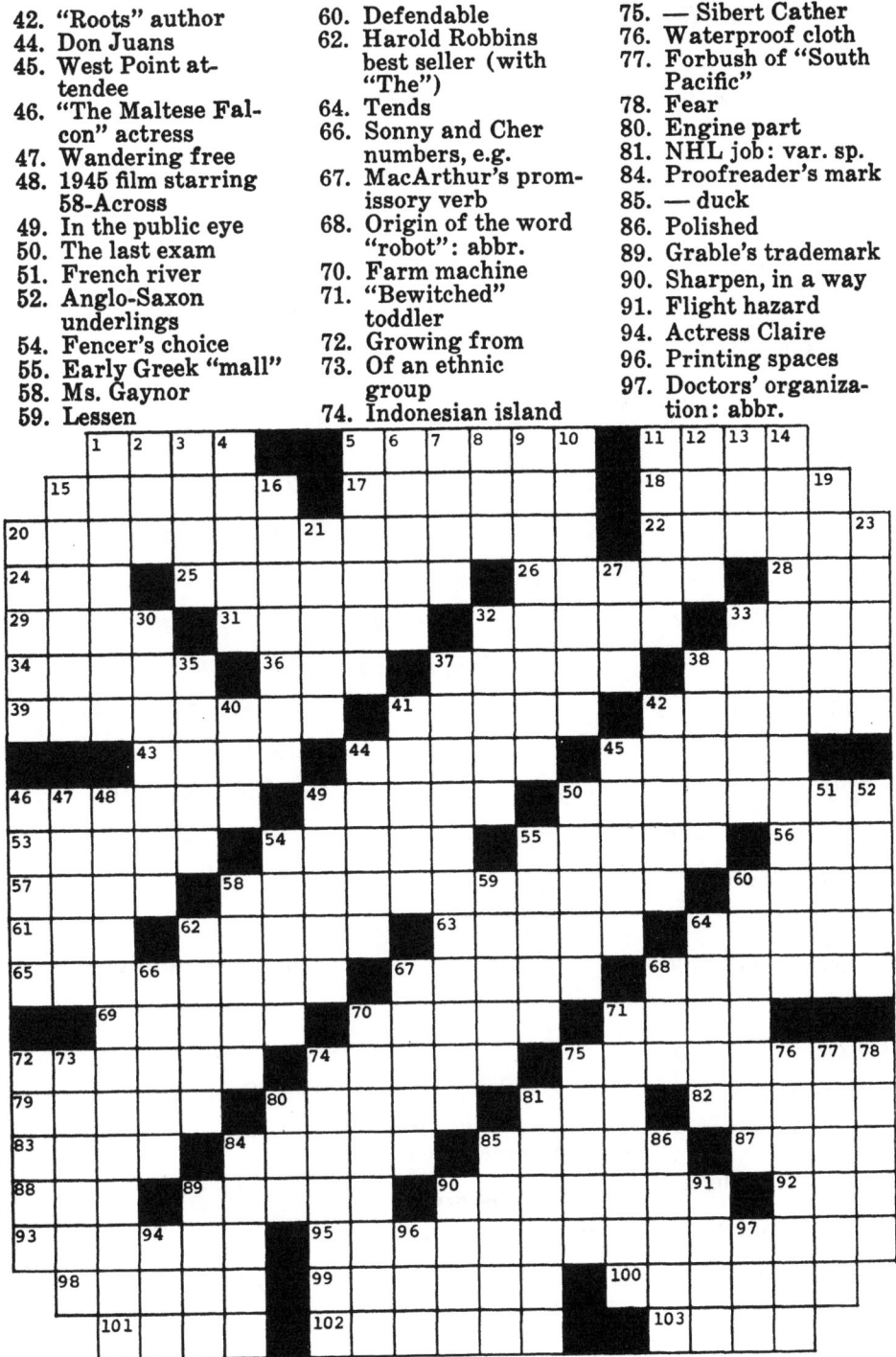

Solution is on page 404

This Diagramless is 15 boxes wide by 15 boxes deep.

ACROSS

1. Decay
4. Bottle top
7. Enthusiastic
9. Bird of peace
10. Native of Stockholm
11. Perfect
13. Wager (money)
15. Get well, as from an illness
17. Actress Gardner
20. First man
22. Shoe bottoms
23. Mix (batter)
24. Exhausted
26. Affirmative reply
27. Frozen rain
28. Some male voices
30. Very thin candles
32. Also
33. Come out on top
34. Steeple tops
37. Sex
40. Performs alone
41. What an eagle isn't
43. Antitoxin
45. Prophetic sign
46. "Yarns"
48. Actor's part
49. The Caspian is one
50. Some floor coverings
52. Lair
53. Male duck
55. Taunt; make fun of
57. Old
58. Roasting rod
59. Years in a decade
60. Cunning, as a fox

DOWN

1. Uncooked
2. Above
3. Daily ocean movements
4. Ciphers
5. Assert
6. Pod vegetable
8. Artificial birds for hunters
9. Dispossess (of rank, etc.)
10. Look fixedly (at)
12. Not now
13. Nocturnal mammal
14. Revise, as a news item
16. Bullfight cheer: Spanish
18. Competes
19. Skill
21. Refer to
23. Slim
25. Portals
27. Twirls
29. Fish eggs
31. Great wonder
34. A portion (of)
35. Beg
36. Showed mercy on
37. Welcomes
38. Wear away
39. Law
40. Distress signal
42. Lofty mountain
44. Males
46. Spoken for
47. Paces
50. Canary confine
51. Shove off, as a boat
54. A rodent
56. Pigpen

Solution is on page 404

DIAGRAMLESS

HARD

**This Diagramless is 15 boxes wide by 15 boxes deep.
Starting box is on page 407.**

ACROSS

1. Not bright
4. Region
6. Exclamation of scorn
9. '87 Super Bowl champs
11. Before now
12. Cite incorrectly
14. Word with "cloth" or "kick"
15. Actor Wallach
16. Kettle
17. Rum
18. Summer drink
19. Regular customer
21. — Cruces, New Mexico
22. — Magnon
24. Inexperienced
25. Fifty-four, in Old Rome
26. Paid notices, for short
27. Street: abbr.
28. Formerly named
29. Actor Hunter
32. Stings
34. That woman
35. Reduce in temperature
36. At the back
38. Baltic, for one
39. Quartet number
40. Coming twice a year
43. Petroleum
44. Examined by radiation: hyph. wd.
45. Certain trains, for short
46. Always
47. Aliens, for short

DOWN

1. White and yellow flowers
2. Baghdad's country
3. Bill of fare
5. Upon
6. Title of nobility
7. Excited
8. Informal dance
9. Comedienne Radner
10. Brief stay
12. Edible grain
13. Greek letter
14. Sleep lightly
17. Rate
20. Make motionless
22. Uproar
23. Competitor
29. Publishers, for one
30. In the lead
31. Man's name
32. All — Day
33. Bill
35. Twist
37. Weight allowance
39. Enemy
41. Church part
42. No: Russian

Solution is on page 405

CHALLENGER DIAGRAMLESS

As in the Special Challenger Crossword (21), we have not given you such helps as "2 wds.," "hyph. wd.," and "slang"; but in the spirit of fair play, all foreign words and abbreviations are so indicated. This Diagramless is 21 boxes wide by 21 boxes deep. Starting box is on page 407.

ACROSS

1. Fairy queen
4. *Roman-fleuve*
5. Game fish
9. Incarnation of a god
11. Within: prefix
12. Swift's genre
13. Language of Cato
14. British carbine
15. Artist Chagall
19. Indigo
20. "The Crucible" *mise en scène*
25. *Der* —, Adenauer
26. In a —, very shortly
27. Men of mettle
29. Pinky and Peggy
30. Caddoan Indians
31. Cupidity
33. Very: French
35. Traveler to Oz
36. Cartography art
37. Opposite of guzzle
39. Animal or plant body
40. Citizen of our most populous State
44. Synge's "The — Islands"
45. Hart's mate
46. Author Deighton
47. Unchanged
50. And
51. Jellyroll container
54. Grown-up filly
56. *Amore*
59. Supply
60. Bruit
61. Sharing
62. Michaelmas daisy
64. Notable periods
65. Salamander
66. Sir Guinness
70. *Crème de la crème*
71. Rationale
73. Rajput princess
74. Ready for the day
75. "Ma, He's Making — at Me"
76. Kon-Tiki, for one
77. Some

DOWN

1. Morning prayers
2. Edible seaweed
3. Unfurnished
4. Surfeit
5. Frosh cap
6. Pranks
7. A step up for fence-sitters
8. 41-Down, to Hera
9. Ninny
10. Dye container
13. "Penates" partners
15. Capital of the Maldives
16. Porter
17. Cop's beat: abbr.
18. *It's me!:* French
21. Cry of triumph
22. Bulgarian coin
23. Part of Q.E.D.
24. Filipino
26. Quarry tool
28. — on, audits (a course)
32. Salon creation
34. Incarnation of Vishnu
38. Foot: suffix
39. Furtive ones
40. Visitor

41. God of war
42. Hand-lotion ingredient
43. Artist Bonheur
48. Altered: prefix
49. Poems as oral history
50. Originated
51. Lincoln's coin

52. Receiver Monk
53. Once named
54. Mouse or rat
55. Cremona masterpieces
57. Washington bill
58. Solemn pledge
60. Pass on

63. Sanction
67. Inventory
68. Woman's name
69. Time period: abbr.
70. "... — I saw Elba"
71. Name chosen by Naomi
72. Algerian seaport

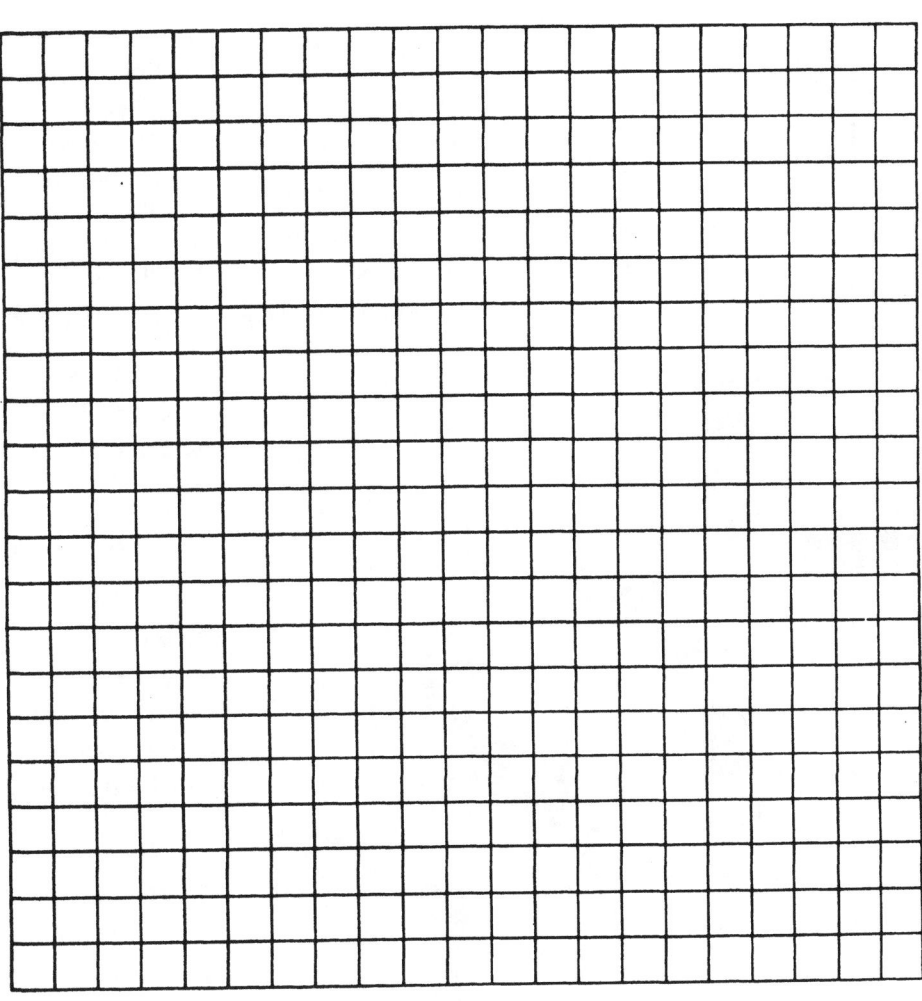

Solution is on page 405

ACROSS

1. Male sheep
4. Cease
8. Boxer, Muhammad —
9. Sixty minutes
10. Baseball club
13. Auto fuel
14. Aware of: slang
15. Lyric poem
16. Ripped
18. Tantalize
20. Speak in a singsong
22. Dressed fur
23. Prefer
24. Bag
25. Carpenter's tool
28. Fruit drink
29. Long, narrow cuts
30. Gift for Dad
31. Ballpoint
32. Lubricates
33. Musical group
34. Bugle call
35. Canvas shelters
36. Brings up
38. Dandelion, for one
39. Annoy
40. Jack rabbit
42. Belonging to us
45. Mine output
46. Unlock
47. Patriotic monogram
48. Cozy rooms
49. Decimal base

DOWN

1. Tattered cloth
2. Southern State: abbr.
3. Incorrect; wrong
4. Brief
5. Musical sound
6. Not at home
7. Shields
10. Watercraft
11. TV commercials
12. Golf mound
17. United
19. B.P.O.E. members
20. Applaud
21. Conceal
22. Buckets
24. Careless
25. Show up clearly: 2 wds.
26. Ungrammatical "am not"
27. Marries
29. Fly aloft
33. Hive dweller
34. Capture
35. Certain voters, for short
36. River: Spanish
37. Miscalculate
38. Small bird
41. Gorilla
43. Put in service
44. Sprinted

Solution is on page 405

ACROSS

1. Drink, cat-style
4. Energy
7. Not high
10. Conceit
11. Historic age
12. Ocean current
13. Final course of a meal
15. Went out with
16. Fido's dad
17. Ten-cent coins
18. Drove too fast
20. Motorist
22. Lessens, as pain
24. Assert
25. Public notices
26. More pleasant
28. Feline
31. Chinese dish
32. Follow the footprints of
34. Lids
36. Prophetic sign
37. Contended (with) successfully
38. Like a sage
40. Become unwoven
41. Word-for-word
44. Mimicked
45. Smallest bill
46. Commotion
47. Encountered
48. Jewel
49. Adjust, as a clock

DOWN

1. Guided
2. Mature
3. Own
4. Look (at) closely
5. Made a mistake
6. Dab
7. Metrical unit
8. Lyric poems
9. Marry
12. More docile
14. Faction
15. Distract the attention of
17. Go under water, as swimmers
18. Red or Baltic
19. Cushion
21. Indy-500 contestant
23. Sniff, as from a head cold
27. Frosted (a cake)
28. Photographers need these
29. Highest card
30. Five pairs
31. Lassoed
33. Flower for a sweetheart
34. Long for with envy
35. Pigs
37. Garment for Dracula
39. Article
40. Male sheep
41. Ship's journal
42. Fruit drink
43. Land parcel

Solution is on page 405

ACROSS

1. Sorrowful
4. Walking stick
8. Rowing team
12. Frozen water
13. Hymn ending
14. Assistant
15. Assign to an inferior position
17. Roasting rod
18. "Beware the — of March"
19. Takes to the proving ground
20. Confront
22. Long adventure tales
25. Inclines
27. Water barrier
28. Touch lightly and quickly
31. Monet's field
32. Selected
34. A Gabor
35. Boot part
36. Belonging to us
37. More secure
39. Exhausted
41. Finch, for example
42. Writing tablet
45. Unfolded
47. Flooring piece
48. Tranquilizer
52. Allay
53. Like some exams
54. Trifle (with)
55. Goad
56. Methods of doing something
57. Female sheep

DOWN

1. Galahad's title
2. King beater
3. Pleasing in its lightness
4. ". . . a bird in a gilded —"
5. Accumulate
6. Clear as profit
7. Compass reading
8. Window frames
9. Tears
10. Work on copy
11. Makes moist
16. Paradise
19. Makes docile
20. Level
21. Prefix with "dynamics"
23. Add beauty to
24. Kind of fuel
26. Extent; range
28. Explicit
29. Assert
30. Singer of poems
33. Color
38. Assist in an unlawful act
39. Spirited mount
40. The present time
42. Staircase part
43. Deceiver
44. Too
46. Chums
48. Scatter (seeds)
49. Historic period
50. Solemn pledge
51. Ogle

Medium

Solution is on page 405

ACROSS

1. Roll of dollar bills
4. Extra tire
9. Dove's call
12. Wide street: abbr.
13. Showed concern (for)
14. Owned
15. Car fuel
16. Picnic pest
17. Very angry
19. Rational
21. Good thing to "wish upon"
22. Toboggans
24. Grooved, as a spoon
27. Ripped
28. Disfiguring marks
29. Richmond's State: abbr.
30. Decay
31. Uses an ax
32. Distant
33. While
34. Displays
35. Manufactured
36. Annoys
38. Was in the Indy 500
39. Sunrise direction
40. "You — Take It with You"
41. Sow, as seeds
43. Kettle
44. Ancient
47. Have a meal
48. Wear away
50. Dark bread
51. Commercials
52. Motor trips
53. Evergreen tree

DOWN

1. Move, as a dog's tail
2. Miss Gardner
3. Sweet dinner course
4. Reads (a page quickly)
5. Window glass
6. Mr. Carney
7. Scale tone
8. Newspaper chiefs
9. Map; graph
10. Grain morsel
11. Lyric poem
18. Rodents
20. Fruit drink
21. Hits; smacks
22. Watch band
23. Wiggly, as a tooth
24. Flat-bottomed boats
25. Avoid
26. Challenged
28. Brief
31. "Gunsmoke" role for Dennis Weaver
32. Manufacturing plant
34. Mr. Musial
35. "Ol' — River"
37. Chairs, pews, etc.
38. Fixed prices
40. Morse system
41. Small, green vegetable
42. Young boy
43. Casing for 41-Down
45. Caustic substance
46. Grass moisture
49. Smallest of USA: abbr.

Easy

Solution is on page 405

349

Medium

ACROSS

1. Popular song
4. Hawaiian dance
8. Hart
12. High card
13. Without any changes: 2 wds.
14. The Pointer Sisters, for example
15. Automobile device: 2 wds.
17. Deserve
18. Foray
19. Pass, as time
21. Expel
23. Derived out of
24. Solitary
25. Courageous person
26. Born
29. Wyoming river: 2 wds.
32. Excitement
33. Like cheese, usually
34. Norway's capital
35. Celebrity
36. Cleaving tools
37. Push ahead
40. One of the martial arts
41. Having vitality and warmth
42. To some extent: 3 wds.
46. Candid
47. District
48. Large deer
49. Watch over
50. Certain sheep
51. Cereal grain

DOWN

1. Possesses
2. Do a baker's task
3. Attack impetuously: 2 wds.
4. Custom
5. Secondhand
6. "— Abner"
7. Starfish
8. Vapor
9. Mouth: slang
10. Broadcasts
11. Departed
16. Silence, in music
20. Taking too much time
21. Miss Fitzgerald
22. Vacuum
23. Thread
25. Make lawful
26. "— said than done": 2 wds.
27. Author, — Stanley Gardner
28. Seth's son
30. Tardy
31. Swarm
35. Be a splurger
36. Blends
37. Scheme
38. Fully prepared (for)
39. Kiln
40. A Fonda
43. Presently
44. Cunning
45. Supplement, with "out"

Solution is on page 406

ACROSS

1. Word with "leaf" or "window"
4. Southern State: abbr.
7. Sad; gloomy
8. Thin layer of ore
9. Cereal by-products
10. Accommodates, at a theater
11. Banquet
12. Extra
13. See 31-Down
14. Bridge triumph, for short
15. As well as
16. Playground item
18. Japanese coin
20. Shoshonean Indian
21. Arrest
23. Autocrat
25. Fish eggs
27. Noticed
28. College group, for short
29. One of the Golden Horde
31. Elevate
32. Sea duck
33. Fortuneteller's card
34. Peruse
35. Always
36. Limb
37. — Moines, Iowa

DOWN

1. Gust of wind
2. Close relative
3. Affirmative reply
4. Dread
5. Tardy
6. Times before noon: abbr.
7. Marked with a hot iron
8. Mariner
9. Bostonian's dish
10. Resorts
11. Italian monk's title
12. Partly frozen rain
14. Attack: 2 wds.
16. Custodian, for short
17. Golden State basketballer
19. Made a snug home
22. Brag
24. Scorch
26. Summer: French
28. Transportation charges
29. Row; layer
30. Seth's father
31. Talk wildly
32. Legislation backed by NOW: abbr.
33. Sen. Kennedy, to friends

Hard

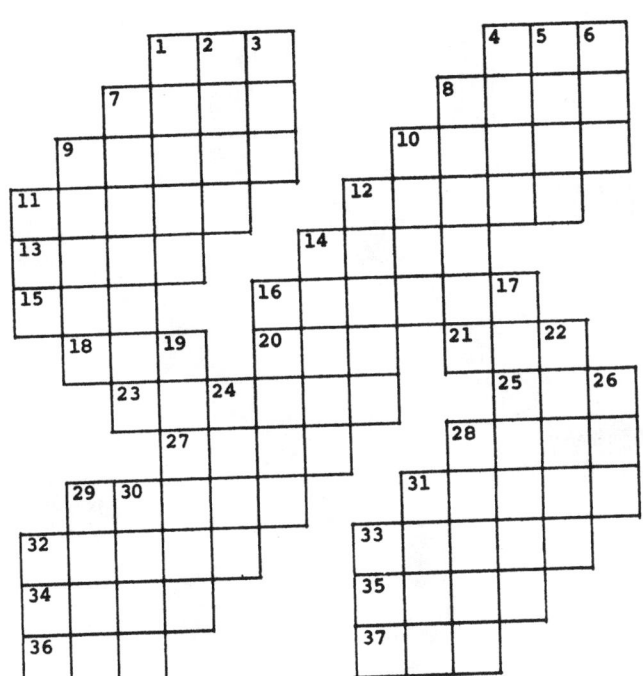

Solution is on page 406

Medium

ACROSS

1. Building wing
4. Picnic area
8. Metal refuse
12. Ocean
13. Great Lake
14. Type size
15. Rank; status
17. Leave out
18. Ember
19. Harangue
21. Shoulder covering
23. Seeks
24. Soft drink
25. Ridicules
26. Refrain syllable
28. Collection of anecdotes
29. Troublesome
30. Cooling device
31. One of us
32. Soiree
33. Requirement
34. French capital
35. Sight or touch
36. Asserted
38. Social group
39. Expectant desire
40. Visionary
44. Portend
45. Mother's sister
46. Lobe location
47. Lively
48. Short letter
49. Secret agent

DOWN

1. Sixth sense
2. Lion constellation
3. Milan, Italy's opera house: 2 wds.
4. Flower part
5. Seed coat
6. — de Janeiro
7. Bluegrass State
8. Baseball and football
9. Certain beans
10. Amino —
11. Means of access
16. Hawkeye State
20. Black
21. "Con game": slang
22. Sharpen
23. Game show emcees
25. Longitude line
26. Girl
27. Poker stake
29. Trim away
30. Comics
32. Inventor's right
33. Lunch or dinner
34. Writing need
35. List of candidates
36. Boutique
37. Large book
38. Penny
41. Twosome
42. Plant juice
43. Attempt

Solution is on page 406

ACROSS

1. Leading actor
5. Practice boxing
9. Small barrel
12. Slacken (up)
13. Assistant
14. Spanish cheer
15. Printer's measure
16. Rational
18. Picture border
20. Gerald or Harrison
21. Order for the butcher
22. Intelligent
24. Lassos
27. Sour
28. Was in poor health
29. That thing
30. Employ
31. "— Hall," Woody Allen film
32. In favor of
33. Negative vote
34. Made a choice (for)
35. Wharf
36. Broke suddenly
38. Convenient
39. Majors and Remick
40. Chore
41. Place for 8-Down
43. Goals
44. Sound heard from Santa
46. Distant
47. Furious anger
49. Biblical garden
51. Explosive: abbr.
52. Toboggan
53. Completed

DOWN

1. Observe
2. Sunbather's goal
3. While
4. Spa
5. Beach "floor"
6. Crusted dessert
7. TV commercial
8. Boxing official
9. Australian marsupial
10. Shade tree
11. Command for Dobbin
17. Mr. Garfunkel
19. Sudden attack
20. Taxi fee
21. Sound, as an argument
22. Shocks
23. Perry —, Raymond Burr role
24. Like most winter coats
25. Weary
26. Tale
28. Poker stakes
31. Comes into view
32. Rosy
34. Unclose
35. Went by
37. "On the ball"
38. Accompaniment with eggs
40. Even, as a score
41. Near the stern of a ship
42. Participated in a marathon
43. Mature
44. Chick's mom
45. Half a pair
48. Mr. Jolson
50. Accomplish

Easy

Solution is on page 406

DIAGRAMLESS

MEDIUM

This Diagramless is 15 boxes wide by 15 boxes deep. Starting box is on page 407.

ACROSS

1. Lids
5. Aid (in crime)
6. — Lisa
7. Milky gem
11. Devour
12. Very unusual
13. Lean-to
17. Allow
19. Poker stake
20. Bees' home
21. Worker at 25-Across
23. Diva's offering
24. Engine-knocking sound
25. Popular U.S. recreational area, familiarly: 2 wds.
33. Songstress Turner
34. Towards shelter
35. Rocky cave
38. Country road
39. Verdi opera
40. Moist
43. Detroit NFL player
44. Farm implement
45. Decay
47. Antitoxins
48. Inspires wonder
50. Oceans
51. Makes a mistake

DOWN

1. Highland cap, for short
2. Wind instrument
3. Word with "code" or "colony"
4. Ohio or Missouri
7. Citrus fruit
8. Sudden feeling of distress
9. "Laugh-In" comedian Johnson
10. Sly, sidelong look
13. Wood-burning locomotive
14. Employ for wages
15. Wicked
16. Transaction
18. Musical group
22. Actress/dancer Miller
24. School group: abbr.
26. Canada's capital
27. Humor
28. TV static
29. Dark or gloomy covering
30. Jai —
31. Nevada city
32. Sharp
35. Mountain passes
36. Annoy
37. Scent
41. Rub out
42. Eiffel's structure
46. Rip
49. Draft organization: abbr.

Solution is on page 406

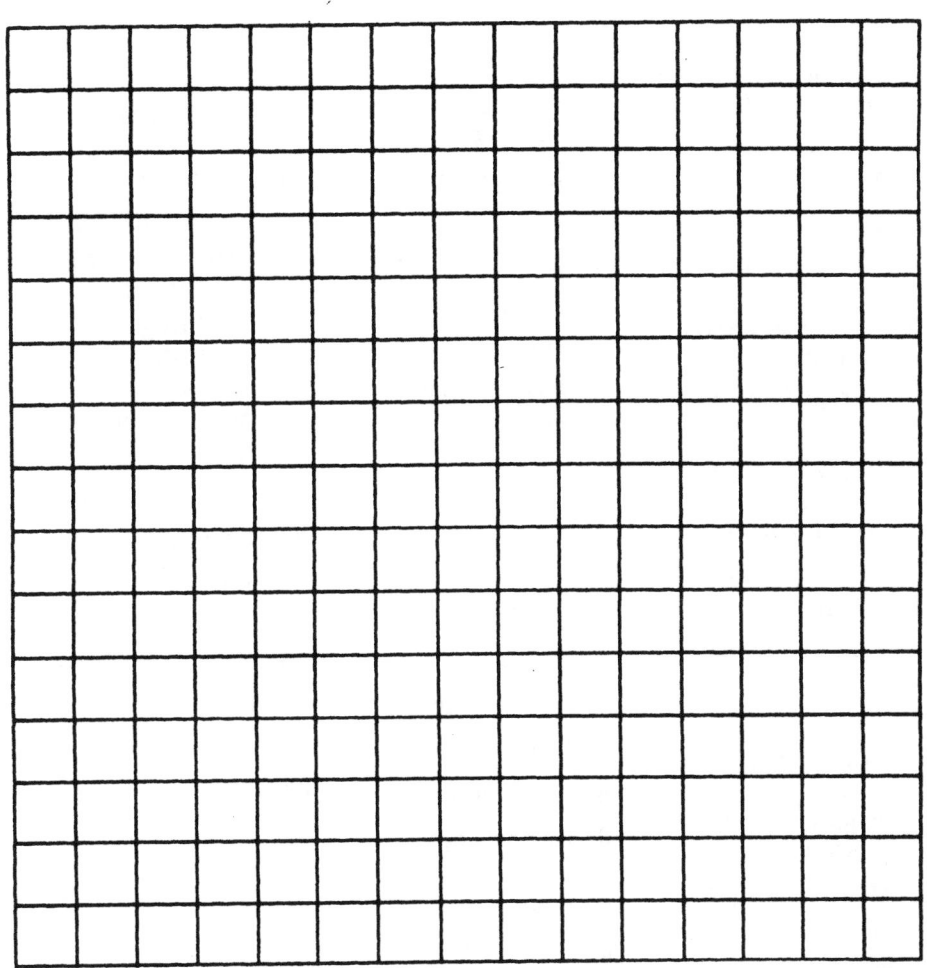

DIAGRAMLESS   EXPERT

**This Diagramless is 17 boxes wide by 17 boxes deep.
Starting box is on page 407.**

ACROSS

1. "West Side Story" gang member
4. Cutting tool
5. Veneration
8. Forbid
9. Having similar qualities
10. Cookbook abbreviation
13. "Brigadoon" setting
15. Ruffle the pride of
17. The Andrews Sisters, for example
18. Outfits: hyph. wd.
19. Relish
23. Finally: 2 wds.
24. Deteriorated: 3 wds.
27. Tiny Tim's daughter
28. "The Big —," Bogart classic
30. Made mistakes
32. Major bargain events: 2 wds.
37. Petitioner
39. Guide (a ship)
41. All
42. Noted U.S. humorist
45. Fred Astaire's sister
46. "To be, or not to be," e.g.
50. Lyric poem
51. Prod
52. African antelope
53. M.I.T. subject: abbr.
54. Encountered
55. Madison Avenue output

DOWN

1. Pokes
2. "On the money"
3. Singing voice
5. Alias: abbr.
6. Bettor's option at Belmont
7. Last word, often
9. Get —, agree
10. Professional boxer's quest
11. Team
12. Young seals
14. Shirt adjunct
15. Mr. Rose
16. Guess: abbr.
18. Filling-station purchase
20. Little bit
21. Burden of proof
22. "Old —," 1957 Disney film
25. Wedding-cake arrangement
26. "Live from the Met" offerings
29. Skin
31. Alphabet letter
32. Located
33. Useful
34. — over, ponder
35. Before, to Keats
36. Feel
37. Red or Black
38. Cancel
40. Stool pigeon: slang
43. Greek letter
44. Sharpened
46. Canadian province: abbr.
47. Vase
48. Person: slang
49. Snacks for squirrels

Solution is on page 406

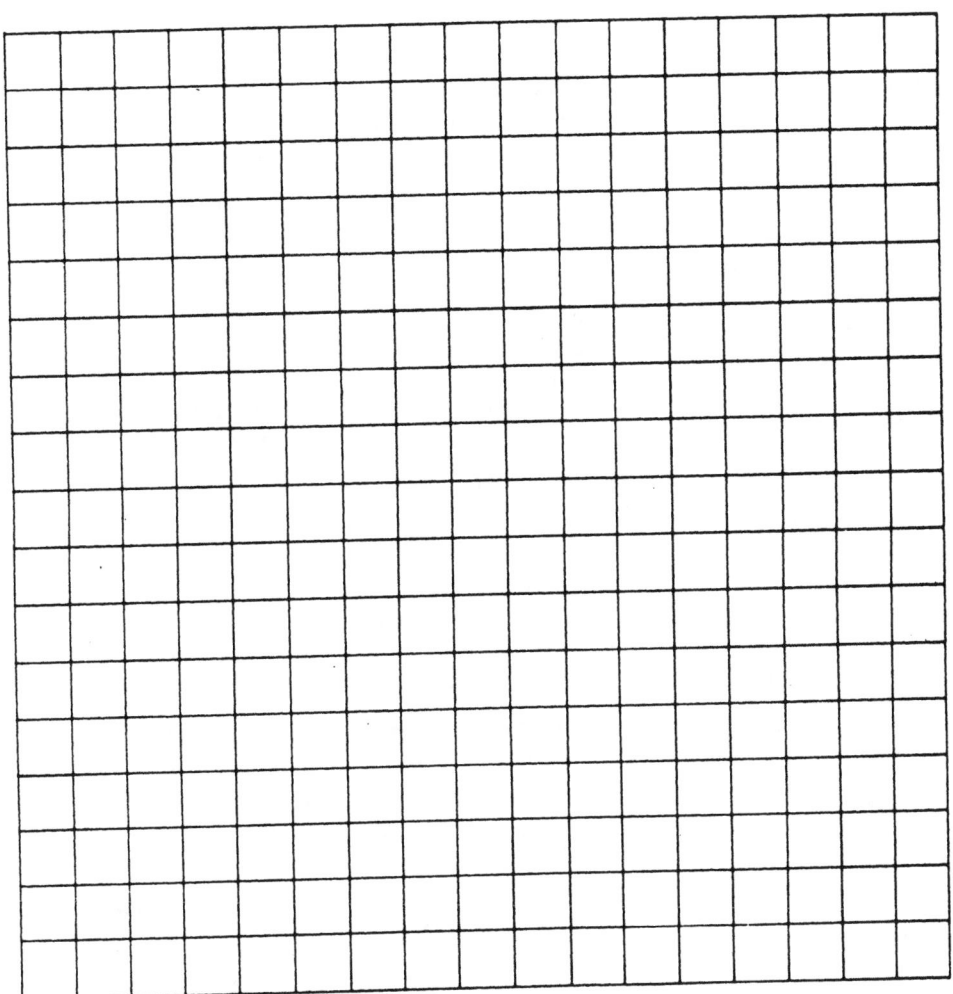

CHALLENGER DIAGRAMLESS

As in the Special Challenger Crossword (21), we have not given you such helps as "2 wds.," "hyph. wd.," and "slang"; but in the spirit of fair play, all foreign words and abbreviations are so indicated. This Diagramless is 21 boxes wide by 21 boxes deep. Starting box is on page 407.

ACROSS

1. Stop up
5. Fixing agent, in darkrooms
6. Chilled
10. Berliner's "alas"
13. Collector's item
14. Old saying
15. Joanne Woodward movie
21. Musical "disability"
22. Twilled silk
23. Time period
24. More central
25. "My country, — of thee . . ."
26. Peruvian capital
28. Actor who portrayed Sonny Corleone
29. Food fish
30. Fit of pique
31. City in Texas
34. Father of Shem
37. Islamic republic
38. Three, in *Roma*
41. Patron saint of sailors
42. Actress Garr
43. Swearword
45. Criticize harshly
46. Army man: abbr.
49. In equal shares
53. Haggard novel
54. Jack-in-the-pulpit's family
56. Himalayan "animal"
57. Mr. Stravinsky
58. Vicki Lawrence role
59. Tape: abbr.
60. Split rattan
61. Stands in (for)
62. Lifeless; dry
63. Harrow's rival
66. — Aviv-Jaffa
68. Form lather
72. Hoarfrost
73. Modeling medium
74. Earth: Latin
75. Usual kind of food
77. Hindu ascetic
79. Figaro's profession
80. James Jones novel
84. Rhythm in verse
85. Expressive sound
86. Certain of the sol-fa syllables
87. Gets rid of
88. Men in baseball
89. Orient

DOWN

1. Bird's low trill
2. Small harp of old
3. "Mayberry" boy
4. Blunders
6. Notions
7. Currency
8. Conceit
9. Oppose openly
10. Garret
11. Twentieth-anniversary gift
12. It tints the hair auburn
13. Burn
14. Sharp-smelling
16. Adolescent
17. Self: comb. form
18. Sniggler's catch
19. Narcissistic
20. Soft, white furs
27. Coral islands
29. Spruce or yew
31. In support of
32. Region
33. Songstress Simon
35. Oriental nurse
36. Base-runner's goal
38. Quinine water
39. Unit of energy
40. Of moral standards
44. Mother of Ishmael
46. Ms. Shriver and Ms. Dawber

47. German woman's title
48. Hinder; hamper
50. "Scarfed"
51. Actress Anderson
52. One of the Flint-stones
55. Powerful watchdog
64. Persian poet, — Khayyám

65. Depraved Roman emperor
66. Available buyer
67. Egress
68. Plant with fronds
69. Satellite's path
70. Mountain ridge
71. Crosby film, "The Bells of St. —"

73. Hawker's goods
74. Mountain lake
76. Jane Austen title
77. Celebration
78. Picaro
79. Brutal fellow
81. Six: comb. form
82. Columnist Bombeck
83. Surpasses

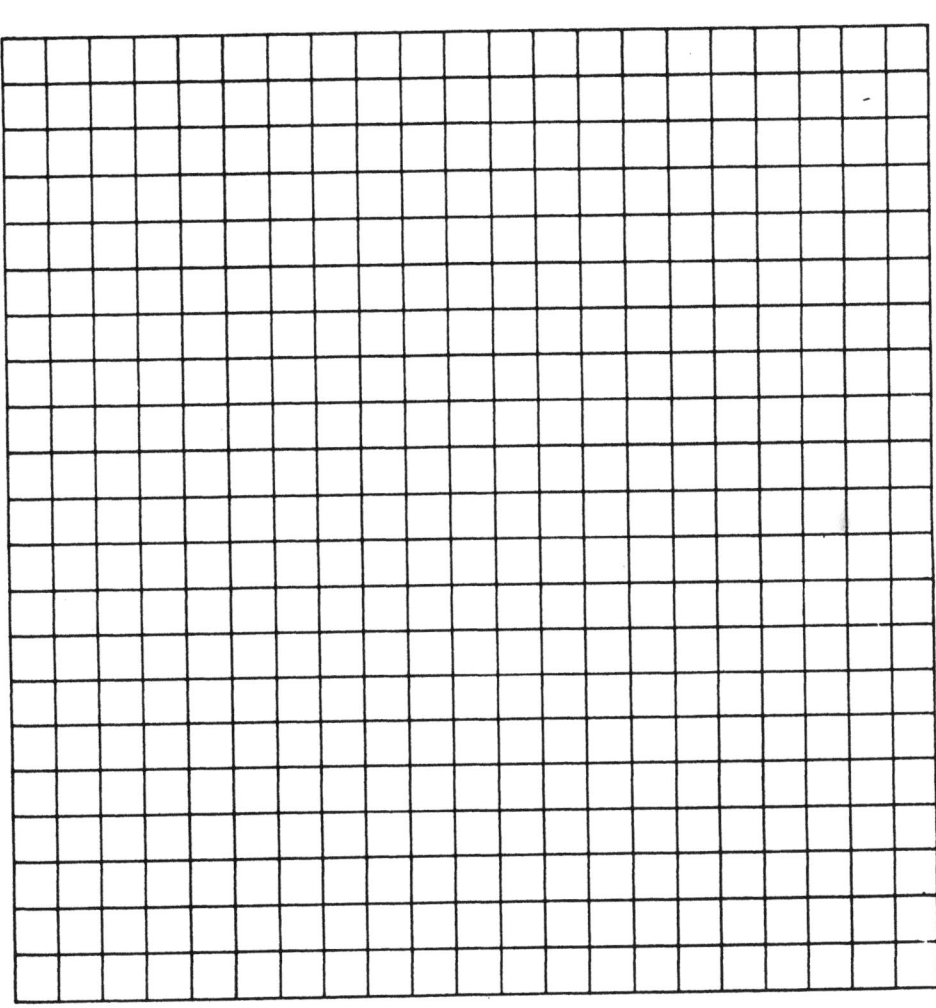

Solution is on page 407

ANSWERS

```
TAB   BREAD   WAR
ALL   LEASE   ICE
PEA   ANT   CARTS
   ZERO   WIDEST
OLIVE   FADES
GONE   DOVES   EM
LAG   TIRES   ARE
ED   HACKS   TWIN
   RATES   POKED
PRINTS   DREW
LANGE   TIE   AFT
ARK   ROOMS   RAH
YES   SHOES   DRY
```

```
AFAR   SWAP   TOP
HIRE   LIME   EGO
ASIA   ERIN   ARE
HALLEYSCOMET
   MAP   SIP
PUP   WEB   LABEL
AGES   RUG   LORE
THROB   NAG   BAG
   DAB   LAB
PARALLELBARS
ACE   LAVA   TOOL
IRE   OMEN   CLUE
RED   TENT   HELD
```

```
WADS   BLT   STOP
OPIE   RIO   OHIO
KEEPSAKE   DELL
   TONE   POSSE
ADDED   LLAMA
PEAT   DYAN   USO
SENSOR   NEURON
ERN   KANE   NULL
   YALTA   SISSY
KUKLA   CHIC
ETAL   SHADOWED
MAYO   POW   ROSE
PHEW   ASK   NESS
```

5-Across: bacon, lettuce, and tomato

```
AVON   SHIP   BIG
RIPE   TALE   UTE
CATTLEMEN   LET
   TAWS   CALMS
APPLY   FILM
GLUE   MILLIONS
RAN   FACES   OAT
ANCHORED   OSSA
   HUMS   DUETS
EMCEE   BAIT
SOO   NEATSFOOT
TOW   TARO   INDO
ADS   STEM   TEEM
```

```
RID   FAR   RAM
ACE   HIDE   BONE
PESTERED   ABET
   TORE   BLEW
PIN   SMALL
CANES   ORE   PAY
ONE   TERMS   AVE
BED   AGO   SOLES
   WRONG   MAR
AGES   EMIT
GIRL   CREATION
EDIT   OUST   ADO
TEN   TEE   LET
```

```
FED   THUS   OMER
ERE   ROSE   WOVE
WINTER   ELEVEN
   HE   ARE   END
THEY   NISAN
HOW   LOT   DESCE
EMEROD   REWARD
NESTS   NOR   FOE
   HEROD   HEWN
DEA   TOE   WE
ANDWHO   WARNED
NOAH   MAIL   OAR
ISMY   SINK   TRY
```

PAGE 10

```
LAMP  CAT  VENT
OVAL  ABE  IGOR
DENY  RENEGADE
ERA ANT  BONES
   CAPE  FOR
BULGE  HEN  SAW
ALEE  VIE  CURE
GUS  MAD  PUREE
   SON  JEEP
PASTA  BAN  ROB
UNTENDED  PIPE
STOW  ATE  ASEA
SIPS  BAD  DENT
```

PAGE 11

```
PUP  STOPS  BEE
IRE  LILAC  RAY
ENGLAND  ADORE
    ANY  STEALS
TRACT  HATED
RISK  FILED  IF
INK  POKER  HOE
OK  CARES  BOWL
  LOCKS  PETAL
SHARKS  PAL
HENNA  TALLEST
ARC  GAUGE  ALE
DOE  EMBER  RYE
```

PAGE 12

```
BARN  CABBAGES
ONTO  HILLSIDE
YTS  RODEO  BAN
SE  TAP  NNE  MD
CABIN  UDDER
ATOM  KNEELERS
MEN  PAIRS  FUN
PRESENTS  MEMO
  SINGS  GARBO
PO  PGA  EAT  AP
ERG  URALS  LII
PENSIONS  MINN
SOURNOTE  YEGG
```

PAGE 14

```
CASTLE  SPEEDS
ACQUIT  HOLDON
STUNT  CAPSIZE
HIES  LODE  TIA
EVA  DAVY  CONK
WELCOME  PORGY
  OVERDUE
DEFOE  GANDERS
ALES  PINT  VIP
POI  PARK  MINI
PINBALL  RANGE
ESTATE  PARCEL
RESTED  OTTERS
```

PAGE 15

```
BAA  SIDE  RAPT
ARC  CLAD  ASIA
SCHOOLTEACHER
SHEAR  ANNE
  SEA  TRESS
MINISTERS  LEI
ABES  ORE  SILL
TEA  SMALLTALK
EXTRA  YEA
  ALAS  VIOLA
TENDERHEARTED
UVEA  MOON  TAD
BEER  SENT  OPS
```

PAGE 16

```
GOD  LOSES  PAY
AIR  EXTRA  RYE
SLAPS  YANKEES
  MASS  SEES
ZEALOTS  RESTS
OR  SNAPS  PERT
NOR  SNOWS  DIE
EDEN  DRANK  BE
SEWED  TREATED
  AXED  MATE
SORTERS  KEELS
AND  DOUSE  MIA
LES  SPEAR  SET
```

```
PAGE 17
JAM  ELSA  SHAM
ANA  LAMB  HALO
WINESBURGOHIO
SLEW   AGILE
     IAN  DERIDE
SOHNE  AGA  GAL
THEGOLDENBOWL
OMS  LID  EARNS
ASSAIL  ERN
   BAYED  TOTE
GREENPASTURES
AINT  AVER  EAT
PODS  DELI  MME
```

```
PAGE 18
       HOP   POD   ACT
       LOBE  BIKES  SHOT
       ROWED  RESET  LINES
MOW   SAFER  REBEL  NAG
COB   ELLA  REED   LAP
ALOHA  SITS  SNAP  TITLE
PETALS  THE  OLD  LESSEN
   TALE  ENTRY  FEEL
   DESIRE  ARE  TUNNELED
MUD  TREATY  BAND  SAVE
LAS   LIE   SIP   BEN
ARTS  OWED  RIDERS  DON
DESERVED  CAN  DINNER
   NEED  BANGS  MOON
ERASER  PAN  LAW  BOSTON
GAVEL  MANE  EMIT  NERVE
ONE  GALA  PLOT  EAT
TRA  EDENS  ALTAR  MEL
   TIRED  AWARE  SOARS
   ROSE  SILKS  TUBS
   YEN   MAS   STE
```

```
PAGE 20
SCANT  GRAPH  DOSE  ACTS
PUREE  ROMEO  EVEN  PORE
ARRANGEMENT  CARD  SLUE
TIER  RAPS  PALE  MILER
SOS  LASS  CURL  NOISE
STRODE  PONY  PAWN  CON
USE  FOLD  LADED  TOO
POSSE  HASTE  ICED  TOPS
ABUT  SOME  RANKS  TERSE
ION  SURE  ASHES  FUSS
REFRAIN  PITON  TACTICS
LIFT  TODAY  PUCK  TOE
STOLE  TOKEN  FONT  MERE
HOWL  GAME  DELTA  MIMED
IRE  BONER  IRIS  DIN
PER  RAGS  SNIP  TICKET
SPATE  PAGE  GATE  LAS
LATIN  RAIN  BENT  SALT
ORAL  PICK  SPEEDOMETER
ONTO  INRE  ERASE  ARENA
POET  PEER  TOTEM  TESTY
```

```
PAGE 22
SPICE  TROT  OLDER  BATH
CAROL  HIRE  TEASE  AREA
ALONE  IDEA  HARPS  LINT
TEN  VINE  CHEST  TREATS
BACK  CHORE  DOOR
CREATE  BEEPS  GIRL  MAP
HORSE  FEARS  PANEL  OWE
AMOS  CLASS  MAZES  SLAT
PAD  SHARE  PIPER  SHAKE
SNEAKERS  PILED  GLARES
WISE  MINER  TRIP
CLEARS  GALES  PRETENDS
HEART  CURLS  GLUES  OUT
OGRE  SOARS  GRAND  MONA
PAL  BERRY  BLANK  LOSER
SLY  LEND  COAST  PUREST
RUDY  WANDS  RICE
DANIEL  DARED  TANK  BAG
OVAL  IRATE  EMIT  IMAGE
MIME  NOTES  SOLE  EASEL
EVES  GEARS  TOES  REEDS
```

```
PAGE 24
POLA  NOTRE  ORD  BRACER
APED  OCREA  LAI  CANADA
SHOOTTHEBREEZE  SPIRIT
TEN  AIRES  NAOMI  TRES
ELI  LOE  HERR  SCARY
LINDEN  ATOMY  PLACATED
AEON  STUDY  BOAST  HEY
STOKERS  MANNE  MERE
PACE  BEEN  SATED  BET
UNO  POI  TOWIT  BATONS
STOLLEN  ULINE  VALERIE
HELIOS  RISEN  ASK  CLE
OLD  TOTOS  DENT  SHED
TINY  PEALS  CONCEPT
ORE  CEASE  BOWIE  ROTH
NASTIEST  FROND  DEARER
HOARE  SEAT  PAS  ELA
SEEM  RIPEN  GHOST  ALI
PLEASE  HOLDONESHORSES
CELTIC  ADE  PAREE  HONE
ASSORT  DER  SWORD  ONER
```

```
PAGE 26
HOCKS  ASHE  SPAR
SHEEP  PLAN  ERIE
TONER  PAIR  VERY
SPACETRAVEL
STU  IRAS  GARAGE
PARTNER  BET  TOY
AXES  WELLS  WERE
TIDAL  DIE  OASES
RUB  EDICT
FLUSTERS  STEPPE
RAP  ERA  EL  ROAN
ETON  AT  RAH  LIV
TENANT  ANNUALLY
TIERS  DEW
EQUAL  ETA  SALEM
BULL  SNOUT  RENO
BIT  BID  THREADS
SPIRAL  SHOE  PST
MARVELOUSLY
BOAZ  EMIR  HOERS
INTO  RICE  OKAYS
BEER  SLED  WIRES
```

PAGE 28

```
W E B                       L E G
A R I D                   S O R E
C A D E T S             S H O R T
      T O O       S L A M S
    S P E N D S     C A R S
    P L A C E     C R A T E
S A I N T     M A I L S     L A P
A L P S     C A R T E     P A N E
Y E S     F O R C E     O U T E R
      F L A K E     S T R E W
    S E A S     R A T H E R
    S T A R T       P I E
S P A R E         E R R A N D
P A L S               S I R E
A R E                 L A W
```

PAGE 30

```
            F A R E
            E W E R
            E L L A       S H O E
            S A T         C E D E
L O S T         Y O U     H A I L
A L E E           S C O R N S
T E A R S       R E A L
H O L M E S A N D W A T S O N
          V A N S       R E E S E
  R E P E N T             S A L E
  O D O R     E A T       T R O D
  A G R A       I R E
  R E E L       D A V E
                E D E N
              S E N D
```

PAGE 32

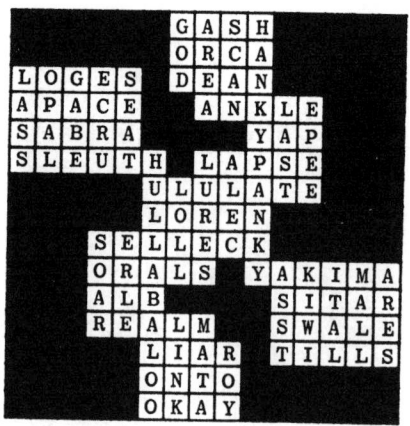

```
            G A S H
            O R C A
L O G E S   D E A N
A P A C E     A N K L E
S A B R A       Y A P
S L E U T H   L A P S E
          U L U L A T E
          L O R E N
        S E L L E C K
        O R A L S   Y A K I M A
        A L B       S I T A R
        R E A L M   S W A L E
          L I A R   T I L L S
          O N T O
          O K A Y
```

PAGE 34

```
M A Y   C H O I R   W H O
I C E   H O U S E   H O W
D E S S E R T   S H A W L
        H E N   S T A L L S
A L T E R   S P I T E
L E A D   S H A V E   M A
S A G   S T O N E   B O G
O K   S T A C K   B O R E
  S H A R K   S O W E D
C H A I R S   P A W
H A U N T   B U L L E T S
A R C   L A U R A   L I E
T E E   E N D E D   F E E
```

PAGE 35

```
H A S   S T O P S   N T H
A L E   T R I A L   A R E
M I C H A E L   E A S E L
    R O C K   P E L T E D
C R E E K   H A P P Y
L E T S   L A N E S   L A
A L S   C O V E R   S O N
M Y   N O V E L   C H A T
    H E L E N   S H A D E
S T E A L S   T H E M
C R A T E   S H A R P E R
A I R   C A P E R   O N E
T O T   T H A N K   O D D
```

PAGE 36

```
L A S   G O A D   F A I R
E L I   U N D E R L I N E
G A M B L E   C O A S T S
    P U P   D O T   L E T
W I L Y   J O Y   H E R
A N Y   T A U   R A S P S
I T   P E B B L E S   R E
L E M O N   L A D   H E W
  R I P   V E X   P O T S
A C T   F A D   N I L
R E T A I L   T I T L E S
I D E N T I C A L   O A K
D E N T   D O N E   W R Y
```

```
F I R   S P E A R   L O T
E R E   H E L L O   A D O
W E D L O C K   T O D D Y
      A R K   H A U L
S M A R T   R E T R E A T
H A R K   H O L E S   L A
R I M   G A S P S   T I N
E N   B A S E S   S A C K
D E S E R T S   T U B E S
    L A N E   M A R
M I A M I   B U F F A L O
A C T   S H E L F   P I N
Y E S   H O N E Y   T E E
```

```
L E T   C H E E R   L E E
A V A   L E D G E   A W L
W A L K E R S   L A P E L
    L E A D   B E N S
J O I N T   P L A N E T S
U S E S   C H A S E   A L
L I S   B R A K E   S H Y
E E   A R O S E   T O O L
P R O M I S E   H O N E Y
    W E D S   W O R N
F L I N G   E A R N E S T
I O N   E A R N S   T A R
B U G   S T A T E   S T Y
```

```
  E J E C T   C R A M P
S Q U A R E   R E W A R D
C U S T E R   O N E   O R
R A T   A M E N D   E V E
A T   S T I L E   A X E S
P E R M I T S   C L A S S
    E A V E   F O A M
A Z U R E   R E L I S T S
W E S T   P A T E N   E T
A R E   G E N T S   A N E
S O   O L E   E L A P S E
H E L P E R   R A S P E D
  S A T E S   S W A T S
```

```
    T A L E   R A I D
P O P   A L A N   A C R E
E A R   R E N T   T E E N
W R O N G   D E N T
    E E L   R E L A T E
S C A T T E R   W E I R D
C A T   D A M   D O G
A R O M A   H O N E S T Y
R E M A I N   P E R
    I R O N   A R I S E
O P A L   M O A T   C O Y
W I N E   A N T E   E W E
L E N D   D E E R
```

```
P U P   D R E W   C A L L
E R R   R U D E   O L E O
A N I   O N E   B O O T
    V E N T   B A R N
K N A V E   G A R A G E S
N O T E   C O N E S   L A
E R E   P A R K A   L I L
A S   B E R G S   M A T T
D E F L A T E   C A N E S
    O A R S   P I N T
S I A M   P O D   E B B
A C M E   P I L E   R Y E
M E S S   S E A R   N E T
```

```
T H E M   S P O T   L E T
H O L E   P U R E   E N O
U P O N   I S E N   A T E
S E N D E T H   D O N E
    I R E   D E N   R O
A L O N E   H E R   S I N
L O N G   S O W   B O N E
M A Y   W A R   W I N G S
I T   B I T   M E N
    H I L L   H E R D M E N
P E N   D E E R   E A V E
A T T   E V E R   T R E E
W H O   R E L Y   H A N D
```

```
  V I C A R   S H A K O
F I B U L A   P A R O D Y
A C I D   P S A L M   D O
I T S   P H O T O   F E Y
N O   G E A R S   P E S O
T R I N K E T   P E L T S
    T O O L   C A T O
F R A M E   E R R A N D S
R U L E   B R O I L   U P
A N Y   B R I E S   A R E
I N   M O A N S   E L B A
L E M A N S   U P R O A R
  L Y O N S   S I R E N
```

```
F O G   F L E A S   D A B
E W E   R O A S T   I C E
E N T W I S T   R A K E S
    A L E   M O D E S T
P E A R L   P O K E S
E A R N   L A N E S   I F
A S K   L I N E S   C O O
R E   H O N E Y   B A W L
    R I N K S   S A L A D
S W I N G S   P E N
P A S T E   C A N D L E S
E V E   S W O R D   O A K
D E N   T E N T S   W R Y
```

```
  S M A R T   J E A N S
S T O G I E   U P R O O T
P I L O T S   B I S T R O
O R O   E T H I C   E G O
I R K S   S O L   I D O L
L U A U S   T E E D
S P I L L T H E B E A N S
    L Y R E   B A N A L
A S H Y   Y A M   L O R E
R H O   D O D O S   I R E
M U U M U U   C A T N A P
S T R E E T   K N O T T Y
  S I L L S   S E N S E
```

```
O W L   G R I M   F E A T
L E E   L I N E   R A C E
D E T   A N N   C A R E D
    T U S K   D E N T
B L E S S   B E N C H E S
R A R E   C R A T E   N O
A D S   T A I L S   G A L
I L   C A R D S   F A C E
D E S E R V E   S O R T S
    P A R E   W A R D
D A I S Y   W I N   E L F
O G L E   T A R T   N O R
G E L S   I D E A   S T Y
```

```
M A R T I N I S   H E M S
O V E R D O N E   E L I A
W E D   L I T E R A L L Y
    O B E S E   O V A L S
L A L A   E N J O Y
A V E R T   T O T   P E A
D I N E R O   B E D L A M
D D T   I N T   R O A S T
    O V E R S   U S E S
S H A P E   A L E R T
P O L I T I C A L   E L M
U P O N   D E P L O R E R
R I C E   A S S E S S E S
```

```
F O R   T O N   H E W
A P E   S O L O S   E R E
T E N   O P E R A   L I E
E N T E R   T A M E D
    W E D   G A R
B A S E   R A I N C O A T
A G O   B I L L S   A D O
D E S E R V E D   F R E T
    V I E   S H E
B O N E D   A W A R D
O N E   E L D E R   M A R
A C E   S O U N D   I C E
R E D   B E D   D E W
```

PAGE 51

```
JAR  STIRS  GAP
ORE  TOOTH  AGE
BEDDOWN  UNION
  TORN  STAN
PLANE  STEPSUP
ROPE  SLAYS  NO
ONE  SPARE  TIS
BE  REAPS  MATE
ERRANDS  CAKES
  AIDE  CANE
SIGNS  SAVESUP
ODE  IMAGE  USA
SOD  NOTES  PEW
```

PAGE 52

```
BAD  FILES  ALA
EGO  ASIDE  LOP
DECIDED  TRACE
  TREE  TENOR
STOOD  FEEDS
WORN  BOAR  HE
IRS  SOURS  MAD
ME  WARN  MILE
  POETS  MASON
MAINE  FUSS
OCTET  LASTING
SEC  EPOCH  LEE
SSH  NASTY  EWE
```

PAGE 53

```
 ADAPT  MOUNT
BRACER  INFERS
RAVINE  GLOBAL
IBID  ASHY  UNE
EST  SCOT  ELSE
  LULU  AWAIT
 SPIRE  TWEET
 MAIZE  VEER
ANNA  BAND  MSS
KGB  PONS  MATA
ERASER  ICEBAG
SILKEN  LOSERS
 ALIKE  EXALT
```

PAGE 54

```
WRAP  TAR  FEUD  CART
HAIR  TINA  OGRE  PACERS
AIDE  ADDITIONS  AVENUE
TD  PALE  SAL  SANE  TEN
 CAPE  BEG  WEED  BESS
SCORE  GAS  TEARS  CARTE
TAME  COT  BEAST  FOR
IRE  PAD  CRAVE  HARNESS
RETURN  PHASE  SODA  LEE
 SO  CLONE  CAMEL  SEA
LATE  BOARD  SALES  BENT
ONE  PRUNE  COLAS  PA
ATE  AIRS  WORLD  TANGLE
DENTIST  RANTS  AIL  RON
 INK  ROSES  INN  WAND
SLEET  SOAPS  ACT  PINES
PENS  OARS  OLE  FIND
AVA  KIDS  ADE  SENT  VA
TEMPER  TANGERINE  EVER
SLEEPS  ERIE  TOOT  REST
 SLAT  REPS  SUB  SETS
```

PAGE 56

```
 GOOD  FIRST  SHAG
SERVE  IDAHO  LOCAL
STREET  SEWER  OPENED
HAM  NESTS  NAPE  DAY
ORAL  SOS  SPADE  HERE
PENALTY  RAIDS  WARNS
 YES  HELLO  NOR
TONED  TASTE  FOMENTS
APER  RENTS  RATE  OWE
PEW  CARDS  DOZEN  VIE
ERE  HISS  COPED  LEND
SARDINE  PAVED  SALES
 ENS  LINES  FAT
FALLS  MINDS  COWERED
OPAL  PASTY  PAR  REDO
OAR  DART  SINEW  PIE
DRIVER  ELATE  SABOTS
 TAINT  NEVER  TIERS
 TASS  SEEPS  STET
```

PAGE 58

```
PATS  MAPLE  REBEL  OAHU
ECHO  ERROL  ELUDE  ISER
ARIL  TIOGA  LARGO  LEAN
RESULTED  PSI  RENEWALS
 TELL  ASPEN  SIRE
RELIVE  CLEAVER  DALLAS
ALLOY  SOO  NEVER  SLIME
STAN  STING  RIVER  SLAV
POM  SHINERS  LETUP  ATE
SNAPPERS  INALL  NIACIN
 ALAS  SNORE  IBEX
SPIRIT  TUDOR  GRATEFUL
PAN  THAIS  TAPIOCA  ETE
AILS  SCAPA  SHANK  MATE
SNEAD  ERECT  INS  WISER
METRIC  ACROBAT  PANTRY
 ANOA  TYROL  DALI
GIOCONDA  LAB  OINTMENT
ROVE  DELHI  CANNA  IDEA
OWEN  OPTIC  ABEAM  ZERO
WARS  STOPS  TERRA  ENOS
```

PAGE 60

```
A P S O   P R I C E   A C T I   O L E O
G R A D   R E R A N   S P A H N   B A R T
R E N O N E V A D A   T O L E D O O H I O
E X T R E M I T Y   S E D   D I V E R S E
E Y E   W I S E   E T A   N O T E
S U I   R O L L S O V E R   O P T
M A S H   M O R E N O   U N E   R O L L O
A N N U L   N A T   U R N S   R A G L A N
R O O M E R   J U L I E   U P E N D I N G
C A B I N E T   R O S S   C H A   E E K S
L A N S I N G M I C H I G A N
A S T I   T A N   G I S H   S A L U T E S
S T E A M E R S   E S T O P   N A T U R E
W A N T A D   E A R S   R O D   S A T I E
A L O E S   O R R   O V U L E S   H U C K
N E R   C O N T I N U E S   F E N
A M A S   O R E   R I T E   T O P
S T A R R E D   E R I   S A N T A R O S A
N O M E A L A S K A   B O W I E T E X A S
O N E S   E R I E S   I R E N E   D I G S
W E N T   T E N D   B E R G S   S N E E
```

PAGE 62

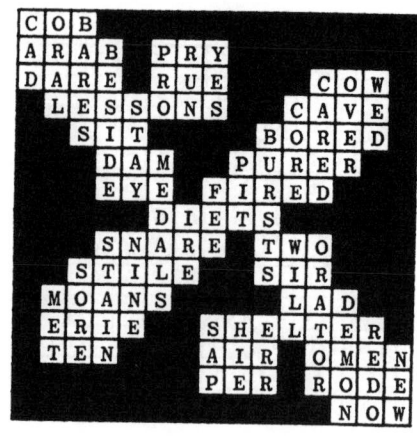

```
C O B
A R A B   P R Y
D A R E   R U E         C O W
  L E S S O N S     C A V E
    S I T       B O R E D
    D A M     P U R E R
    E Y E   F I R E D
      D I E T S
    S N A R E   T W O
    S T I L E   S I R
M O A N S         L A D
E R I E     S H E L T E R
T E N       A I R   O M E N
          P E R   R O D E
                  N O W
```

PAGE 64

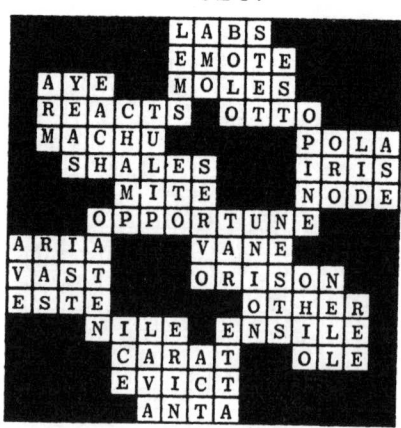

```
        L A B S
        E M O T E
A Y E     M O L E S
R E A C T S   O T T O
M A C H U       P O L A
  S H A L E S     I R I S
  M I T E       N O D E
  O P P O R T U N E
A R I A   V A N E
V A S T   O R I S O N
E S T E     O T H E R
  N I L E   E N S I L E
  C A R A T   O L E
  E V I C T
  A N T A
```

PAGE 66

```
C A S T         S O M E
A L T A R     H I R E D
S L A T E S   P I R A T E
H O T   D O P E S   T E N
  W E T   L O W   P O D
  D I V E S   A I R
    R E S T O R E
    S E X   A V E R T
  L A D   A G E ' S I N
N I L   L I E N S   R O T
A M U S E D   S E D A T E
B I T E S     T I D E S
S T E W       P E S T
```

PAGE 67

```
H I D   A L O N E   S A M
I D O   D A R E S   C U E
T A C   O N E   C L A N S
    T I R E   P A I N T S
S T O N E   D O P E S
E A R N   E A S E D   T O
E L S   F A R E S   S I D
M E   B A R N S   F L E D
  S O I L S   D E E D S
S K I N N Y   W A D E
C A D E T   S I T   V A N
A T E   E R O D E   E V E
T E D   D I N E D   S E W
```

PAGE 68

```
S A F E   R A M S   B O B
E R I N   A N E W   A P E
A T T R A C T   E A S E L
    A R K   R E L E N T
S T A G E   D A T E S
L I N E   L I K E S   T O
A D D   H A V E N   T U B
B Y   W A K E S   F A R E
  P A R E S   S U N N Y
S T A I N S   P O T
W A S T E   R E S U L T S
A P T   S H U T   R E E L
B E E   S O M E   E D D Y
```

```
ARC   SOD     LAD
POOR  OUR   PIPE
TENACITY   OMEN
   VIAL  GALAXY
CRISP   HOSE
RACE   LOOKSFOR
ART  MENDS   LAY
MESSAGES   BATE
    ALAS   SIGHS
THRILL   PURR
REAL   INUNDATE
IRIS   TEN   SNAG
MEN   YET   TWO
```

```
WAG   STAMP   ALA
EVA   LOSER   PER
BALLETS   IMAGE
   ADS   EVER
OMENS   BLASTED
POSE   SEATS   LA
EVE   PLATE   FOR
RE   MOORE   TAPE
ARTISTS   LATER
   ANTS   SIR
SLIDE   STOPPED
HAL   RIPEN   ORE
EDS   SNAPS   PAN
```

```
PET   PALS   PATH
ORE   EDIT   ASIA
OIL   NOSE   SPED
RELIC   TEST
   LIP   POETIC
CHILLED   SLICE
HOD   RAP   LED
ALLOW   REPULSE
TEETER   WAS
   HEAL   LEGAL
LANE   DOSE   ARE
OVER   ASIS   SIS
GETS   RENT   PAT
```

```
HATS   LAP   GROW
IRON   ERR   RISE
SEPARATE   ABEL
   RID   SENSES
CREEP   SENT
LAWS   WONDERED
AGE   WANTS   ELI
WEDDINGS   BASE
   ENDS   WARES
TRANGE   SON
HURI   REPENTED
ALOE   ERI   EASI
TEND   DEN   RITE
```

```
GNU   SOBS   BEAT
RON   INON   ARCH
ARF   LEGISLATE
MAUVE   PALS
   RINSE   DEEDS
SELECTED   TRUE
AM   EARED   PA
SILT   NINETIES
STOAT   ETNAS
   CREE   OGLES
AMAZEMENT   ARE
COLA   MOUE   NNE
EDEN   ANTS   DEN
```

```
WAS   AREA   SLAB
EWE   SEAT   TIRE
TEACHER   SINCE
   RED   FINE
BASIS   PILGRIM
ARAB   ALLY   ME
SEW   MONEY   CAT
IN   HOPE   PAGE
NATURAL   SABER
   ORAL   WON
PEARL   LIBERTY
ELSA   AIDE   OWE
WITH   DEER   DOT
```

PAGE 76

```
G O A T   A S H   P A L S
A N N A   P E I   A L O E
G O D S P E E D   C E D E
      T A X   E L I X I R
R O V E R   G A I N
U S E D   C O W P O K E S
I L E   C O L A S   A V A
N O R M A N D Y   S T E W
      A L T A   H E E L S
G R I L L E   R A N
L E N D   S W A N S O N G
O N C E   T O P   O L E O
W E A N   S E T   R E D O
```

PAGE 77

```
T O E   S H E D   J A W S
W A X   P I N E   A R E A
O R C H A R D S   P I L L
      H A R E   C R A D L E
S H A V E   G R I N
T U N E   F L I P   P I P
E G G   G L O B E   A R E
W E E   R A V E   S T I R
        S I T E   W A I S T
A C C E P T   R A G E
C L A N   E V I D E N C E
M I S S   R I T E   C O Y
E P E E   S E A S   E W E
```

PAGE 78

```
    B E A S T S   M A R E S
S O L I C I T   A N I M I S M
P R O D U C E   D I G I N T O
R O P E D   A C E   S T A R T
I D E S   S M I L E   S T E T
T I R   D A Y T I M E   R E L
E N S U E D   E N E R V A T E
        S U D S   E R I A
S A R A C E N S   G E N D E R
E V E   E N E M I E S   I R A
D A S H   S E E M S   S V E N
A L O O F   R E P   S P E C K
T O R T O N I   A S T A R T E
E N T E R O N   C H A N G E D
    S L A N G   T E N S E D
```

PAGE 80

```
P E P   S L A B S   S A W
O A R   H O T E L   T I E
P R O M I S E   E R O D E
      A N T   L E E R E D
S T A K E   L A P S E
L A C E   R O B O T   D A
A P E   R A V E N   L I D
M E   L E V E L   P I N E
      P A V E S   R A T E S
S T O N E S   D O G
T O W E R   G I V E S U P
O N E   S L A V E   U S E
P E R   E A G E R   M A T
```

PAGE 81

```
R O O F   R O O M   P A Y
O R A L   E R G O   A C E
A L T O   S O L O I S T S
N E S T L E   E L L A
      S O A R   A L D E R
P A R A G R A P H   E L A
I T E M   C P A   O N L Y
T O M   T H I R D B A S E
A M I S H   D A Y S
      N O R A   K E E P E R
E N D T A B L E   R I T A
G E E   S L O E   V E N T
O E R   H E A T   E R A S
```

PAGE 82

```
R I B   S T E W   S A S S
A D E   T A L E   T R U E
P O T L U C K   P A I N T
      T A N K   H E R S
T W I S T   L I S T E N S
R A N T   F O R T S   O H
E G G   L A N E S   B O O
S O   S I D E S   C A S E
S N E A K E R   B A S E S
      L I E S   T A L K
I D O L S   C O L L E C T
C A P E   D A R E   T O O
E Y E D   O N E S   S O N
```

PAGE 83

```
BRAC  OHO  NAVE
LANA  DUB  OBIE
EGGS  AMOEBEAN
BALED  BEVEL
   ERATO  ELLEN
CONSOLES  FRO
SAFE  FDR  COAL
ORR  OUTSMART
SPELL  SERRA
   PELEG  SEDAN
AROMATIC  FACE
MESA  RFD  UNTO
OPEN  ETS  LOAN
```

PAGE 84

```
ADD    FRO    FLY      PRO
CROW   GLIDE  SLIER   SOAR
EASE   RINDS  LOOSE   SPIRE  PURE
WEEPING  CROWN  SPIRE
   KING  BOOTS  COIN
SPEND  CARDS  CARTERS
ALONE  PASTE  FORTS   OWE
HELD   SIDES  FARES   STOW
SEA    SPEED  TAUNT   SHORE
PROTECT  POLLY  HEARD
   PACE  ROOST  BAND
SHARK  TASTE  BURDENS
STOLE  WIVES  FLIPS   OAT
KITS   DIMES  GOALS   HOLE
IRE    SIREN  BURST   HASTE
SLIPPER  ELECT  FIRES
   RIPS  CAUSE  WAND
STONE  PAGES  MITTENS
TORN   RAISE  EVADE   SEAL
ALAS   STEER  DARES   TAME
PEP    ESS    TEN     RED
```

PAGE 86

```
CAD   SHOT   DART   RED
TAXI  HOLE   EVER   ERIE
PARES AMEN   PESO   NAVAL
APE   TAME   THE TONE  EVE
LETTUCE  INN  POWERED
   ORE  SLENDER  WED
SHRUB SHORT  SAW   DITTO
TEAR  SPINE  STIES TWIN
ARC   EIRE   BOLSTER IRE
REEK  VET    MELEE RANGES
   EYES  LINED  FINE
SINGER SANDS TOO   WHIP
ADO   SALUTES PERU ADE
GONE  LOGES  TANKS HILT
SLEEP PAR    RENDS CARES
   LOG  RAVINES  MAR
BLESSED  LET  FENDERS
AIR   TEAM NET MITT  RAH
TERSE LAUD   AFAR  EVOKE
DOUR  ELSE   MISS  RIDE
RES   SEED   PEST  SEE
```

PAGE 88

```
BASE   SASH   SPELL  SPOKE
ALAN   TIKI   TENET  TRAIL
SILT   EDIT   RADAR  ROSES
STARVES  COUPON  MANTRA
   DUEL  SHADOW  GAIT
AROSE  PECKED  REYNOLDS
WAIT   RECOIL  CHAOS  EDS
EEL    REDUCE  SHIRR  VOTE
   NEWARK  COINS  MAN
AIREDALE  CHINO  RESALE
PLACERS  HAULS  SEESRED
BETTED  WATTS  POLKADOT
   TAM  SAUTE  RAPIER
OMAR   CORNY  CAMPER  PAY
ROI    SHUNT  GRIPES  DARE
BELLHOPS  WEANED  WOLFS
   EERY  BARTER  SHOO
MORALE  DAYBED  STORMED
UPEND  AISLE  OILY   MITE
SANTO  MOTOR  URAL   ANTE
ELTON  ARENA  TETE   TOAD
```

PAGE 90

```
DISC   PANDA   AMATI   DENT
OVER   ACORN   CARON   ERIE
LORE   GROUNDCREWS     LINE
TRESBIEN  OWENS  TOUCAN
   SAND  GUIDE  LAUD
RACING  TINGE  CONCEPTS
ERODE  LARCH  WORTH   RUT
COMA   PELLET  ORES   HORA
AMP    EAVES  DEMON   TACIT
PALANCE  SEVEN  SERENE
   INTERNATIONALISTS
ACCORD  ERASE  ATTESTS
GRATE  PAIGE  TAMES   IOU
ROTE   BITS   NOISED  POND
EWE    TEPEE  HUMID   MANTA
ENDORSER  MOTES  GARSON
   BETS  SEWER  ENNA
POSTER  ENTER  KLONDIKE
IGLU   INTERREGNUM     IDES
ALAS   DANAE  ANODE   GERT
FETE   EGADS  RUBES   MANE
```

PAGE 92

```
POD              BOY
TRUE            COME
SHORN          FRUIT
HARMS         SLANT
OLEO         SPEND
TEETH       SLIDE
   EAT TAN
   THEATER
      RAG  SAD
GEESE         PRESS
DELAY          ERIE
BEAST         CARTE
FLARE        MODES
RUNS          APED
YES           RED
```

```
        AWOL
        NIRO
      BANKS      AHAB
      SOLD      AMARA
      ACORN    DIGITAL
      MAGOO     AMIN
        AVALON
      WOLF MIME YAMS
    STD KILLED   ERIK
    HART MOOLA   TILE
    OKAY BEGIN   ALPS
    TEMPOS ADD  NETTLE
      SIZE GESTS  IRAN
      CONK OCEAN  CATO
      ANNO LAWMAN YES
      LEAH RUIN SPUR
        LOOKAT   MELBA
          ABET   BAIRN
        TURKISH    LEAN
        ASHEN    ALIGN
        NEON      PETE
                  TOYS
```

```
PAR  SHIRT  POP
EVE  CATER  AWE
PASTORS    ALTER
   CORE  SPAT
FLUTE  SPECIAL
LIES  SEIZE  LO
END   STAKE  DON
ED   SHORE  FINE
TACTICS    MISER
   HUNK  PART
ALIBI  PASSAGE
PAL  ELECT  NEW
EYE  RANTS  TEE
```

```
DAD  SAME  BLOT
ODE  IDOL  REAR
GEL  RAM  TIARA
   ITEM  PANS
RAVEN  FINGERS
OVEN  WINKS  ON
PER  WINES  AGO
ER   SAVED  OVER
STINGER  ALERT
   SEES  WREN
PALER  HAM  USE
ICER  LOVE  EAR
NESS  AGED  SPA
```

```
LIP  AVOID  LOS
ERA  CEASE  OUR
GAL  IRK  FISTS
   ANDY  RICE
TACOS  GENERAL
AGED  FREED  WE
LES  MAILS  CAN
EN  CALMS  WARD
STARTLE  FINES
   ROTS  WIND
SLOPE  OIL  LOT
HEM  RINSE  EAR
YEA  SNEER  STY
```

```
WAS  RASH   PEP
ACE  ALTO  FARE
IRE  CLEOPATRA
TERSE  ATOM
   ARID  WEDGE
SWIG  TYPE  RAY
PIRATE  ARRIVE
ADO  OMIT  APES
RENEW  SHAG
   DEER  DETER
ALTERNATE  ORE
SEEN  DEEP  WIN
PEN  SLAT  NET
```

```
RAM  ABEL  PEEK
EGO  NORA  ERLE
BONANZA  SPAIN
   TRIO  SIPS
PLATE  STREETS
HENS  SHEER  ON
AVA  PARES  ATE
SE  SEVER  AREA
ERECTED  FLASK
   FRED  LAMB
RARER  JAMAICA
FLEW  NOTE  AIM
DIMS  SEED  NAP
```

PAGE 101

```
PROMPT  SLUMPS
RANCOR  TANDEM
OF  CREVICE  RI
UFO  EMILY  FIR
SLIP  OCT  BOOK
TELLER  STANDS
  CAY    END
CRATES  EAGLET
RENO  PAX  SETH
ASS  LAGER  SHY
NU  CAROTID  EM
ELLENS  EDIBLE
STRODE  REMISS
```

PAGE 102

```
JAM  SHAM  SLAP
EVE  NOTE  PAGE
TAR  APE  BONER
  RAKE  GLUE
MAINE  CLASSES
ALLY  GLAZE  LA
JOY  PROSE  PEN
ON  QUITS  FACT
RETURNS  PASTA
  EARS  WANT
YANKS  PAR  USA
ELSE  SALT  ROD
TIES  ONLY  END
```

PAGE 103

```
ALAS  DOC  HASH
BOIL  IRA  ECHO
STREAMER  IRIS
  ICE  REGENT
STAGE  WISH
LUSH  SHATTERS
UNIT  WIG  OLIO
GASOLINE  FALA
  FINE  AFTER
GUSHED  IDO
ARIA  LIFELINE
DARN  ELF  LOIN
SLED  SLY  YULE
```

PAGE 104

```
HIS  POWER  SHE
INT  AROSE  COW
SHEAR  TEN  ATE
SEALED  KEPT
  LANES  WATER
IS  STEAD  WERE
ROW  SPIES  RAN
OARS  STREE  NO
NKING  HIELD
  TOLD  SMOOTH
WET  AIR  ENTER
ARE  SNOUT  ERE
SIN  SEETH  DEW
```

PAGE 106

```
SALAD  HAULED
PALACE  OCTAVE
ELIXIR  NEE  IN
RIP  DIMES  ANT
KNEE  DAY  MICA
SADDLED  MODEL
  GAS  MAR
SPRAY  CANASTA
THOR  SON  LEAN
RAW  SLOTS  DIG
IS  PEA  LOCALE
PIRACY  ELATER
SCENTS  SOWED
```

PAGE 107

```
SIP  CANOE  WEB
ORE  LIONS  ADE
SEAPORT  CAKES
  ICY  TALENT
STACK  TAPES
HACK  TILES  SO
ONE  ALL  LAD
OK  HOLLY  HALO
  PARES  POWER
GRINDS  COO
RANGE  CUSTARD
ART  ROUTE  CUE
YES  SHRED  TEN
```

PAGE 108

PAGE 110

PAGE 111

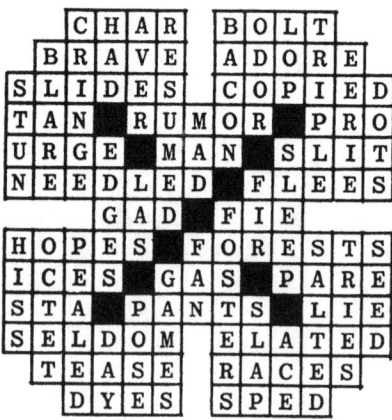

PAGE 112

PAGE 113

PAGE 114

PAGE 116

```
SPAR STEP MARS ROLL
HALE EWER EDEN ERIE
ERAS RELY TOGA CENT
DESERVE    ARRESTS
   NEEDS  TREAD
SALTS SAP CAD VENTS
TRUSTS WATER DESIRE
AIM SIP NOD FAD PEA
NAP NOW PAGED   SET
      WIT RAW
PET SENOR BET   ROB
ALE SIR WAD ROW APO
CLASPS METER MISTER
TASTE PAL WAS SCENE
   RELAY  PALER
PARADED    CAREERS
ANON ADDS CARS ABEL
STAG PLEA ABET MODE
SIDE SENT BEDS SNOW
```

PAGE 118

```
LIMAS  AWED  SIVA
OSAGE  SITE  ANOS
STRETCHTHETRUTH
ELIS  HAHA  RAREE
SEN  GAMIN  ACERS
 SAMISEN    EDS
  ABED  GMEN
FAWNED  HAIL  PAT
ALOES  NEWSFLASH
DIRT  PARKS  ORCA
END  FERRY  HITON
DEFILED  PETITE
  ORALS  LOREN
STROPS  EMERGES
LAWNS  CAVES  SMU
OBOE  TUBES  SHIP
SORROWFUL  WHOLE
HOD  RIFT  CRATER
  SOTS  HAIR
CUT    CONTEST
CAPES  LORDS  POP
ORDER  AFRO  DIDO
ATALOSSFORWORDS
TETE  USER  ANILE
SLED  NOES  GATES
```

PAGE 120

```
LOT  MILE ACTOR RIPE
ALUM POSER SHADE ARIA
MITE IGLOO PIPES TINS
BOUTIQUE SHINE OUTSET
   HAUL TIARA CURL
 STAGE THOSE SERGEANT
CHINO FERN STANCE COO
LATE CORE  RITE SCOT
ELL GARNET FANS THESE
FEELING EDICT HORSE
  HORDE FEINT FETES
 HOLLY RANGE LEADOFF
CELLS FOBS SCROLL RIO
ODDS BILL  LESS PILL
AGE BALLET BUNS FIELD
TERRACES RILED GUESS
  ASKS FOCUS PURR
RADISH SATES HASSOCKS
ERAS ADULT HAUNT GONE
ANTI NURSE EDGES IDEA
LOAN DEFER REEL  EEL
```

PAGE 122

```
SALTERS CASTOR PELOPS
STANDEE ASTUTE INAROW
TONTINE CHOCOLATECAKE
SPA TED HOOK ENOS NED
 SHEPHERD CAAN OGRE
CARPS LATE FAST TRESS
IGOR FANS CIRE BOLD
TRAILING CORM ORDERER
EARNEST MORSELLED IRE
 GAT COURTLIER SNIP
ARCED BANTERING PEKES
BAHS POSTULATE BAN
EYE REITERATE TOLDOFF
TARHEEL RITE ARRESTEE
ROIL FREE SNAG OISE
FLYNN TIER AEON GUSTS
RATE DORY PLEASANT
ESA TENT LAHR AGO COT
STRAWBERRYPIE COMPOSE
NITWIT EELERS TREACLE
ONSETS EXERTS SASSOON
```

DIAGRAMLESS STARTING BOXES

Page 30 begins in the 5th box across.

Page 32 begins in the 7th box across.

Page 64 begins in the 7th box across.

Page 94 begins in the 4th box across.

Page 126 begins in the 1st box across.

PAGE 124

```
   POP    FOE
  LAVA   SLAP
  SIREN  SPIRIT
 REFINE TWIN COLD
TINTS SPRING  TOO
ODDS   LINE SLATE
YES   FATE  POOL
   FACE DRAW
   FIRE GEAR
  DONE BRAY
 PURE GRIN  MAR
SLIDE DRIP  DOPE
OIL TRADES LIVED
NEED HONE TRACED
 SILENT RACES
 RARE   AGED
 EWE    WED
```

```
BALI      LEES
EMIL      ELSE
TEAL      NASA
ANN     SHINER
  ABERDEEN   CPA
   ARRIVE  THEM
   TESTED  HERO
DAFT       IDES
INRE  VASSAR
STAN  IDEALS
HEN   ELONGATE
  KNAVES    REB
  LEDA     AIRE
  IRED     SCAT
  NOSE     PASS
```

```
FAMOUS  HEARD
AVERSE  INROAD
CE BEVY DIANE
ENE DEER DRUB
TUNS NAIL   BA
SETUP ROOSTER
  ERIE TRUE
SCREECH DIXIE
OR  SHUN TANS
LESS ONUS SAP
IDAHO TREE  RR
DIVIDE SALAMI
 TENET ENLIST
```

```
APE  BLOTS  RIP
NET  ROAST  ERA
TRACE  TAR  SAL
   OWS RANT
ARTISTS  NASTY
RAIL RANDY  HA
EVE  PALES  FIR
NE  POPES  FIND
ANDES STRINGS
  EATS  SON
WAN  ELL SEVEN
ACT  RAISE AWE
YES  STEMS  TEE
```

```
TAC  SCAB  SHUN
IDA  CAVE  PESO
PER  ONE  DOLED
   TROT  POOL
SLOOP BALLOON
TOOT DENTS  NA
RON  SOLES SIS
AS  SPOTS SCOT
PESTERS LOONY
  CONS SOLO
SHOOT TOO  TAP
PILL COOP  EGO
ADDS  ANTS  RED
```

```
 CEDAR  SLANG
THRONE LABORS
RAIN  TRADE OH
USE DUETS  DUE
ME  SIRES FIND
PRETEND HANDS
  VATS HALE
SPATS BOULDER
CODE WALLS  LA
ALE CORDS  MAT
RI HORNS GATE
SCHOOL OPENED
 YIELD NAMED
```

```
EMS  CLARA  AMA
SAT  HARES  GAS
PREVENT SAILS
 EASE  MAIL
TARTS PAYMENT
ALES RATES  OH
HAD HATED  VIE
OR SATES CASE
EMOTION POMES
 BARN GASP
ACORN SALTINE
ROE ELATE  ROY
COS TAPER  ETE
```

```
M A L E . S E T . S P A T
E R I N . A L E . P A L E
S E N S I B L E . I D L E
S A T . R O S T E R . . .
. . L I T . E V E N T S
C A R E S . A R E . O R E
O M I T . A D S . S N O W
P E N . O L D . D I E T S
E N G I N E . F U N . . .
. . N E R V E S . S A D
M A I N . T E N T A C L E
A C R E . E T C . V A I N
P E E R . D O E . A N T S
```

```
A L E . T H E M . S H O P
R E X . E A S T . P A N E
E X H O R T S . W I N C E
. A R M S . H I N D E R
C L U B . F A D E . .
H I S . S H A V E T A I L
A N T . H O V E L . P R O
T E S T I M O N Y . P I G
. O V E R . P A S S
D R A W E R . W E A R .
R I V E R . D I A L E C T
I D O L . T I N S . N O W
P E N S . I N K Y . T O O
```

```
P A L . S O A R . S P A R
O R E . T I D E . K I T E
K I D . O L D . D A T E D
E D G E R S . S E T . .
. E V E . S W E E T E R
F T . E D I T O R . O W E
I R A N . M A R . S E E D
L E D . G A R D E N . S O
M E S S A G E . V A T .
. A L E . R E P E A T
S T O V E . W I N . A C E
A I D E . B E N T . S I N
D E E D . O D D S . E D S
```

```
E L I . S P A K E . D I R
L I O . C A R E S . E N O
D E P A R T . E R R A N D
. I R A . P O O R .
S H A R P E N . M O L E S
T A N . E N O S . T Y R E
A M . D O . A S . R E
R A L D . C A M E . H O R
S N O R T . L E T T E R S
. D E E D . T O R .
B E G G A R . F L O O D S
O W E . R E L I E . D I A
Y E S . S W O R D . S P Y
```

```
W A S . M A L E S . S O B
A I M . A D O R E . E W E
D R A W S . G R A N T E D
. R A T S . S L O T .
P A T I E N T . S A L E M
A L . T R A I L . H E R E
L E E . S P L I T . D A N
E R A S . S T O R M . S D
S T R U T . S N E E Z E S
. N E A T . S A N E .
G U E S S E D . T U B A S
E S S . T E A S E . R I O
M E T . E N D E D . A D D
```

```
T A P . T O W E L . E L M
I L L . O M A H A . W O O
P E A . A I R . D R E S S
. C A S T . A D O R E S
P R I N T . S L E D S .
L A N D . S T I R S . T O
E G G . S O A K S . P I N
A S . S I N G E . P I L L
. B U L G E . T A L L Y
S C A R E S . F A L L .
T A K E N . D A M . A D D
A G E . C H O R E . R Y E
Y E S . E A G E R . S E W
```

ARMADAS LEASE
FREEPORT IDIOMS
IMPROPER KERMIT
CERISE OMEN ANO
KNIT AVID CLEO
LIN BENES GOING
EATAWAY NARRATE
GASP ALAN
CHANNEL MANUMIT
HOSEA ATEST ACE
AVIS OCHS LIEN
MEN PLEA AKIMBO
PRIMED MORAVIAN
SENATE EARRINGS
DETER STALAGS

WAN ECOLE ESS
AVA CRUET SEA
REGULAR EDSEL
RAM TRUANT
GRANT MONEY
RUGS CARAT HP
ALE BANAL CAL
ME BRUSH LULU
GOOSE SORTS
CANUTE PIN
LOATH HUGGING
ANT EPOCH CIA
DES ROPES ELM

BRAG DAYS PER
LORE EDEN ORE
ELIMINATE LIL
WED RIM EBONY
AIM PRO
LAIRS POSTAGE
ODOR PAD HIES
GENERAL BERET
SEW FUR
CASTS PIN SIR
ART TRANSLATE
LIE EARN AGED
LAP DYES DAMS

APE WAS ABASE
LAX IRE NAPES
IDA NEA TYPES
ARCED RAISE
SETS ACT AWE
SIGH TALON
SEDATE POISED
TREYS BUMS
SAP MET LEAD
LONER FEVER
ELOPE ALI IRA
MIRES TEL CII
SPENT EWE TEN

CAPP CAN SODA
OVAL APE WRIT
LISA NOW INCH
LASTED ESTATE
ATE FLORA TUN
RED FED TEEMS
PEDDLED
TOPIC LEE OWS
ORO TRYON RAP
MIMOSA PSYCHO
AGAR SPA OHIO
TIDE POR KINK
ONES SID ODES

HERE SWAT ELSA SNOB
EVIL TINE NEAT HAVE
MEL WEDNESDAY MOPED
PREPARE TIED RIVERS
URN MEND BALE
CHURN BARK CARELESS
RIPE WARS ROSES MOO
ADO PINS LURER TILL
BENDING WINKS RULED
AND PANTS FIB
ADORE RAKES CANASTA
PIPE HARES PARK HAG
EVA SAVES CALM DOPE
SELECTED GOLF SOWED
REEL PONE GOO
STRAND LOAF HAMMERS
AROSE FORTUNATE RAH
LIME MUSE SANE DICE
TOPS ANTS EGGS REED

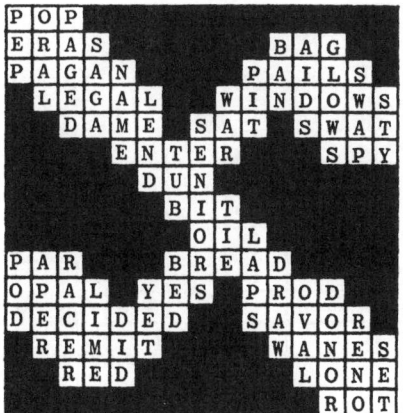

PAGE 148

W	A	R	D		S	T	R	A	W		M	A	L	T	S		A	R	C	H
A	L	A	E		O	R	I	B	I		A	M	O	R	E		N	A	H	A
N	A	N	C	Y	L	O	P	E	Z		J	U	D	Y	R	A	N	K	I	N
E	N	T	R	E	A	T	S		E	R	O	S	E		G	L	U	I	N	G
			E	A	C	H		S	N	O	R	E		H	E	E	L			
D	E	B	A	S	E		D	I	E	T	S		M	I	S	C	A	S	T	
I	D	E	S	T		F	O	R	D	S		K	I	N		S	T	A	I	D
D	U	N	E		F	A	C	E		S	U	N	D	A		E	L	M	O	
I	C	C		J	A	C	K	N	I	C	K	L	A	U	S		L	E	G	
T	E	R	M	I	T	E	S		S	O	Y	A	S		S	A	T	Y	R	S
			E	I	G	H	T		S	H	U	C	K		C	U	P	E	L	
L	A	N	O	S	E		S	C	A	L	A		S	O	M	E	T	I	M	E
E	S	S		A	R	N	O	L	D	P	A	L	M	E	R		T	O	M	
A	C	H	S		D	O	A	L	L		D	U	E	S		S	T	U	B	
R	O	A	N	S		O	R	D		S	H	I	R	T		P	U	L	S	E
	T	W	O	T	I	M	E		B	O	A	T	S		P	U	R	E	E	D
		W	A	R	Y		D	A	R	N	S		M	E	R	V				
A	R	A	B	I	A		W	I	N	E	D		F	O	R	G	I	V	E	S
B	O	B	A	N	D	B	I	N	G		L	E	E	T	R	E	V	I	N	O
B	A	L	L		E	A	S	E	L		E	R	A	T	O		O	D	O	R
A	M	Y	L		S	T	E	R	E		R	A	T	O	N		R	E	S	T

PAGE 150

B	E	E	R		H	O	P		S	A	D		O	G	R	E
L	A	R	G	E		A	L	E		P	I	E		G	R	A	N	D
D	E	S	I	G	N		R	E	P	A	I	R	S		L	A	N	C	E	S
R	A	K	E		E	L	M		P	I	N		S	H	E	D		O	N	E
U	S	E		O	W	E		F	E	D		L	E	A	D		A	R	I	A
M	E	T	E	R		S	P	U	R		P	A	R	T		I	T	E	M	S
		L	E	S	S	E	N		C	A	R	T		P	R	O
B	A	R	K		T	O	T		S	L	I	D		P	R	O	M	O	T	E
I	C	E		M	A	N		G	E	A	R		L	E	A	N		R	O	E
B	E	T	T	E	R		W	R	A	P		R	O	S	Y		O	D	O	R
	A	I	L		P	O	O	L		R	U	S	T		H	U	E
S	L	I	M		G	L	O	W		B	O	N	E		F	E	R	R	E	T
T	O	N		F	R	E	D		S	A	L	T		C	U	P		E	V	A
A	U	S	T	R	I	A		D	I	L	L		A	H	S		E	D	E	N
			H	E	M		B	A	N	D		C	R	E	E	P	S
A	G	R	E	E		B	A	N	K		D	O	M	E		A	P	R	O	N
L	I	O	N		B	I	T	E		S	O	D		S	O	W		A	D	E
A	L	T		W	A	N	T		D	E	N		H	E	N		H	I	D	E
S	L	A	V	E	S		E	D	U	C	A	T	E		T	R	A	D	E	D
	S	T	A	L	E		R	U	E		T	A	R		O	T	H	E	R
	E	N	D	S		Y	E	T		E	G	O		P	E	A	R

PAGE 152

R	A	T	E		A	C	E	S			A	C	R	E
A	W	E	D		B	O	L	T		S	H	O	O	S
S	A	M		C	E	D	A	R		L	A	N	D	S
P	I	P	E	R	S		T	I	D	Y		T	E	E
S	T	O	N	E		W	I	N	E		B	R	O	S
		G	A	P	I	N	G		C	O	O
S	I	N		T	A	N	G		B	U	L	L	E	T
I	R	O	N	I	N	G		B	I	R	D		D	O
P	A	T	I	O	S		C	A	L	L		K	I	T
	I	N	N		W	A	L	L		B	E	T	S
S	H	O	E		H	A	N	D		A	L	E
T	I	N		C	A	R	D		S	P	E	N	D	S
A	D		P	E	R	M	I	T	T	E	D		L	A
R	E	M	I	N	D		D	O	O	R		B	I	N
	A	C	T		H	A	R	P		E	R	I	E
F	O	R	K		G	A	T	E		S	A	O
A	G	E		P	A	V	E		A	P	R	O	N	S
I	L		M	A	Z	E		P	R	I	N	C	E	S
R	E	T	I	R	E		S	E	E	N		H	O	T
	A	N	T		O	C	E	A	N	S
W	A	R	D		I	D	O	L		E	A	T	E	R
A	R	T		U	N	D	O		A	R	G	Y	L	E
D	E	E	D	S		E	T	O	N	S		P	I	N
E	N	S	U	E		S	E	N	T		B	E	S	T
D	A	T	E		T	R	E	E		O	D	E	S

PAGE 154

W	A	D	E	R		F	L	U	F	F		S	C	R	A	P
P	A	R	A	D	E		L	O	N	E	R		A	L	A	R	I	C
P	I	T	C	H	E	D	B	A	T	T	L	E		C	O	P	I	L	O	T
A	L	E		S	N	O	O	T		O	L	E	A	R	Y		A	L	M	A
C	U	R	D		S	U	R	F	S		S	H	O	E	S		B	A	M
E	L	I	A	S		T	I	E	T	O		A	N	D		S	H	O	T	E
S	E	N	N	A	S		S	E	A	L	A	N	E		C	O	A	X	E	D
		G	A	L	A	S		T	I	D	E	D		T	O	N	S
P	I	P	E	S	T	E	M		R	F	D		L	O	N	G	S	H	O	T
I	L	L		A	C	R	I	D		A	E	S	O	P		S	L	O	S	H
S	I	A	M		H	A	N	D	K	I	S	S	I	N	G		E	R	I	E
C	O	C	O	A		P	E	T	I	T		S	N	O	O	P		S	E	W
O	N	E	L	I	N	E	R		P	H	D		S	T	A	R	K	E	R	S
		O	D	E	S		B	U	F	F	S		E	L	E	N	A
P	L	A	C	E	T		P	O	P	U	L	A	R		S	P	O	N	G	E
L	A	T	H	S		S	A	W		L	A	T	E	R		S	U	D	R	A
A	S	H		L	I	L	L	E		T	U	B	E	S		T	H	A	T
N	E	L	L		E	M	P	I	R	E		R	E	S	E	E		O	P	E
T	R	E	E	M	A	N		G	R	A	N	D	C	H	I	L	D	R	E	N
	S	T	A	R	V	E		H	O	S	E	A		U	N	L	E	S	S
	E	D	S	E	L		T	R	E	E	Y		T	E	A	S	E

PAGE 156

P	O	P
E	R	A	S					B	A	G
P	A	G	A	N			P	A	I	L	S
	L	E	G	A	L		W	I	N	D	O	W	S
	D	A	M	E		S	A	T		S	W	A	T
		E	N	T	E	R			S	P	Y
			D	U	N
			B	I	T
			O	I	L
P	A	R			B	R	E	A	D
O	P	A	L		Y	E	S		P	R	O	D
D	E	C	I	D	E	D		S	A	V	O	R
	R	E	M	I	T			W	A	N	E	S
		R	E	D				L	O	N	E
								R	O	T

PAGE 158

```
            D I S H
            M A N I A     I N C H
            E N T R Y     M O L E
            A C H         P O O R
            N E E D Y     U N T O
T O E       F I E L D
H A L L     I S S U E S
A T L A S
W H I S T   A R K   I N T O W
    S T E E R S     S C A L E
    S P E N T       E R I N
S E C T   R O P E S   T O T
E V E R     L A P
A I D A   A D A G E
S L E W   D I C E D
          O N E R
```

PAGE 160

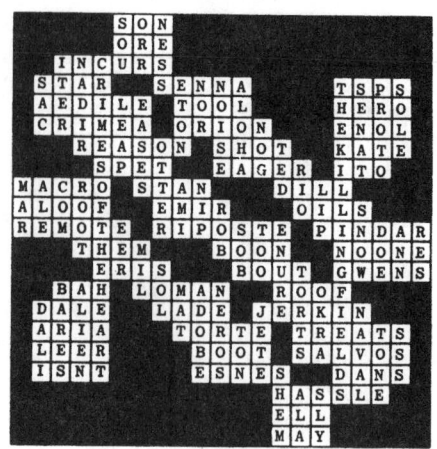

PAGE 162

PAGE 163

PAGE 164

PAGE 165

```
C O P   O L D E R   P E W
A I R   M A I N E   E V A
P L O W I N G   M E T E R
    M I T E   T O W E R S
A M I D   R I V E R
L O S E   P I N E S   W E
T O E   R E N T S   H I D
O N   W E E K S   C A S E
    B A L L S   O P E N
S T O R E S   C A R P
A R O M A   B A N D I T S
W I T   S P U R T   L I E
S O S   E A S E S   Y E A
```

PAGE 166

```
J A R   C A S E D   A S H
I D O   A L I V E   L E I
B O B S F O R A P P L E S
  B E E T     E R A
S T E P S   B A N A N A S
P O R T   W I N D Y   L E
R O Y   R A N T S   P I N
A T   M E L D S   O R E S
T H R U S T S   A L O N E
  I C E     A C E D
I N T H E D O G H O U S E
L E E   D O N E E   C U R
L E S   S E E R S   T E N
```

PAGE 167

```
R A W   L A D   T A N
O D E   H E R O   S O L O
B O L D E S T   S T E P S
  L E N S   C L A S S Y
F A D E S   P A I L
L O O P   W O R D L E S S
I N N   S H O V E   V I A
P E E P H O L E   B E N T
  L O S S   L A R G E
R E L A T E   H A R M
I R O N S   T A K E O F F
P I N T   P U R E   R U E
S E E   A G E   E N D
```

PAGE 168

```
B I T   S T A T E   G A P
I D O   T A L O N   R I O
G A R B A G E   T R A D E
  N A B S   D E E D
S C A R S   G A R D E N S
P A D S   P A R E S   O H
A D O   T O T E D   P I E
R E   P A N E S   B A S E
S T R A N D S   S O R E R
  E G G S   F A I R
S T E E L   B A L L O O N
P O D   E V A D E   T W O
Y E S   D A T E S   S E T
```

PAGE 169

```
A L P S   F E T E   I M P
R E A L   O V E N   S E A
E A S Y G O I N G   I N N
A N T   A L L   I S S U E
  H I S   G N U
C A B I N   F E E L E R S
O P E N   A I M   T R U E
W E D D I N G   B A R G E
  E N D   M E N
S W O R D   L I E   A R C
L A P   I D E N T I C A L
E V E   A O N E   R I T A
D E N   N E A R   E D E N
```

PAGE 170

```
L A Y   P O O R   C O A T
A R E   R I V E   A L S O
S E A   A L E M   L I K E
T A R R Y   R I A L
  E E K   T H E N C E
K I N D R E D   A D O R N
I N E   Y E S   T O O
S T A T E   N E W N E S S
S O R R O W   T H E
  A N O N   A R M E D
R O A D   R O L L   E V E
O N C E   D R I E   E E N
D E E D   S T E S   T R Y
```

PAGE 172

```
  B E L L I   C H A O S
S A L A A M   H E I F E R
T H A W   P S A L M   S O
R A N   F I O R D   P A M
A M   A L O U D   P I M A
P A S T E U R   G R E E N
  T O E S   W R I T
S M E L T   F R I G A T E
H U R L   R A I N S   A L
I N N   S O U N D   S P A
P I   Y O U N G   T H E N
S C H U S S   E D W A R D
  H E L O T   R O O M S
```

```
S A L . I T E M S . S I T
O R E . R I V E T . E R A
S T O R E . A L A . V A N
. . O N E . T R E E . . .
B O R D E R S . T E N D S
E R I E . R A V E L . A L
A D D . D O L E D . A V A
S E . P A R E S . S N I P
T R A I N . S T R A N D S
. L E G S . S O N . . .
P A L . E L L . S K A T E
I D O . R A I S E . R O W
N E W . S T E P S . E Y E
```

```
. S P U D . S E C T O R .
S T A R R . T R O O P E R
P A T I O . R E N T . S E
I S T . P I E C E . P U P
T H I C K S E T . G A L A
. . H I L T . F A C T S
E F F A C E . P R I E S T
F L A S K . R U I N . . .
F O R E . S O N G S T E R
E R E . W I D T H . E G O
T I . M A R E . T I A R A
E N L I V E N . E L M E R
. S I L E N T . N E S T
```

```
A P E R . B A R . P O L O
R O V E . L I E . A M I D
M E E T . A L A . R I N D
S T R I P S . C R A T E S
. . R O T A T E D . . .
L A C E D . D E L E T E S
A C E . R O D . A V A
S T E A M E R . R E N E W
. R I P E N E D .
M A R I N E . E X I T E D
A L A S . A T E . T I D E
M A N E . T E D . O M E N
A N T S . S A Y . R E N T
```

```
T O M . S T E A L . S W I N G
I D A . E R A S E . H O N O R
M E R R I E R . T H I N . M A
. O N E . S T O P . H A S
C H A S E . M E E T . B I D S
H E R E . N E A R . M I D
I R K . F O R T . P E T E R S
N O . R I D E . C O N E . O N
A N G E L S . L A N D . C U E
. L E E . F O R D . J U T E
F R E D . C O O L . M A T E R
R U N . D A R K . L O N
A L . B A R E . G E N E R A L
M E T A L . S H O N E . A G E
E R O D E . T O D A Y . T A T
```

```
F I R . S T R I P . R U M
A C E . P R O N E . O R E
R E S C U E D . D R A G S
. T I D Y . D O M E S
S L I T S . D O L L S
P O N Y . G A V E L . M O
R A G . T A L E S . B O W
Y D . T A M E R . H U R L
. T I L E S . D A T E S
S T A L L . W A I T
W A S T E . M I R R O R S
A P T . S H A D E . N A P
B E E . T I R E S . S H Y
```

```
B A H . R E P A Y . R E B
E G O . H A I T I . O D E
T O U R I S T . E L M E R
. S E N T . C L I E N T
P A T I O . R O D E O
U P O N . W I V E S . M R
T E N . C O D E D . M I A
T D . P A V E R . C E N T
. P A R E S . C R A T E
S W E D E N . T H I N
T E A S E . A R A B I A N
O A R . R A R E R . N C O
P R Y . S L E E T . G E T
```

PAGE 180

```
CHAT        WREN
RIVAL       CAIRO
OREGON    BURDEN
PEN   GETUP   ICE
  SUN  VAN  ANT
   EAGER  EGG
    MAR  MAN
   LEG   SIREN
  LAD  GIN  SAT
FAD  BONUS   TEN
INDEED    SECURE
SCENE      WORSE
HERD         WEED
```

PAGE 181

```
TOSH   IRA   HERO
AREA   DAS   APED
PREVIEWS     VINE
    EVA   ELECTS
ASSAY   DREW
CHOW   RATIONAL
TODO   EVE   RODE
STARTLED    DRAG
    DRAY  TSARS
NITWIT   LOW
ETUI   EDITIONS
VENT   TIN   TRIO
AMAH   OPT   HELP
```

PAGE 182

```
SALAD  SHE   PEP  RAMS
ALIBI  CURT  CRIED  EVIL
GAMES  AREA  HURRY  VICE
ESP  COLT  TRADE  NEEDED
  TALE  STARE  CALL
SPIRE  SPLIT  BOSS  SAW
BLAND  SHIED  TASTE  LIE
EASY  CLOTS  PARTY  RIDE
TNT  SHARE  PARKS  DICED
TERMITE  FAIRS  SALES
  EAVE  FUNNY  CITE
GLARE  CADET  FREEDOM
TRACT  SONGS  SLUGS  BAR
RASH  STAGE  SPADE  METE
APT  GLASS  SUITE  FUSED
YES  RENT  SIGNS  GATES
  FIND  HINGE  RUSE
REMIND  HORSE  WANT  DIM
ODOR  ELOPE  SCAT  ELATE
OGRE  ROSES  TUNE  NINES
FEED   WED    BED  STEMS
```

PAGE 184

```
CHAR  SENOR  DODOS  DREW
LOBE  ELOPE  ERODE  EIRE
APES  NAMES  CASED  STIR
DELICATE  TRITE  APIECE
  DATE  BRIDE  STAR
SPHERE  PRICE  SHIVERED
PRINT  PLACE  ALIVE  ERE
AUNT  GRANT  BRINE  FLAT
TNT  FROND  PRIDE  TEASE
SESSIONS  PROSE  LAWYER
  ELSE  SLAKE  COPE
STAVES  STATE  DIVERTED
CAGES  SPITE  RIDER  WAR
OPEN  SMILE  LACED  DIRE
PEN  ATONE  GIVER  FINNS
ESTIMATE  MATES  CARESS
  CORE  MELTS  PARE
RESIST  VITAL  DETECTED
ALEC  LOOSE  ELITE  TAKE
FILL  ENTER  SEVER  OMEN
TALE  SEERS  TIERS  REST
```

PAGE 186

```
PEEKS  STEED  SOUP  PRIM
AERIE  PURSE  ARNO  LORE
PROTAGONIST  LAIN  ALOE
AIDE  RUIN  REALTY  CENT
WEE  DISC  GOLD   TEEM
  HOLE  PAIL  STANDOFF
SCRAWL  MART  APHID  DOE
CLOWN  BULB  MURAL  HERE
ROOK  POSE  TENET  FILET
ANT  TASK  BUTTE  MUG
PESTERS  NOTES  FASHION
  OAK  TENOR  LASS  RUE
SHAWL  BOWER  MISS  MATE
EARN  CANTS  COST  RATED
ERG  SONGS  CAST  LITERS
PEELINGS  BOLT  HASH
  NEXT  MEAL  CODE  BUS
LETS  ROBOTS  HURL  TANK
IRIS  ABET  TOURDEFORCE
MINE  CORE  EAGLE  ANKLE
BEAN  TENT  DRESS  RESET
```

PAGE 188

```
  TENOR  BETAS  SCRAM
CREATE  AROMA  TAILORS
RAILROADTRAIN  ARCADIA
ORE  DEMOTED  DONNE  EOS
MOSS  SEWED  SLICE  ARTS
PLOTS  DER  POOLE  RANEE
SENATE  LIBERTY  CURERS
  NOLA  NESTS  COLON
SUITOFLIGHTS  REVENGES
ENROL  MORAY  HONED  LAP
LION  SATAN  BOUTS  RIDE
MON  MADAM  CORGI  BASIE
ANIMATES  CLOSEMOUTHED
  NIXON  CAINE  EAST
SIGNIN  CARPETS  FEARED
ABBES  PORES  ROB  SNEVA
LEOS  ARMOR  BALER  SLAT
ARA  AEIOU  DADDIES  ADE
DIRECTS  STATIONMASTER
SADDENS  EATIN  GATHER
  STRAY  SLANG  SNEER
```

```
PAL           WEB
PANES         CAGED
CURTAIL   BARGAIN
ART  PLANETS  TEE
DENT TIERS   MITT
  REAP ROE  FANS
  RILES  THING
  LAY      INN
  VOTES  STEEP
CARE   TOP  DRAT
HOGS  PAIRS  STAG
ERR CEILING  HIE
WEATHER  GALLANT
SNEER      POINT
TNT          WED
```

```
POP  STAMP   PEN
EAR  PAPAL   AYE
PROMISE   UPSET
   INK  ONES
PROSE  MUGGERS
LOPS  BITES   OT
EAT  CIDER   DUE
AS   POLAR  DATA
STALAGS   JEWEL
   MUSE   PEA
TRUST  TRANSIT
WAS  AGAIN   ACE
OWE  LONGS   GET
```

PAGE 198

```
FADE  GEAR  ADO
OPEN  ONCE  RAM
REST  ADEQUATE
   PIED   URBAN
START  WHIGS
ERIE  SHORE  GO
EAR  SMILE  HAD
MY  STONE  BAND
   STAGE  SONGS
GREAT   FOOD
LANGUAGE  TOAD
ITS  TIER  HUGE
BEE  EDEN  STEW
```

PAGE 199

```
BAG  ALAMO  ONE
ACE  DONOR  PAW
ATTEMPT  DRAPE
   LIE  DEALER
TRUST  PARIS
ROSE  FRILL  SO
ICE  FAIRY  WEB
OK  FANCY  LANE
   BARGE  DADDY
STORMS  RAW
PUREE  FURNACE
ABE  ROUSE  RUG
NED  SHRED  MEG
```

PAGE 200

```
BETS  POPS  EBB
AREA  IDEA  DOE
TIED  LOTS  EWE
SENDFOR  SANE
   LET  SEW  DO
HOPED  HAD  TOW
EVES  LAG  SHUN
LEG  HIT  BEETS
DR  SAT  PAN
  TIPS  PADDLED
PAT  TARS  SURE
IKE  EDIT  IRAN
GEM  NOME  NEST
```

PAGE 201

```
MADAM  STOKE
ALIBI  URGENT
LEVEL  NARY  WE
ERE  KATIE  SIN
STRAWHAT  WANT
  NEON  SINGE
OFFKEY  PICKER
WOULD  BALK
NOSE  BACKSEAT
ELS  RESEW  DUE
RE  DOLT  OVENS
  DOUBLE  RENTS
  ROSES  MESSY
```

PAGE 202

```
HERE  ABLE  WET
IRON  LEAN  EVE
DIED  LENT  REN
   USE  DESERT
SPARKLE   RO
HATE  UNBELIEF
ERE  SI  AD  SLE
MERCHANT  EASE
  RI  OTHNIEL
SLAYER  EAT
HAM  LEAR  INTO
ONE  DARE  RAIL
TEN  SPED  EYED
```

PAGE 204

```
MEL  STAGE  AMONG
AVA  HONOR  WAFER
REDFORD  ROAD  VA
  ARE  LADY  DEN
SPACE  HAND  BURT
LINE  SAND  TIE
INA  LIZA  DALLAS
DE  RIDE  FALL  SO
ESCAPE  BALL  ANN
  HIS  FORE  LIEN
CHAN  FROM  MARRY
HOT  MEET  DAN
IT  TOWN  RANDALL
PENAL  CHARO  RAE
SLOPE  HOMER  TWO
```

PAGE 206

```
C A B A N A S   ■ O P E R A
O V E R A C T   ■ D E N I M
M O D E S T O   ■ E R A S E
A C ■ ■ H O N E S ■ ■ T E N
K A N S ■ R E V ■ B E N D
E D I C T ■ S E E R ■ ■
R O T O R S ■ S L E E P S
■ ■ T I E R ■ M A R I E
L A P S ■ L O S ■ M A R X
A M A ■ C L O N E ■ A T
G U S T O ■ M I G R A T E
E S T E S ■ E P A U L E T
R E A D Y ■ R E D N E S S
```

PAGE 207

```
G O T ■ S P I N E ■ S S W
A D E ■ T E N O R ■ P I E
S E A S O N S ■ A P A R T
■ E L S ■ U S E R ■
S H I N E ■ S N E A K E R
P O R T ■ L A I R S ■ R I
A T E ■ H U N T S ■ R O D
R E ■ P A R E S ■ H I D E
S L E E P E R ■ S I D E S
■ L A P S ■ L E T ■
S H O R E ■ W E A S E L S
P I P ■ N A V A L ■ L E E
A P E ■ S N A P S ■ M O W
```

PAGE 208

```
S L I V E R ■ C A S T O R
P O T A T O ■ O P I A T E
R A ■ T O D D L E R ■ I N
A F T ■ N E E D S ■ P O T
N E A R ■ O R E ■ L O S E
G R I E F S ■ R A I N E D
■ L I E ■ R A T ■
B L O N D S ■ S E R I A L
A I R S ■ A R M ■ S A M E
S T S ■ F L I E S ■ C U V
T T ■ O R I O L E S ■ S E
E L E V E N ■ T A U T E R
S E N A T E ■ S T R E S S
```

PAGE 210

```
■ B L E A K ■ M O N K S ■
O R A N G E ■ E V E N T S
G A R D E N ■ R A T I O N
R I G S ■ N A I L ■ T R A
E N E ■ B E L T ■ S T I R
■ F A D E ■ S T E E L
F I E R Y ■ B E A D S
D A M E S ■ G L E N
I R I S ■ B E A R ■ G N P
A M T ■ B E E N ■ O H I O
N E A T E R ■ K I M O N O
A R T I S T ■ E R A S E R
■ S E C T S ■ T A R T S
```

PAGE 211

```
T A R ■ P A R T S ■ P R Y
A L I ■ A D O R E ■ R O E
N E V E R ■ B A L L O T S
■ E A R S ■ P L O T ■
C A R T O N S ■ S T E M S
A L ■ S T I N G ■ S C O T
R I P ■ S P O R T ■ T O E
T E R M ■ S W A R M ■ S E
S N O O P ■ S M E A R E D
■ M O O S ■ S A N E ■
T W I N K L E ■ T E N O R
W A S ■ E A G L E ■ T R Y
O N E ■ S T O O D ■ S E E
```

PAGE 212

```
G A S ■ S T A B S ■ A C T
A R T ■ H O T E L ■ D O E
P E A ■ O N E ■ E R O D E
■ L E T S ■ S N A R E S
B E L L S ■ B A D G E
O R E S ■ P O L E S ■ N C
A I D ■ S A N E R ■ L E O
S E ■ T A L E S ■ P E A R
■ S I D E S ■ P A S T E
S T E E D S ■ O I L S
E R A S E ■ E V E ■ O L D
L I T ■ N E V E R ■ N O R
L O S ■ S T A R S ■ S T Y
```

PAGE 213

```
SCRIBE SHOPS
LAUREL TAILOR
INNATE ALLUDE
CONN VEIL MAC
KEY WARN TAPE
TATA LAGOS
STRIKE BICEPS
CRUDE WEST
RIPE SORT MAL
APT STOA DECO
PLUSHY TAURUS
SERIAL EXCITE
SERGE SETTER
```

PAGE 214

```
WAY SPURT EWE
ERE PAPER GAY
DENTAL DANGLE
ORES DESKS
FAILS ODES
ABODE CARTONS
DEW AIM LEI
STARTLE SHEAR
EAST QUOTE
STEAL YOUR
HIDDEN WILTED
ONE NEVER AGO
PEN TWIST POT
```

PAGE 215

```
BEE ALLOW SEA
OAR PIANO PAN
GRASPED ROOST
SOLD SKIRTS
SPICE BUILT
LANK PENNY PA
EGG CLANG CAD
DE SHADY THUD
CLANS BOILS
APRONS COAL
BRAWN CANDLES
LOT ELOPE EVA
ESE LANES DEW
```

PAGE 216

```
CORE AMID SPAN
OPAL LIMO MARCO
REV BASIN ALERT
ARENAS TAME SEE
LANES FATE BESS
DEBATE WIN
CAR MINE WINTER
OPENERS HAND VA
DEPEND DONE PET
EAT CENT MESS
SWAT DOCK FOE
OAT POLO DULLER
AD DEPARTURE DO
RECITE ARMS PEP
ONE ATOP MANE
FILE DUET BOP
AND WORD FOREST
IT LIMA WATERED
LOCATE WASH STS
ASH CARTER
BARS TERM ROLES
OUT LOAF BEWARE
ADORE SAVED TAN
RIOTS ERIE LESS
SONS DEEP TREE
```

PAGE 218

```
BETTE GREY SILO LASER
ORION RATE CROW ELOPE
MINOT AVON ROVE GLUED
BEETHOVEN NINE TIERED
SURER BABY LEROY
MADISON CURE EDEN RIA
AGREE IVORY OTIS BARD
BIAS SMALL MUTT CEDED
ELM GIANT PETE ARCANE
LEAVINGS MILER GEARED
EDGE HONOR KEEL
SPONGE SIDON WINDMILL
HORDES OVEN FINDS RIO
ALLOT FUEL CONGA MAME
DIOR MOSS SHAGS PATES
EON DONA SEAL CARNEYS
SANDPAPER PALED
SHRANK HOOK SUNFLOWER
COULD CORK RELY ALAMO
OLIVE ANTE ALSO TIRES
TENOR PEAS GLEN ENSUE
```

```
PLED  SLOE  OBOLS  ADMIT
RENO  WARD  SATIE  NOISE
URDU  ENDO  ENTER  GULLS
DOUBLEDOME    DOUBLEBASS
   ESS    AMIS    ILL
   ESS ASSET PRESENCE
SKATE CRIED SIEG POOL
TOLA DOUBLEEAGLE LOLL
ERIK ERMS DULY CANES
RAKEOFF PAINE TOY
NNE DOUBLEFEATURE BWI
  DUG RANTS PEDDLED
BOSOM MAMA OMEN OISE
ETTU DOUBLEAGENT UTES
EREB OONS MIRED IBERT
ROWLANDS FIRED ALL
ETE SERE ALLEGED
DOUBLEDATE DOUBLETIME
ATSEA OVALS ALII AMON
SHADS SIREE KNEE LETS
HORST EVERT SASS KLEE
```

```
      LAP
      CAPE
      WATER        HAS
      PARED        LOST
COVER              RISKY
USE         CENTS
RESTS       TALES
      KORAN
      HABITAT
      SALAD  TESTS
      FINED        TOO
LINKS              BRAND
HANGS       FLARE
AIDE        ORATE
MRS         WADE
            EYE
```

```
STOP        BEG
LAVA        OXEN
AMEN        RITES
TENTS  PET  SET
    SAVES   TRAP
    LID     VIA
    STEAM   PINT
  TOE  LAD  ACT
COLD    TERSE
AND     NOT
REIN    STEEP
  SEE  HIS  DOMES
    RACER    RARE
    TORE     ERIE
    WON      SEND
```

```
MET   CAIN   CRAM
AVA   ONTO   HAIR
PARENTS  PAIRS
   VEE  TENS
DATES  PRETEND
EDEN  MEALS  IA
POE  SEEDS  HER
OR  STARE  FACE
TEAPOTS  CAGES
  PALS  TAD
EVADE  ARRESTS
RARE  SLOT  PIE
ANTS  OATS  YEA
```

```
FAD  GALA  SEED
ICE  ARID  PLAY
RELATED  GRATE
   IDEA  GRIT
PAVES  CRATERS
OWES  NOISE  AH
WAR  DARNS  LIE
ER  DIMES  MADE
RECOVER  FIRST
  ODES  SING
BANGS  CONTEST
EDGE  AONE  SEE
GOOD  TOSS  TAN
```

```
SAVORS  KAISER
EMPLOY  ENTICE
AP  DARKENS  HA
LUG  DIANA  HOC
ELLA  AYE  POET
DEADEN  DURESS
  MER   SED
SLOPES  BESOTS
TOUT  ALE  SWIT
OUR  SLAVE  NNE
IV  ELICITS  DE
CRETAN  ENAMEL
SEDATE  SATYRS
```

PAGE 229

```
HAM  BERET  TOT
USE  IVORY  AVA
THANKED  PAPER
   SEEN  MINERS
BLUES  LASTS
LARD  WAITS  PM
ONE  CORNS  POE
WE  BARGE  BLOT
   TENSE  TEARS
PIRATE  FRAT
ADORE  TAUNTED
ILL  RAIDS  ERR
REL  SHEET  RAY
```

PAGE 230

```
READ  EATS  FEW
ERLE  TROT  AVA
DAISY  CLEANER
   KEEP  DATA
OVERALL  MOTOR
PA  TREES  MIME
ELF  NAVAL  CAP
ROOT  DETER  HE
ARROW  LATERAL
   TRIM  NOME
BLUNDER  NINES
ION  TRUE  SETA
DUE  HEED  SWAY
```

PAGE 231

```
PETER  FLORID
ERODE  LIMITED
AROID  ACADEMY
COTTONGIN  RON
HRH  LOOT  MATA
   BERN  TOTEM
PATINA  TOLEDO
AVAST  HERD
TOME  MEAN  CUR
TIP  MARMALADE
EDIFICE  DAVIT
RECALLS  OVINE
   DORSEY  SALEM
```

PAGE 232

```
ASS  TENT  ALAS
NOI  AWAY  BADE
NOE  BER  WIDOW
ANGELS  SAD
   EVE  REVENUE
SO  ESTATE  AND
AMAN  AZA  INTE
NEW  SPOTOF  ON
GREATER  THE
   WAS  WHENCE
ARRAY  SEE  DAV
ROAR  BEAR  ERE
MINE  EARS  DEN
```

PAGE 234

```
AGES  AWAY  HAS
NEXT  CASE  ONE
DECADES  ALONE
   IRIS  BROKEN
OFTEN  BANGS
SEED  JOKES  ME
LAD  TAXED  DAY
OR  TAMED  BITE
   RATES  EASED
QUARTS  HELP
UNITE  PILLOWS
ITS  RAIN  ASEA
TOE  SLED  DEBT
```

PAGE 235

```
AGE  STAR  CLAW
SAY  AIDE  HOLE
SLEEVES  FOOLS
   WED  EARS
TONES  SADDENS
APES  DATES  ON
MET  SOLES  TOE
ER  SATAN  ROSE
RATTLED  DINER
   ROTS  ROD
ALANS  LESSONS
RIDE  NONE  LEO
TEES  CUTS  DEN
```

PAGE 236

```
MAST ■ DECIMATE
OLEO ■ EDUCATOR
WEAR ■ LOT ■ ITES
■ LOWER ■ SNIDE
BO ■ NID ■ SUER ■
ABATE ■ ERR ■ IMA
CORONA CORONAS
HER ■ INA ■ EAGLE
■ OBEY ■ CYR ■ TA
RAGES ■ LISLE
ALAS ■ WIG ■ OLAF
PANORAMA ■ CAGE
TITTERER ■ KNOW
```

PAGE 238

```
WASP ■ FAD ■ ASHE
OLEO ■ ONO ■ WHOA
KEEPSAKE ■ FOPS
■ PUMA ■ GUEST
TOTEM ■ REALM
OMAR ■ BAAL ■ ACT
TINSEL ■ TACKLE
OTT ■ BUGS ■ LEES
■ AMBER ■ FARMS
WALES ■ ABET
ALIT ■ EVENTIDE
DOZE ■ TEN ■ EROS
SEER ■ END ■ RAGE
```

PAGE 239

```
FOR ■ STEP ■ SPAR
ADO ■ PORE ■ ERIE
SOLDIERS ■ WEDS
TREAD ■ SOS ■ SET
■ MET ■ SAGE ■
BID ■ RAM ■ WANTS
ACID ■ TAR ■ STOP
DEVIL ■ NOD ■ STY
■ IDOL ■ BET
BED ■ TIP ■ FADED
OBEY ■ SERENADE
NONE ■ PEON ■ TEN
ENDS ■ SLED ■ ANY
```

PAGE 240

```
■ WANTS ■ SALAD
■ PILEON ■ EVADE
CADET ■ ASEA ■ DA
ORES ■ SKIN ■ TON
MAR ■ DEEP ■ WINS
ED ■ PINS ■ RID
TENANT ■ HONEST
■ ICE ■ TASK ■ HI
FACE ■ MATE ■ RAM
ARE ■ PATS ■ HIRE
LO ■ AINT ■ SIDES
SMITE ■ LOADED
EASES ■ ENTER
```

PAGE 241

```
ELIE ■ EGGS ■ ADO
BANC ■ FRAT ■ NOD
BOTH ■ TAME ■ DUD
■ HOE ■ PALMERS
SKI ■ SHELLER ■
PESETAS ■ ASSAM
ANOA ■ MOA ■ OONA
TOURS ■ FLANNER
■ RENEWAL ■ VWX
MOLDIER ■ ELI
OBI ■ TRAP ■ OLGA
OAF ■ CITE ■ FLEW
NNE ■ HEHS ■ TELL
```

PAGE 242

```
SHIN ■ SAGS ■ ANEW ■ SWAB
WIRE ■ PLOP ■ MEAT ■ LADE
ADO ■ SEPTEMBER ■ GAVEL
PENNIES ■ COLD ■ LATEST
■ AND ■ TILE ■ DALE
FLAPS ■ BEAD ■ HONESTLY
LACE ■ BALL ■ PAVES ■ RUE
EWE ■ DOLL ■ SALES ■ CARL
ENSNARE ■ TENTS ■ CAMEL
■ IRE ■ FREES ■ FOR
SHOCK ■ SLIPS ■ PROPOSE
LOVE ■ SEATS ■ BOOK ■ VAN
ABE ■ SHAKE ■ CALM ■ REND
PORTHOLE ■ WORE ■ BANDS
■ HOPS ■ WANE ■ LAP
SCARES ■ BEST ■ WINTERS
HOMES ■ PREPARING ■ DUE
AREA ■ REAP ■ CAPE ■ OGLE
DENT ■ EGGS ■ THEN ■ REED
```

PAGE 244

```
LED      SAP      HIP      MET
ORAL   STIRS  DARES   SORE
GATE   TALON  ADORE   HARE
SANDALS OFTEN   TROTS
  DIRE   BORES   STAR
THERE  DAZED   FELINES
SHORT CARET  LIVED   RIB
ARMS  SHUNS  LINER  WADE
DOE   STABS  WOMEN  BASED
WRITERS CASES  RATES
  DAMS   CAGES   TORE
PEELS  FAKES  SEVERAL
MORAL  HOPES  TONES  TAG
AWOL  GALES  CARTS  CONE
RED   LANDS  NESTS  LONER
REGARDS RINKS  WAVES
  RIDS   DENTS   DAVE
GRADE  MINER  PIRATES
BEAT  NIECE  ALIEN  EVEN
ERIE  SCREW  LASTS  DIME
TEN     YES     WAS     LIT
```

PAGE 246

```
OPERA   ACRE    DAZE
RELIC   BRIM    EDEN
ERECT   DEBS    TOED
   PEONIES   PEP
RAH   ROCK   CARTED
USA   SEA   ION   ILE
SINS   START   NOSE
TATER   ELK   SONAR
   WEB   ASSET
STA   JABS   ALERTS
COB   ERA   AVE   AHA
ATE   CRY   DOC   VET
ROTATE   PERT   ENE
   PEDAL   YON
METED   REF   RURAL
AXED   HEARD   NEMO
TIN   PEA   EEL   VOW
STEELY   AQUA   ESS
   MAY   FLUSTER
AGER   ERIE   HASTE
DONT   BEEN   EVERS
MOTH   BENT   RESAT
```

PAGE 248

```
APRON  STAND  SHED  SHAD
SHOUT  HOVER  POLE  PERU
SOUTHDAKOTA   LOST  RAIL
ANTS  OMEN  WRITER  EDDY
YES  NOUN  FIAT    AGES
   HERS  PONY  ANCESTOR
SCHUSS  TANG  FLUTE  ADO
CHANT  FACT  FALLS  PROM
RUST  COLT  RAVEL  OUTRE
ART  FORK  DECOY    HUT
PRELUDE  MISER  FURTHER
USE  WANTS  BASS    ORE
CEASE  SILKS  BOTH  SURE
HASH  BULLY  MORE  POSED
ESS  BANDS  RILE  COMEDY
FEELINGS  CELT    RAKE
RANK  CAGE  LIME    MAR
HITS  STRATA  TINE  SALE
EDIT  HOAR  TRANSLATION
FLOE  ONTO  TEPEE  DINED
TEND  TEEM  AMEND  DRESS
```

PAGE 250

```
ORATE   PRORATA   MASTED
AMULET  AERATOR   ASLOPE
MADISONCARTERMICHENER
PRETTIES   EMS   NEEDIER
   ELY   HARPO   URNS
SARTRE  VERSO  PTA   ANT
ALIA  FERN  SUIT   CLEO
BOSWELLDOOLITTLEBROWN
RUE  MAYAN  ELATE  RENEE
EDS  INNS  STIRS  MOTELS
   BRAN  TATAR  GAME
MADRAS  CURED  ALTA  PAL
AWAIT  BORER  ELECT  ONE
GARNERARNESSVANHEUSEN
ERIE  ENNS  PIRN   TENT
SEN  ANY  PSALM  PRESTO
   SAGE  TROTS  ERE
CHAPTER  HEM  EMINENCE
COBURNSTEWARTDUNNDEAN
CLARET  ITALIAN  TIGERS
LOSSES  MARIMBA  SEEDY
```

PAGE 252

```
   FAD        CAD
GAPE   HAS   AVER
RACES  ART   PAPAL
ALE  TORMENT   ORE
MASSIVE   POINTED
   ONES   SAVE
PAPER      HERDS
FIR          VIE
CLAWS      STONE
   NETS   THOU
DEPOSIT  ROASTER
IRE  TRIPODS  ODE
ERASE  LIT  TAMED
SLUR   LES  EVEN
SEN          RES
```

DIAGRAMLESS STARTING BOXES

Page 158 begins in the 7th box across.

Page 160 begins in the 6th box across.

Page 192 begins in the 13th box across.

Page 224 begins in the 1st box across.

Page 254 begins in the 3rd box across.

```
MAZE
AGOG
DIDO
ALI          SPA
MEAL      PEERS
   CANDLEPOWER
     DORA    SORE
BUS ANTE SON  ERIN
EDEN    OWES   NET
ROMANCANDLE
   SCRAP   YARD
   TAN      SIR
          TIDE
          KEGS
          ORES
```

```
HAY  BREAD    CAB
ICE  RINSE    ONE
DESCEND   PLANE
     HAG  WAITER
STEAK  HARES
TILT   RESTS   TO
ARM  BOATS   PAW
RE  FLUTE   CALL
  BOOTS  DOLLS
SPARSE   PEA
LAKES   PULLING
AGE   OPERA  RUE
BED   MONEY  ANT
```

```
  STORE    TAME
SERMONS   AMENS
ALIEN   POSTAGE
GLEN  SINS   SAW
ESS   MANE  HUGO
   CAVE   KAREN
   SCARE  DINES
SEARS    HUSK
LABS  DONS   SRO
ICI   CURE  SPED
PONTOON   AHEAD
SWEEP  SECONDS
  STAY   DEEDS
```

```
JUST  SLAP  FLEA  THAW
OTTO  HALO  LAGS  HONE
BAA FASTENING  PRONE
SHRIEKS  TEND  SEEPED
  RAY  REST  SITS
ASCOT WEST OKLAHOMA
LOAN HOES FRILL  PAN
ELM DELL BADLY  RAID
SEE ELF CAMEL HOLLY
  FAD POKER  BOB
CHOIR HIRED TIN INN
HERE BANKS MILK DOE
IRA CENTS ROLL HOST
COLORADO SELL BALES
  PUTS PAVE BAR
STRESS RULE RESPITE
PRINT PORTRAITS OIL
EASE PEAS SINS OWLS
DYED OGRE EDDY FATE
```

```
PEEL  BERT   PEG
EAVE  ANTE   AXE
PRETENDED   SIT
   TAG   DUSTS
COVET   RAYS
EVER  RAP  ADES
NET   ODE   OLE
TROT  PAR  ROSE
   USER  CARED
GLOBE   BAN
RIP  ENDANGERS
AVE  PAUL  ERIE
BEN  SPED  RAGE
```

```
TWO  SEAR    TEN
ORB  WAVE   PAVE
MYSTICAL   ALEX
  CASH  INSERT
SLUSH  MEET
PARK  GIVEAWAY
ACE  LINED  RUE
RESPONDS   GIRL
  RUGS  VITAL
ALLUDE  MINE
DEAN  RHAPSODY
DAZE  LIME  FOE
SKY   YEAR  FEN
```

PAGE 262

```
LOT . TAPE . HEWS
IDA . ACID . ERIE
FOR . MET . SLATE
TRACES . SIPS .
. AS . STREETS
SCOT . SPEED . IN
PAN . ROOMS . IRA
AN . FORTS . STEP
STRIPES . BE .
. ALES . PLANTS
PAILS . ARE . ERA
ELSE . ALAS . EEL
APED . DAMS . DEE
```

PAGE 263

```
BLAND . GLOBE
LINER . SHINERS
AMIGO . COVERUP
HIS . PROSE . ADO
STEPSOUT . STIR
. HOOT . RHETT
. SPOUT . PAUSE
SLANT . FACT
CANE . BACKSTOP
AVA . MATTE . ARA
DICTATE . DECAL
SNEAKED . UNITE
. GAPED . PETER
```

PAGE 264

```
YAM . DATE . SPAT . SHE
EVER . OMEN . PAGE . STAY
SITES . TINT . IRON . STATE
DEPOSED . RACE . TOTALS
RULED . MANES . RAGE
TEA . PANTS . SCARE
METES . PRICE . CLOT . SLAP
IRED . CRONE . CRAVE . AVE
LIE . SHINE . GRAVE . POKES
LEMONADE . PRUNE . REVERT
POSE . GRADE . CASE
REVERE . SLOPE . FAVORITE
ALONE . THOSE . HADES . DIE
PST . WEAVE . TAKEN . DOLL
TEES . ISLE . VALET . MILES
PASTE . DALES . SOS
CODE . MISER . HILTS
BAKERY . OVEN . SANDALS
CORES . ACRE . TAPS . SNAIL
ONES . ROAR . EXIT . TIDE
WED . DOLT . DENY . NET
```

PAGE 266

```
WED . FATE . SCAN
ACE . APES . TORE
FRAGRANT . ANTE
TUNA . RESERVED
. MATT . ATE
ALLEN . SIS . ROY
BOASTS . TISSUE
EBB . HOE . EWERS
. OWE . CARE
CARAMELS . LETS
IRIS . GAINLESS
TINT . AIDE . RAT
EDGE . DREW . YRS
```

PAGE 267

```
OWE . STAMP . COO
DEL . ORDER . RAW
DEE . FAD . ACORN
. CLAP . SNOW
SATES . DECIDED
TREE . PANEL . LO
ROD . LANDS . POT
AM . SAVES . TAPE
PARADES . SORES
. AIDS . SLOT
SMILE . ALE . NEE
EEL . RAPID . ELL
ENS . STEMS . RIM
```

PAGE 268

```
FED . THUS . ESAU
ERE . HOPE . LOSS
WINTER . ENDURE
. HE . LSE . RID
THEY . SATAN
HOW . GOD . REMIT
ELEMEN . HERODI
NISAN . AIR . TOE
. NESTS . HELD
ART . ROE . ME
BURIAL . HIRAMS
EDEN . EYES . SEA
LEEK . SENT . ANT
```

PAGE 270 grid:

```
ECHO  SAVOR  STRAP  TROT
THAW  TRADE  PEARL  HOUR
HONE  RESEMBLANCE  RATE
ERG  CANE  OAR  AVERSE
REGALIA  CANTS  ASIA
LION  SALES  CLUSTERS
DAIRY  RIGID  FLORA  VET
RIDS  BERET  MAINE  EGO
ADE  ALLEY  COUPE  BANAL
MERIDIAN  MOONS  CATTLE
ROPY  PANDA  DARK
STAIRS  WARDS  BIGNAMES
POSSE  PINTO  TOTES  ORE
RUT  FADES  ROOTS  STAR
ACE  BORES  MOTTO  CLOSE
THRILLER  VIBES  SOUR
MOLD  SALEM  DETECTS
POTATO  ANA  CAVE  YAW
AGOG  WAITINGGAME  ACME
TRUE  EGRET  INFER  FLEE
HERS  REEDY  GUESS  TEST
```

PAGE 272 grid:

```
PARIS  PAD  SPA
EDITH  ALE  PUB
NOSEY  SINCERE
KM  PTG  HALL
SPY  SLENDER
TO  PAUL  REELS
ALIENS  GARDEN
BONET  HOGS  NO
DRAGONS  SAW
ERIE  ARE  HA
READERS  TALON
MAN  ABE  ALONE
ALA  ROD  TONED
```

PAGE 273 grid:

```
BIT  STAB  ACTS
ADE  TALE  TREE
TORTURE  COUNT
RANT  PANS
SLANT  BASEHIT
NICK  WAGES  DR
ONE  CAKES  PIE
WE  SAVED  BOOS
SNAPPED  HOOTS
NEED  HOUR
RAGES  LETTERS
ABED  HIRE  SIP
HERS  IDOL  TOY
```

PAGE 274 grid:

```
SCOLD  SUPPERS
STADIA  TRIOLETS
TENDER  ENTREPOT
RET  NEAR  SECTOR
OPAL  DIES  TILE
BETAS  LOOSE  LIE
ERASERS  UPSWEEP
SMU  ASA
APPOINT  STAGING
REO  STOMP  YEMEN
ARTS  TAUT  DOMO
RIATAS  GRID  GEM
ALBANIAN  TALESE
TELLTALE  ADONIS
DELIMIT  NOTES
```

PAGE 276 grid:

```
FACE  FIN  CHOW
AGOG  UFO  HIDE
REGGAE  CEASED
NIL  TAR
ACTOR  CUSTOM
CRAG  BORE  SOP
MUM  POUND  CUR
ESP  LURE  CANE
TALENT  PARTY
LAD  MAN
SONATA  ADOPTS
IRON  RBI  PINK
REDO  YEN  YETI
```

PAGE 277 grid:

```
ALA  BAR  EVIL
HAL  OVAL  MINE
OVERTAKE  PEND
YACHT  EAST
OLD  PAYDAY
THEDEEP  PHONE
RARE  NOD  ANNA
AVAIL  PIONEER
YESSED  MUD
LEOS  TESTS
SODA  TEARDOWN
IRON  SAGA  MIA
REED  TEN  EGG
```

PAGE 278

PAGE 280

PAGE 281

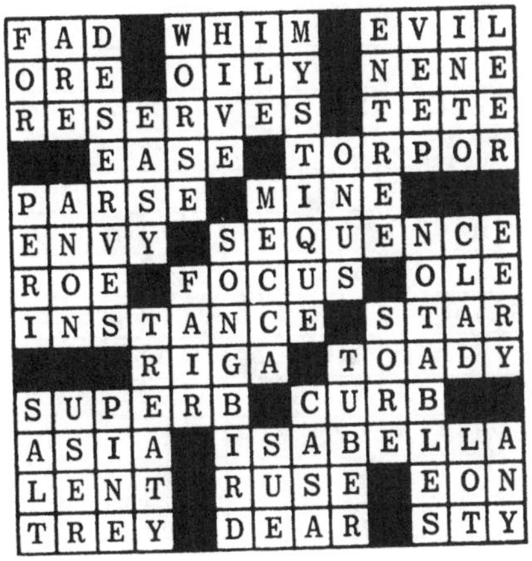

PAGE 282

PAGE 284

PAGE 286

PAGE 288

PAGE 289

PAGE 290

PAGE 291

PAGE 292

PAGE 293

```
HOLD  BOAS  SAD
ALEE  ARCH  ERA
SEATED  HEFTED
HONOR  REAR
    URGE  REALM
INCREASE  TREE
NOR  DRAMA  EEL
OPEN  BLIZZARD
NEWER  TRUE
    CUBS  RAJAH
FICKLE  HELENA
ORE  EASE  ODOR
GEE  STAY  TINT
```

PAGE 294

```
ASK  USES    IAM
FOE  NOAH  ACRE
ALENT  TORMENT
REPAIR  TIE
    KLED  SNARE
FREE  BITE  GAL
LEAD  EER  DENS
ASS  ALSO  EDGE
STEPS  TOMB
    OIL  POTTER
SUSTAIN  NOISE
PRES  EESE  MAN
YEA  STAY  BUT
```

PAGE 296

```
GOVS  ANTS  NOD
EDIT  CURT  UBI
MESA  ERIE  RIO
   IST  SPENSER
METHANE  LEE
ELI  MORO  ADAM
TIN  STYLE  ABA
SAGS  ARID  GET
   NAB  HOGARTH
ACUTELY  EMU
SUR  LIMA  EDDA
ELS  OVER  EGOS
ATE  WEST  REEK
```

PAGE 297

```
TAC  GRASS  ART
ALA  RIVET  LEE
REPLACE  ERODE
   TONE  SPAN
STAND  PUPPETS
ERIE  BORES  IT
VAN  CARED  TRA
ED  SORER  PEER
NETTLES  CLASS
   WELD  HOOP
SLIME  HARPOON
AIR  GLARE  TWO
GEL  EASES  SET
```

PAGE 298

```
LAMP  SPY  SWAB
AFAR  TEE  TARA
STEAMER  FORTY
   TAM  MART
USHER  FORESTS
REED  SAVED  AL
ADE  GATES  TKO
LA  TILES  SEEP
SNARLED  ROANS
   PALS  HUM
CARDS  LUMBERS
ALOE  BEN  ERIE
PINS  BET  RAPT
```

PAGE 299

```
LOS  STARS  ABE
EAT  TULIP  LAD
ERA  ICE  ODORS
   TANK  LION
SLING  GALLERY
TOOT  CAMEL  HA
RON  DOTED  FIR
AS  SORER  POND
WEAPONS  CARES
   CARS  PANT
STORM  DAN  USE
EAR  ADORE  NOV
ANN  TONES  EWE
```

PAGE 300

```
T R A S H E S   . A L A M O
P R E S C O T T . M O L A R S
R U N S O V E R . A R I S T A
E S T A T E . A B I E . S O B
S T A Y . M I E N . M A L I
E E L . D A U N T . P A G A N
T E S T I N G . H E L L E N E
      A N D   . R A T
D I S M A Y S . S I N A T R A
E T H E R . A G E N T . O A R
S H O D . P I L E . C O D Y
P A R . A L D O . I T A L I A
O C T A V O . A R M E N I A N
T A I L E D . T O R M E N T S
N E A R S . S E E P A G E
```

PAGE 302

```
N A B . H O O P . S L A P
U S E . A D A M . T A T A
T H E A T E R . F I R E D
  H O E S . R I N G
S P I N S . D A N G E R S
L I V E . L I K E S . A T
A L E . B O N E S . P I E
M O . R A V E S . D O S E
S T R I K E S . H O S E D
  O V E R . P A L S
P A G E S . C O L L E C T
E V E R . T O O L . S U E
W A R S . O W L S . S E E
```

PAGE 303

```
E L S E . M O P . S H A M
L E A D . A W E . H E R O
F I G U R I N E . I R I S
  C A N . K A N S A S
B O G E Y . S A V E
L A N D . T U B E . O P T
A H A . V A P O R . P O I
H U T . O L E O . C U R L
  S T I R . H A S T E
L A S H E S . P A C
O B O E . M O U T H F U L
F L O E . A R T . E A S Y
T E N T . N E T . T R E E
```

PAGE 304

```
G A P . T O P . B O W
O I L . A W E . T I M E
D R E A M E R . T R A I T
  A C E S . L E A S T
C O S T S . L E A D
A L A S . S E A . E D E N
M E N . T A P . E R E
P O T S . A R T . A S I A
  T H I N . F L E E T
S P O O N . B E E R
P O I N T . E L E C T E D
T O N E . L E D . E R R
A N T . M D S . D A Y
```

PAGE 305

```
H A M . A P A P . P O T
E T T U B R U T E . R U E
R E S P E C T . A C O R N
  I T S . C R A M
A R E N A . T A L L E S T
T E X T . W E D . I N T O
L A T H . O N E . F A R M
A C R E . M O T . O D E A
S T E A M E R . B R E W S
  M I E N . D I N
S H I R T . M A R I T A L
P E T . A B U N D A N C E
A N Y . L E D A . T E E
```

PAGE 306

```
C A B . P R A M S . F I G
A D O . R E G A L . A R E
T E X T I L E . I D I O T
  C O Z Y . S C O R N S
S T A T E . J O K E S
W O R E . D A L E S . L A
I N S . H O M E R . M E N
M Y . C A V E S . F A S T
  L A N E S . H O R S E
S T I N G S . B O U T
P O K E S . B O W L I N G
I R E . U S U A L . N E O
T E D . P O S T S . S A D
```

PAGE 307

```
SPENT  SOLIDS
COLOR  PRIVATE
AWARE  LADY  ON
LET  EDITS  NUT
DREW  ONE  MATE
    RANT  TIMER
STRIPE  BONERS
TRITE  GONE
RACE  PRO  RAFT
ADE  PLATE  LIE
WE  LEAD  ACORN
SILENCE  TUNED
NOOSES  SEEDS
```

PAGE 308

```
HOPS  AMEN  SWAM  SLAW
AGED  LOSE  TIME  PINE
IRE  FIRSTLADY  PLANE
REPLACE  WIRE  FEARED
    ICE  POST  SITS
SLANT  CART  OKLAHOMA
TANK  MASK  SPILL  LID
ATE  EAST  WEEPS  MEND
NEW  ART  BEANS  BOOKS
    ASK  HEALS  HEW
JELLY  BEARS  MID  BIB
ORAL  WANTS  WINS  ADE
AIM  BARNS  REST  PILE
NEBRASKA  FEAT  MILES
    ANTS  DOCK  BIN
STRIKE  FREE  HOTTEST
IRONS  PRESIDENT  CAR
PIPE  TEES  VALE  OHIO
SPED  OATS  ENDS  FOLD
```

PAGE 310

```
SLOB  BRAG  HEARD
SPIRAL  TRIVIA  TERRIER
TATTLE  RODENT  EXAMPLE
ACT  INVOKES  HOMES  TUB
YELL  DOWER  SWAPS  WIDE
SEAM  TEN  START  MODEL
TOWEL  TOURS  CURED
CLEVER  TAUNT  PINS
CLOSET  JILLS  CONCEAL
LOOTS  CAGES  PARCH  DEE
ASS  MODES  HATCH  MAY
WEE  BOWER  WITCH  SWINE
DRAINED  MATCH  BLARED
BRED  DITCH  ROUSED
TRACY  PINCH  COAST
FRESH  POACH  GOO  HELP
LUSH  TINGE  GRASP  SOIL
IMP  FAKER  FLIRTED  VEE
EPITOME  AVAILS  NOVICE
RETIRES  MIDDLE  TWINES
TEEMS  ZEES  NAGS
```

PAGE 312

```
PORTS  BOMBER  GOADS
GENIAL  AREOLE  LILAC
LETSWELLENOUGHALONE
ERIE  EYES  SAID  HUN
NAM  SPED  CHILD  BABE
STEPPES  CLOVE  LOSE
AIR  SUEDE  TOW
SCANT  SORAS  COVERUP
TART  PALER  LITERATE
RUM  MAGISTRATES  PIT
ISOLATED  HONES  MILE
PERUSES  PEAKS  CIDER
CON  TEARY  DOE
SPIN  BASIS  DIMNESS
SCUD  TENOR  FIVE  LOT
TIL  DOLT  DOVE  TALE
ALLWOOLANDAYARDWIDE
SLIER  ORIOLE  GAINER
HANDY  WALTER  ENTER
```

PAGE 314

```
STATE  TOILE  HANDS
CARBON  ARRAY  OPORTO
AMOUNT  RAISETHEROOF
ROUT  IRONS  SOUR  GOT
TAB  SCAT  DORM  HUGE
LAKES  FLIRT  QUEEN
PERI  PALACE  CUR
ALMOST  BOSK  GUITARS
LEAS  APORT  HARP  NAP
BAKE  MADASHOPS  SARI
USE  PINE  TERSE  OXEN
MERGING  GRAD  SAFELY
LEG  PRATES  KATY
SMEAR  DRAWS  CAIRO
POND  BOOM  BONN  GEE
ORT  LOUD  SHOWN  BRAY
RAISEARUCKUS  ARRIVE
TYRANT  COILS  LOANED
SEPTS  TODAY  SENDS
```

PAGE 316

```
ALIBI  HEATER  STAG
SMOKES  EXPOSE  LILAC
WHOSESOIREENOW  ARENAS
IRR  SETTERS  TRINE  DNA
RIOT  TOAST  DEIST  THIN
ENURE  PLY  BARTH  CAINE
DESERVES  HENIE  LARDER
ANIS  RELIC  MALTA
GRODIN  TESLA  COMMENCE
RENEE  GEESE  HONES  CAR
AGED  SEESERPENTS  PENN
SAM  THANE  IRATE  CARTE
PLAGIARY  SNIPE  TORSOS
YANKS  SAGES  PROA
SMARTY  LITER  SLAPDASH
LANES  VALOR  COO  TITLE
ORBS  LENIN  SANTA  STIR
PIA  MEDOC  SUMATRA  IDO
ENNEAD  LOEWEPRESSURED
ADANO  INVADE  ROSTER
STEN  NEATER  SNEAD
```

PAGE 318

```
            R I C H
  L E T   D E T A I N
  E L A T E D   P L O T
  E L B O W     T O R E
    A S P         N U T S
          S E A     S O P A
    A B E   U R N   E T N A
    R E G U L A T O R
B E S T   A S K   I N N
E A T     D E S
D R E W         C O W
  N E E D     D U N E S
  L E A F   B A T T L E
    P R U N E D   O D E
        T R O T
```

PAGE 320

```
B U F F
O P A L         F L E W
S T R A P     O A S E S
S O C I A L   S C I S S O R S
    E R S E   O U R   T R A P
    S T A T U S   P E T T Y
      G E L   P A R I S
    V A L U E   B O R N E
    C A N O E   P A T
H A U N T   R I G H T S
I S L E   T O E   E R A S
M E T A P H O R   R I C H E S
  S L E E T       P R O N E
  S A Y S         E R N E
                  D E S K
```

PAGE 322

```
T A R   G R A T E   O L D
I R E   R A Y O N   P E A
M E A S U R E   D R E A M
    P O N E     L E N D S
S H I F T   C H E S S
T U N A   F R O S T   H I
E G G   C O O P S   H A D
W E   W O R S E   H U L L
  F A R M S   P A S T E
S T A I R   B O M B
W R I T E   S E E S A W S
A I R   C R U S T   N A P
T O Y   T E N T S   D R Y
```

PAGE 323

```
M A C   B I S O N   S P A
O I L   A D O R E   H A L
B R O N S O N   P H O N E
    S A I L   S T I R
T H E M E   S T U D E N T
R O T E   D I A N E   I A
I T S   C A R N E   M E L
B E   S A L E S   P A C E
E L E C T E D   C A S E S
    L A S S   C A R T
A L O N E   L A N T E R N
D I P   Y I E L D   R A N
O D E   E N E M Y   S E W
```

PAGE 324

```
  H E S S E   A M A S S
B O D K I N   M A R O O N
A W A Y   G A B L E   L O
N A M   C A B L E   R O I
J R   E A G L E   S A N S
O D Y S S E Y   B U L G E
  U S E D   D R I P
H O K E Y   F E A T H E R
A N O N   C L A N S   N O
R A N   G U A R D   E R A
E G   B L O K E   O T I C
M E D I U M   S T E N C H
  R O D E O   T O R A H
```

18-Across: National Association of Manufacturers

PAGE 325

```
S A P   R E L Y   O P U S
T I E   E R I E   L O R E
A D E   P R E S I D E N T
R E P L I E D   M E
      A N D   S P R U C E
A L O N E   W A S   N O R
P O L E   F O X   S T A N
E V A   E O N   Q U O T E
R E V O K E   C U E
    R E   R A I D E R S
D R U G S T O R E   Z E E
I O T A   A B E T   R A N
E D E N   N E T S   A D D
```

PAGE 326

```
LIT  SLAW   SPAN
IDO  AIDE   TORE
NOR  LED  WASTE
ELOPED  PINS
    IS  SADDENS
TIME  TILES  OH
ODE  RIDER  TOO
AL  SANER  TINT
DESIRES  PA
   ALES  CANTER
DIVER  HAS  ARE
EVEN  CART  RIN
NEST  ALEE  ANT
```

PAGE 327

```
 CRISP  PLATE
SEABEE  ROLAND
LANIER  OLIVER
ISIS  FOWL  EMU
MES  FIRS  CRIB
   LADD  BONES
 QUERY  CRASS
DUNNE  PAIL
RAND  HARM  EGO
IRE  AARE  SLAV
ERRING  FINITE
DEVOTE  UNISON
 LENIN  LATER
```

PAGE 328

```
ARE  SHAKE  WIN
WAY  TARES  IVO
EWE  INK  COVER
  LONG  CAREST
BRING  ROPES
RODE  ISLES  HA
ASS  BROOD  DEN
YE  RUINS  FRET
  SORTS  GOODS
ROMANS  HARP
ABIDE  FAT  POT
GET  THINE  EAR
EYE  HERDS  DRY
```

PAGE 330

```
POD  SLAMS  ALA
IRE  CADET  RIP
TEN  ACE  ABODE
  TORE  CRAM
SPINE  CATNAPS
POSE  DANES  EL
EST  PARED  LEO
AS  TARTS  HELP
REPORTS  TEASE
  ARTS  MEND
HERON  WIN  EVE
ARK  EVICT  REV
TRA  RAGES  SEA
```

PAGE 331

```
MAR  SILO  CHAR
ALI  EDAM  REDO
MAO  LAKEHURON
ANGEL  ENID
  RISER  REBEL
BOAR  ASHE  EVA
OWNERS  OSPREY
WED  ATOM  OILS
SNEAD  LEARN
  RAVI  REGAL
MOONRIVER  SPA
ALAI  NINA  EER
PETE  EASY  ADD
```

PAGE 332

```
SONS  CLEM  HULA
ALEA  OHARA  ONUS
MARLENEDIETRICH
END  PITY  UNTIE
  LEO  HARE
GREEN  DORN  SOL
RUE  SERGE  ADA
FALSE  HES  RODEO
ONE  SWEDE  MIT
EDS  TOES  ARIES
  SHEP  RAT
ALICE  TRIS  SHE
GENERALHOSPITAL
ANON  COUPE  DILL
LANE  HUGE  AREA
```

PAGE 334

```
TARA  ROB  OPAL
EGAL  ERE  RAGE
ERIK  PEDIGREE
MALAGA  SLIDES
   LAIR  LEO
FILIGREE  SNOW
ADA  AETNA  EWE
TACT  DISAGREE
   RIA  APAR
AKIMBO  HAILED
JAMBOREE  SORE
ALAR  BAR  TOIL
RILE  STE  SNEE
```

PAGE 335

```
PALM  PIN    PIE
AREA  ROO  TELL
REAL  ENTHRALL
INSTEP  SOO
SAT  TAP  PUPIL
   ACRE  BONE
HITTHECEILING
IDEA  ANNE
MEANS  NET  WEB
   EAT  MOBILE
SHANGHAI  OPAL
POND  EWE  LETO
ADD  YES  DREW
```

PAGE 336

```
AFT  LESS  AHOY
NOR  OMIT  MUTE
TREASUREHUNTS
STAVE  PAST
   SERUM  DEISM
SPUR  RIDE  NEE
PAR  GAMES  GAS
ICE  ALEE  ACTS
NEHRU  DRAMA
   OOZE  DONEE
HOUSEBREAKING
EASE  BOOM  NOG
RTES  SENS  ESS
```

PAGE 337

```
CAPS  DADO  FAT
UNIT  ABOU  ONE
RACY  WESTERNS
TALENT  LAMAS
   TEN  MIS
MAYS  PRINTING
SEP  FABLE  NEA
SCENARIO  STET
   ODE  APE
ALTO  SATIRE
WORKSHOP  READ
EVE  HANS  ESSE
SEE  EDGE  STEW
```

PAGE 338

```
MOSS  REGINA  DOOM
CEREAL  EDISON  ORRIS
WHATPRICEGLORY  MARSHA
ART  TAMALES  STEEL  TAB
VOID  HIRER  HEIRS  MESA
ENERO  NED  POMME  CARTS
DORISDAY  RUPEE  HOORAH
   VIOL  ROBIN  CAIRO
ALBEES  FOALS  FALLIBLE
SOLAR  SAUDI  AIDES  EOS
TOOT  JAMESCAGNEY  TRIN
OSO  BABES  EBOAT  METRE
REDDENED  SNARL  RINSES
   OUTER  THETA  TUNA
ERNEST  SHAME  WARDBOND
NATTY  CURLY  GIB  SLIER
ACHS  CAMEL  POLIS  ELLE
TIE  LAMAS  HEALTHS  SLA
EASIER  THEOKLAHOMAKID
LUNGE  RENNIE  ANOMIE
NAST  ARSENE  EGAN
```

PAGE 340

```
ROT  CAP
AVID  DOVE
SWEDE  IDEAL
BET  RECOVER  AVA
ADAM  SOLES  STIR
TIRED  YES  SLEET
TENORS  TAPERS
   TOO  WIN
SPIRES  GENDER
SOLOS  PAR  SERUM
OMEN  TALES  ROLE
SEA  CARPETS  DEN
DRAKE  TEASE
AGED  SPIT
TEN  SLY
```

PAGE 342

```
    DIM
    AREA           BAH
  GIANTS           AGO
MISQUOTE        DROP
ELI     POT   GROG
ADE       PATRON
LAS   CRO     RAW
      LIV     ADS
      AVE   NEE   IAN
    SMARTS        SHE
    COOL    AFT   SEA
  FOUR      BIANNUAL
  OIL         XRAYED
  ELS           EVER
                ETS
```

PAGE 344

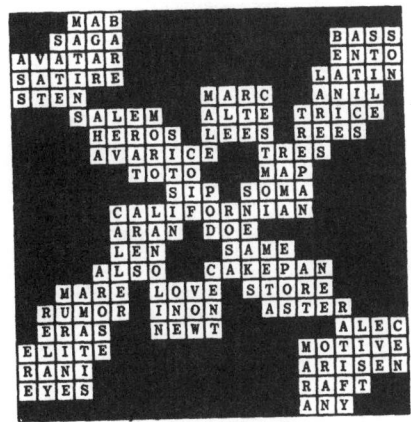

```
      MAB                      BASS
      SAGA                     ENTO
AVATAR                         LATIN
SATIRE              MARC      ANIL
STEN     SALEM    ALTE   TRICE
         HEROS    LEES   REES
         AVARICE    TRES
         TOTO       MAP
         SIP      SOMA
       CALIFORNIAN
       ARAN    DOE
       LEN     SAME
       ALSO   CAKEPAN
  MARE  LOVE    STORE
  RUMOR INON    ASTER
  ERAS    NEWT
ELITE                        ALEC
RANI                         MOTIVE
EYES                         ARISEN
                             RAFT
                             ANY
```

PAGE 346

```
RAM    STOP          BAT
ALI    HOUR          ODE
GAS    ONTO          DE
       TORE    TEASE
CHANT    PELT
LIKE     SACK    SAW
ADE      SLITS   TIE
PEN      OILS    BAND
         TAPS    TENTS
  REARS    WEED
  IRK      HARE    OUR
  ORE      OPEN    USA
           DENS    TEN
```

PAGE 347

```
LAP   PEP          LOW
EGO   ERA          TIDE
DESSERT    DATED
     SIRE    DIMES
SPED    DRIVER
EASES   AVER
ADS     NICER    CAT
        RICE   TRACE
      COVERS   OMEN
      COPED    WISE
RAVEL    LITERAL
APED     ONE   ADO
MET      GEM   SET
```

PAGE 348

```
SAD    CANE    CREW
ICE    AMEN    AIDE
RELEGATE       SPIT
    IDES        TESTS
FACE    SAGAS
LEANS    DAM    DAB
ART     CHOSE   EVA
TOE     OUR    SAFER
    SPENT      BIRD
SLATE       OPEN
TILE    SEDATIVE
EASE    ORAL    TOY
PROD    WAYS    EWE
```

PAGE 349

```
WAD    SPARE    COO
AVE    CARED    HAD
GAS    ANT    IRATE
    SANE    STAR
SLEDS    SLOTTED
TORE    SCARS    VA
ROT    CHOPS    FAR
AS    SHOWS    MADE
PESTERS    RACED
    EAST    CANT
PLANT    POT    OLD
EAT    ERODE    RYE
ADS    RIDES    YEW
```

PAGE 350

```
HIT   HULA   STAG
ACE   ASIS   TRIO
SEATBELT     EARN
    RAID  ELAPSE
EVICT    FROM
LONE   LION   NEE
LITTLEBIGHORN
ADO   AGED   OSLO
   STAR    FROES
PROPEL   JUDO
LIVE   INASENSE
OPEN   ZONE   ELK
TEND   EWES   RYE
```

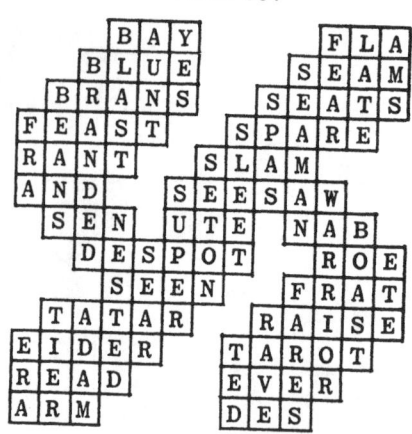

```
     BAY        FLA
     BLUE      SEAM
     BRANS    SEATS
FEAST        SPARE
RANT        SLAM
AND        SEESAW
SEN      UTE  NAB
   DESPOT      ROE
      SEEN   FRAT
  TATAR      RAISE
EIDER        TAROT
READ          EVER
ARM            DES
```

PAGE 352

```
ELL   PARK   SLAG
SEA   ERIE   PICA
POSITION     OMIT
   COAL   TIRADE
SHAWL   HUNTS
COLA   MOCKS   LA
ANA   PESKY   FAN
ME   PARTY   MUST
   PARIS   SENSE
STATED    CLAN
HOPE   IDEALIST
OMEN   AUNT   EAR
PERT   NOTE   SPY
```

PAGE 353

```
STAR   SPAR   KEG
EASE   AIDE   OLE
EN   SANE   FRAME
   FORD   VEAL
SMART   LARIATS
TART   AILED   IT
USE   ANNIE   PRO
NO   OPTED   PIER
SNAPPED   HANDY
   LEES   TASK
ARENA   AIMS   HO
FAR   RAGE   EDEN
TNT   SLED   DONE
```

PAGE 354

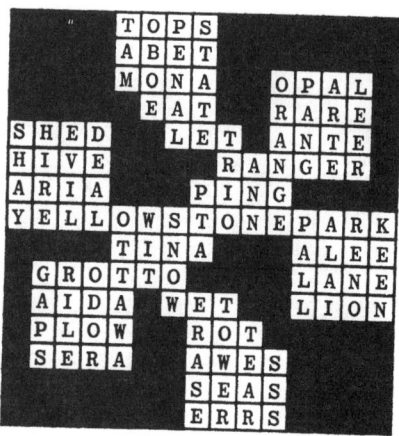

```
     TOPS
     ABET
     MONA    OPAL
      EAT    RARE
SHED    LET  ANTE
HIVE        RANGER
ARIA     PING
YELLOWSTONEPARK
     TINA      ALEE
GROTTO        LANE
AIDA   WET    LION
PLOW   ROT
SERA   AWES
       SEAS
       ERRS
```

PAGE 356

```
JET
AXE      AWE
BAN    AKIN      TSP
SCOTLAND       PIQUE
TRIO        GETUPS
    ENJOY   ATLAST
    GONETOSEED
    TULIP
    SLEEP
    ERRED
   SUPERSALES
SUITOR   STEER
ENTIRE    NASH
ADELE   QUESTION
ODE    URGE   GNU
       ENG    MET
              ADS
```

PAGE 358

Page 286 begins in the 10th box across.

Page 320 begins in the 1st box across.

Page 342 begins in the 3rd box across.

Page 344 begins in the 4th box across.

Page 345 begins in the 5th box across.

Page 356 begins in the 1st box across.

Page 358 begins in the 6th box across.